Science and Technology Concepts for Middle Schools™

Earth in Space

Student Guide and Source Book

NATIONAL SCIENCE RESOURCES CENTER

The National Science Resources Center (NSRC) is operated by the Smithsonian Institution and the National Academies to improve the teaching of science in the nation's schools. The NSRC disseminates information about exemplary teaching resources, develops curriculum materials, and conducts outreach programs of leadership development and technical assistance to help school districts implement inquiry-centered science programs.

SMITHSONIAN INSTITUTION

The Smithsonian Institution was created by act of Congress in 1846 "for the increase and diffusion of knowledge. . . ." This independent federal establishment is the world's largest museum complex and is responsible for public and scholarly activities, exhibitions, and research projects nationwide and overseas. Among the objectives of the Smithsonian is the application of its unique resources to enhance elementary and secondary education.

THE NATIONAL ACADEMIES

The National Academies are nonprofit organizations that provide independent advice to the nation on matters of science, technology, and medicine. The National Academies consist of four organizations: the National Academy of Sciences, the National Academy of Engineering, the Institute of Medicine, and the National Research Council. The National Academy of Sciences was created in 1863 by a congressional charter. Under this charter, the National Research Council was established in 1916, the National Academy of Engineering in 1964, and the Institute of Medicine in 1970.

STC/MS PROJECT SPONSORS

National Science Foundation
Bristol-Myers Squibb Foundation
Dow Chemical Company
DuPont Company
Hewlett-Packard Company
The Robert Wood Johnson Foundation
Carolina Biological Supply Company

Science and Technology Concepts for Middle Schools™

Earth in Space

**Student
Guide
and
Source
Book**

**NS
RC**

National Science Resources Center

THE NATIONAL ACADEMIES ✺ Smithsonian
Institution

Published by Carolina Biological Supply Company
Burlington, North Carolina

NOTICE This material is based upon work supported by the National Science Foundation under Grant No. ESI-9618091. Any opinions, findings, and conclusions or recommendations expressed in this material are those of the authors and do not necessarily reflect views of the National Science Foundation, the Smithsonian Institution, or the National Academies.

This project was supported, in part,
by the
National Science Foundation
Opinions expressed are those of the authors
and not necessarily those of the Foundation

10   10 9 8 7 6

ISBN 978-0-89278-543-8

Published by Carolina Biological Supply Company, 2700 York Road, Burlington, NC 27215.
Call toll free 1-800-334-5551.

Cover design and illustration by Max-Karl Winkler; cover image compiled by Reto Stockli, courtesy of NASA Earth Observatory Goddard Space Flight Center, National Aeronautics and Space Administration.
Printed in the United States of America

CB787891001
♻ Printed on recycled paper.

Earth in Space

MODULE DEVELOPMENT STAFF

Developer/Writer
Carol O'Donnell

Science Advisors
Stanley Doore, Meteorologist (retired),
National Weather Service, National
Oceanic and Atmospheric Adminstration

Brian Huber, Micropaleobiologist, Department of
Paleobiology, National Museum of Natural History,
Smithsonian Institution

Ian MacGregor, Director (retired), Division of
Earth Sciences, National Science Foundation

David Williams, Planetary Scientist,
National Space Science Data Center,
NASA Goddard Space Flight Center

James Zimbelman, Planetary Geologist, Center for
Earth and Planetary Studies, National Air and
Space Museum, Smithsonian Institution

Editor
Karen Gulliver

Illustrator
Max-Karl Winkler

Photographic Research
Joan Mathys
Christine Hauser

Contributing Writers
Phil Berardelli
Lynda DeWitt
Carolyn Hanson
Linda Harteker
Scott Paton
Catherine Stephens

STC/MS PROJECT STAFF

Principal Investigator
Sally Goetz Shuler, Executive Director, NSRC

Project Director
Kitty Lou Smith

Curriculum Developers
David Marsland
Henry Milne
Carol O'Donnell
Dane J. Toler

Publications Director
Heather Dittbrenner

Managing Editors
Linda Griffin Kean
Dorothy Sawicki

Illustration Coordinator
Max-Karl Winkler

Photo Editor
Christine Hauser

Graphic Designer
Heidi Kupke

Researcher/Writer
Carolyn Hanson

Reader Editor
Linda Harteker

Design Consultation
Isley &/or Clark Design

STC/MS Project Advisors for *Earth in Space*

Tom Albert, Teacher-in-Residence, NASA Goddard Space Flight Center

Cassandra Coombs, Director, NASA Southeast Regional Clearinghouse, College of Charleston

Stanley Doore, Meteorologist (retired), National Weather Service, National Oceanic and Atmospheric Administration

Ann Dorr, Teacher (retired), Fairfax County, Virginia, Public Schools; Board Member, Minerals Information Institute

Andrew Fraknoi, Astronomical Society of the Pacific; Professor, Department of Astronomy, Foothills College

Jackie Faillace Getgood, Supervisor of Mathematics, Spotsylvania County, Virginia, Public Schools

Marvin Grossman, Associate Director, Project ARIES, Harvard University, Harvard-Smithsonian Center for Astrophysics

Patricia Hagan, Middle School Science Specialist, Montgomery County, Maryland, Public Schools

Matthew Holman, Astrophysicist, Harvard-Smithsonian Center for Astrophysics

Brian Huber, Micropaleobiologist, Department of Paleobiology, National Museum of Natural History, Smithsonian Institution

Ian MacGregor, Director (retired), Division of Earth Sciences, National Science Foundation

Brian Marsden, Senior Astrophysicist, Associate Director, Smithsonian Astrophysical Observatory, Harvard-Smithsonian Center for Astrophysics

Timothy McCoy, Meteorite Specialist, Department of Mineral Sciences, National Museum of Natural History, Smithsonian Institution

Stephanie Stockman, Planetary Geologist, Science Systems and Applications, Inc.; NASA Goddard Space Flight Center

David Williams, Planetary Scientist, National Space Science Data Center, NASA Goddard Space Flight Center

James Zimbelman, Planetary Geologist, Center for Earth and Planetary Studies, National Air and Space Museum, Smithsonian Institution

Foreword

Community leaders and state and local school officials across the country are recognizing the need to implement science education programs consistent with the National Science Education Standards as we strive to attain the important national goal of scientific literacy for all students in the 21st century. The Standards present a bold vision of science education. They identify what students at various levels should know and be able to do. They also emphasize the importance of transforming the science curriculum in a way that encourages students to engage actively in scientific inquiry—thereby developing conceptual understanding as well as problem-solving skills.

We believe that the development of effective, standards-based, inquiry-centered curriculum materials is a key step in achieving scientific literacy. The National Science Resources Center (NSRC) has responded to this challenge through the Science and Technology Concepts for Middle Schools (STC/MS) program. With the publication of the STC/MS modules, schools now have a rich set of curriculum resources for middle school students that embody scientific inquiry and hands-on learning.

Since its founding in 1985, the NSRC has made many contributions to the goal of achieving scientific literacy for all students. In addition to developing the Science and Technology for Children (STC) program—an inquiry-centered science curriculum for grades K through 6—the NSRC has been active in disseminating information on science teaching resources, in preparing school district leaders to spearhead science education reform, and in providing technical assistance to school districts. These programs have had an important impact on science education throughout the country.

The transformation of science education is a challenging task that will continue to require the kind of strategic thinking and insistence on excellence that the NSRC has demonstrated in all of its curriculum development and outreach programs. Its sponsoring organizations, the Smithsonian Institution and the National Academies, take great pride in the publication of this exciting new science program for middle schools.

J. DENNIS O'CONNOR
Former Under Secretary for Science
Smithsonian Institution

BRUCE M. ALBERTS
President
National Academy of Sciences

Preface

The National Science Resources Center's (NSRC) mission is to improve the learning and teaching of science for K-12 students. As an organization of two prestigious scientific institutions—the National Academies and the Smithsonian Institution— the NSRC is dedicated to the establishment of effective science programs for all students. To contribute to that goal, the NSRC has developed and published two comprehensive, research-based science curriculum programs: the Science and Technology for Children® (STC®) program for students in grades K-6, and the Science and Technology Concepts for Middle Schools™ (STC/MS™) program for students in grades 6-8.

The STC/MS curriculum project was launched in 1997. The overall design of the instructional materials and the process by which they were developed are based on a foundation of research. The STC/MS courses were informed by research on cognitive development, teaching, learning, assessment, and the culture of schools.

The STC/MS curriculum materials consist of eight courses. Through these courses, students build an understanding of important concepts in life, earth, and physical sciences and in technology; learn critical-thinking skills; and develop positive attitudes toward science and technology. The STC/MS program materials are designed to meet the challenge of the National Science Education Standards to place scientific inquiry at the core of science education programs. Specifically, the National Science Education Standards state that "...students in grades 5–8 should be provided opportunities to engage in full and partial inquiries.... With an appropriate curriculum and adequate instruction, middle school students can develop the skills of investigation and the understanding that scientific inquiry is guided by knowledge, observations, ideas, and questions." STC/MS also addresses the national technology standards published by the International Technology Education Association.

Informed by research and guided by standards, the design of the STC/MS courses addresses four critical goals:

- Use of effective student and teacher assessment strategies to improve learning and teaching.
- Integration of literacy into the learning of science by giving students the lens of language to focus and clarify their thinking and activities.
- Enhanced learning using new technologies to help students visualize processes and relationships that are normally invisible or difficult to understand.
- Incorporation of strategies to actively engage parents to support the learning process.

The research and development process has included trial teaching and field-testing nationwide with geographically and ethnically diverse student populations, as well as the active involvement of the scientific and engineering communities. This process has ensured that the learning experiences contained in each module reflect current scientific thinking, and are pedagogically sound and developmentally appropriate for students.

The NSRC is grateful to the Smithsonian Institution and the National Academies for their overall project support and for sharing their scientific expertise—critical for the development of world-class products. Support for project staff and the associated work to produce and publish these materials has been made possible by the National Science Foundation, our publisher Carolina Biological Supply Company, and numerous private foundations and corporations, including Bristol-Myers Squibb Foundation, The Dow Chemical Company Foundation, DuPont, the Hewlett-Packard Company, and The Robert Wood Johnson Foundation.

The NSRC would like to acknowledge Douglas M. Lapp, former NSRC Executive Director, for his vision and leadership on the STC/MS project. The STC/MS development staff, under the direction of Kitty Lou Smith, and the publications staff, under the direction of Heather Dittbrenner, working in cooperation with Dorothy Sawicki, Managing Editor for the first four modules, and Linda Griffin Kean, Managing Editor for the second four modules, are to be commended for their creativity, dedication, and commitment to develop these excellent curriculum materials that will be used to improve the learning and teaching of middle school science in the nation's schools.

We welcome comments from students and teachers about their experiences with the STC/MS program materials and recommendations for ways the STC/MS courses can be improved.*

Sally Goetz Shuler
Executive Director
National Science Resources Center

*Please forward your feedback and suggestions to STC/MS Program, National Science Resources Center, Smithsonian Institution, Washington, DC 20560-0403.

Acknowledgments

The National Science Resources Center gratefully acknowledges the following individuals and school systems for their assistance with the national field-testing of *Earth in Space*:

Bozeman Public School District, Bozeman, Montana

Site Coordinator: Myra Miller, Keystone Project Director

Sheri Konietzko, Teacher, Sacajawea Middle School

Ana Morris, Teacher, Sacajawea Middle School

Joann Watson, Teacher, Chief Joseph Middle School

Anderson Oconee Pickens Hub, Clemson, South Carolina

Site Coordinator: Elizabeth Edmondson

David Pepper, Teacher, Seneca Middle School, Seneca

Alan Weekes, Teacher, Pickens Middle School, Pickens

Ali Wienke, Teacher, Wren Middle School, Piedmont

Fort Bend Independent School District, Missouri City, Texas

Site Coordinator: Mary Ingle, Director of Secondary Science

Tom Grubbs, Teacher, Lake Olympia Middle School

Kirlew Matthie, Teacher, Lake Olympia Middle School

Scott McKie, Teacher, Lake Olympia Middle School

Schenectady City School District, Schenectady, New York

Site Coordinator: Arden Rauch

Claire Godlewski, Teacher, Oneida Middle School

Danielle Hartkern, Teacher, Central Park Middle School

Ed Pfeifer, Teacher, Schenectady High School

Spotsylvania County School District, Spotsylvania, Virginia

Site Coordinator: Katie Wallet, Supervisor of Science

Mary Hardy, Teacher, Ni River Middle School

The NSRC thanks the following individuals for their assistance during the development of *Earth in Space*:

Dennis Schatz, Associate Director, Pacific Science Center, Seattle, Washington

Rose Steinet, Photo Librarian, Center for Earth and Planetary Studies, National Air and Space Museum, Smithsonian Institution, Washington, D.C.

The NSRC also thanks the following individuals from Carolina Biological Supply Company for their contribution to the development of this module—

Dianne Gerlach, Director of Product Development

Bobby Mize, Department Head, Publications

David Heller, Product Developer

Jennifer Manske, Publications Manager

E. Alan Scott, Department Head, Earth Science/Anthropology

Gary Metheny, Editor

29 & Company, Design

Finally, the NSRC appreciates the contribution of its STC/MS project evaluation consultants—

Center for the Study of Testing, Evaluation, and Education Policy (CSTEEP), Boston College

Joseph Pedulla, Director, CSTEEP

Contents

CONTENTS

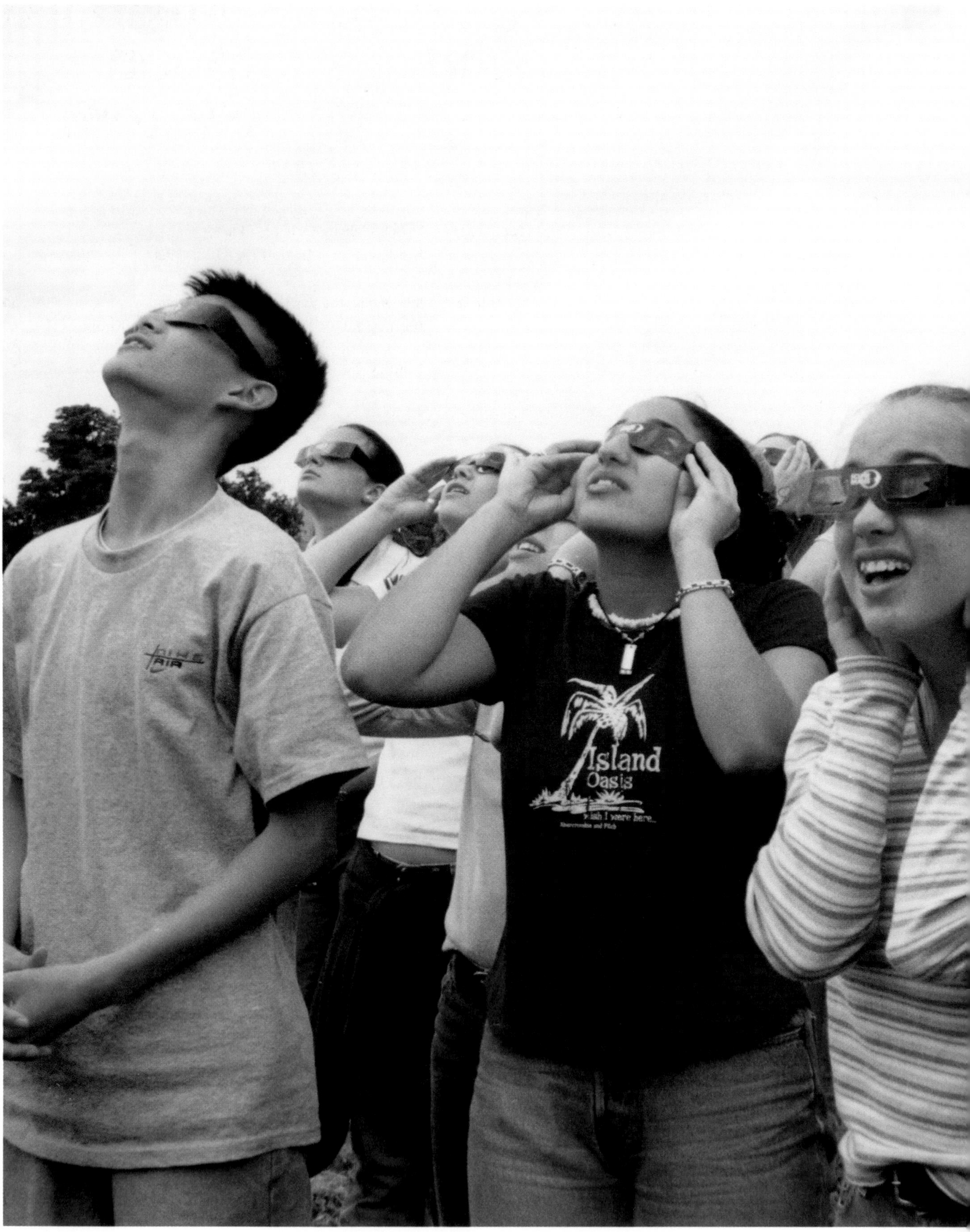

COURTESY OF CAROL O'DONNELL/© NSRC

PART 1 Sun-Earth-Moon System

Thinking About Earth as a Planet

NATIONAL AERONAUTICS AND SPACE ADMINISTRATION/JET PROPULSION LABORATORY

This composite shows several images of the planets that were taken by Voyager *and made into one photo.*

INTRODUCTION

By simply looking into the sky, you have made direct observations of the Sun and Moon—the two most visible objects in our sky. Astronomers historically have made direct observations of our closest neighbors, including Mars and the Moon, but most of what astronomers know about Mercury, Venus, and the outer planets comes from the use of technological tools, especially NASA spacecraft. (NASA stands for National Aeronautics and Space Administration.) For example, *Voyager 1* and *Voyager 2* reached Jupiter in 1979. *Voyager 1* reached Saturn in 1980 and sent back close-up views of the planet. *Voyager 2* moved on to explore Uranus in 1986 and Neptune in 1989. As it orbits Earth, the Hubble space telescope has taken images of Pluto and its moon, Charon. As a result, the solar system is no longer a complete mystery to astronomers.

How much do you know about our solar system? What do your observations of the sky tell you? In this lesson, you will consider what you already know and what you want to know about Earth in space.

OBJECTIVES FOR THIS LESSON

Record your ideas and questions about Earth in space.

Record your responses to 10 common questions about space.

Analyze the class's responses to these 10 questions.

Getting Started

1. Read the Introduction and Objectives for This Lesson. (Try to do this before every lesson.)

2. Record in your science notebook 5–10 things you know about the solar system and Earth in space.

3. Share what you know about the solar system with the class.

MATERIALS FOR LESSON 1

For you
1 science notebook
10 self-stick notes
1 set of colored pencils, crayons, or fine-point markers

Inquiry 1.1
Examining Our Ideas About Space

PROCEDURE

1. Answer each of the following 10 questions individually in your notebook. Label each answer with the corresponding letter (A–J).

A. What is responsible for the length of one day? What is responsible for the length of one year?

B. What causes seasons?

C. Why does the Moon appear to change shape?

D. What causes a lunar eclipse? What causes a solar eclipse?

E. Look at Figure 1.1. What are the points of light in the night sky? Can you see them in the daytime? Why or why not?

F. Look at Figures 1.2 and 1.3. What processes created each landform? Do these land-forms exist on other planets or moons? Explain why or why not.

Figure 1.1 *Points of light in the night sky*

Figure 1.2 *Landform #1*

UNITED STATES GEOLOGICAL SURVEY/HAWAIIAN VOLCANO OBSERVATORY

Figure 1.3 *Landform #2*

G. Where does gravity exist? Where is gravity strongest? Where is it weakest? Why?

H. What keeps the planets in orbit around the Sun?

I. What causes tides?

J. Look at Figure 1.4. What do you see in the night sky? Write what you know about this object.

Figure 1.4 *What do you see in the night sky?*

2. Record each of your answers on a separate self-stick note. Write the matching letter (A–J) in the corner of the note.

3. Your teacher will circulate folders among members of your group. Each folder contains a question (A–J) and a photograph. Examine the photograph and read its matching question. Post your self-stick answers inside each matching folder.

4. Once you have posted all your answers to Questions A–J, your group will get one or two completed folders on which to report. Read all the posted answers on each completed folder. Put all the answers that are the same, or nearly the same, together in piles.

5. From each pile, select one answer and post it on the inside of the folder. On that answer, indicate how many times other students gave it as an answer. Put aside the duplicates.

6. Post any unique or original answers on the folder.

7. When all groups are ready, report your findings to the class. Ask your classmates if they have any questions or want to debate any of the statements. Be prepared to revisit these statements throughout the module.

REFLECTING ON WHAT YOU'VE DONE

1. Discuss the following questions with your class.

   Are any of the questions (A–J) you answered during Inquiry 1.1 related to the same topic? Explain your answer by giving an example.

   What can we learn about Earth by studying the solar system?

   How is Earth different from other planets? How is Earth similar to other planets?

2. Record in your notebook any questions you have about Earth in space and the solar system in general. Label these questions "What I Want To Know About the Solar System."

3. Share your questions in a class discussion. Your teacher will record your ideas. You will try to answer these questions as you work through this module.

4. In your science notebook, summarize what you learned (or did) in this lesson. Date your entry.

ASTRONOMY: Looking Back

What do you see when you look into the night sky? Your first answer may be "stars." Almost everything we see at night looks like a point of light. But did you know that those points of light also include planets, moons around other planets, meteors, asteroids, and even comets? All these heavenly bodies and our Sun—a star itself—are part of the cosmic neighborhood that we call the solar system.

How did we come to learn so much about the solar system? Today, astronomers use such technological advances as Hubble, a space telescope that orbits Earth and takes pictures of the solar system and deep space, and the Solar and Heliospheric Observatory (often referred to as SOHO), a satellite designed to continuously study the Sun. However, while modern astronomy—the science of observing the sky—is only a few centuries old, skywatching has been a pastime throughout history.

Ancient Skywatching

During ancient times, people could easily see the Sun and Moon, five bright neighboring planets, an occasional comet, and frequent meteors. But they did not know what these objects were. So they made up stories to describe what they had seen. To the ancients, everything in the night sky was magical, and the stories that they told, called myths, explained that magic. Astrology grew out of these early myths. (Astrology is the belief that events in the sky—the "heavens"—control our lives and predict the future.)

The ancients tried to identify patterns in the sky. They observed the Sun as it appeared to move across the daytime sky and watched as the Moon seemed to follow that same path. These early skywatchers recognized patterns in the stars' positions, gave those patterns names, and told stories to explain how these constellation "pictures" came to be.

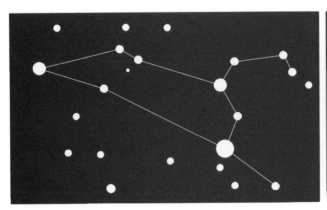 

Constellation Leo, shaped like a lion, is best seen in early spring when it is high in the sky in the Northern Hemisphere. Regulus is the bright star that marks the lion's heart.

The earliest skywatchers who kept records were the Sumerians, Babylonians, and Egyptians. Their records dated as far back as 5000 B.C. The Greeks, in 1000 B.C., continued to try to find order in the sky and in the motions of objects in the sky. They went beyond earlier, simple observations and tried to develop theories or models for the nature of celestial objects and their motions.

Classifying "Stars"

The ancients thought that everything in the sky was a star. They classified stars this way:

- "Fixed stars" that didn't change and didn't move relative to one another (which we know as *stars* today)
- "Shooting stars" that flashed across the sky (these are now known as *meteors)*
- "Hairy stars" that moved across the sky with a tail following behind them (we know these as *comets)*
- "Wandering stars" that moved across the sky following the Sun's path (these are now known as *planets)*

The Greeks gave the name *planetes*, meaning "wanderers," to the Sun, Moon, and planets—which to them were points of light that moved against the background of fixed stars. It became apparent over time that these *planetes* were part of a closely associated group of objects that we now know as our solar system.

Earth-Centered System

The Greeks believed that Earth was the center of the universe and that all the planets and stars moved around Earth. According to Greek philosophy, everything about Earth was perfect. The Greeks believed

that the sphere was the perfect shape, and they theorized that the planets, the Sun, and the Moon were attached to a huge, turning, transparent crystalline sphere that was centered on Earth.

In the second century A.D. in Alexandria, Egypt, the Greek astronomer Claudius Ptolemy proposed that planets moved in little circles that moved on bigger circles around Earth. His theory explained why some points of light seemed to move in strange patterns. For almost 1400 years, people believed Ptolemy's theory to be true.

In the early 1500s, the astronomer Nicolaus Copernicus modified the Earth-centered model with the revolutionary theory that the Sun, not Earth, was the center of the solar system. After Copernicus died in 1543, the Danish astronomer Tycho Brahe used Copernicus's observations to confirm that the planets orbited the Sun. With careful measurements, he showed that comets were well beyond the Moon. But Brahe still believed that the Moon and the Sun revolved around Earth. Finally, Brahe's student Johannes Kepler, who used Brahe's measurements, confirmed that all the planetary objects, including Earth, orbited the Sun.

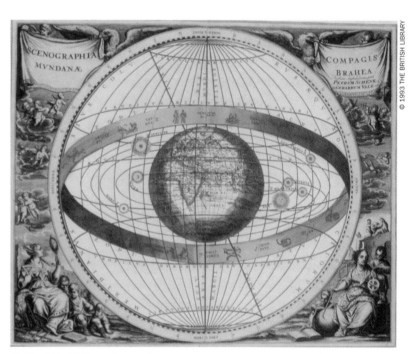

Early map of the solar system

Galileo used one of the first telescopes to look at the sky.

The Italian scientist Galileo Galilei adapted one of the first telescopes for astronomical use in 1610. This new invention made distant objects appear to be nearer and clearer. Fainter objects became visible, and astronomers' measurements became more precise. Among Galileo's first discoveries were four satellite moons revolving around Jupiter. Since Galileo could see for himself that these moons orbited Jupiter, he could demonstrate that Earth was not the center of the universe. Galileo was arrested for his discoveries and claims, which contradicted many beliefs held by the Church. However, Galileo and many others made new discoveries over the years, including the rings of Saturn, satellites or moons around several planets, sunspots, and other phenomena.

Looking Beyond

The sky that we see at night is the same sky that skywatchers of old saw and studied. The biggest difference is that we have the benefit of technology and much more knowledge to explain our observations. Exciting new discoveries about the universe are made every day. □

QUESTIONS

1. What is astronomy?
2. What did ancient skywatchers do to explain the night sky? Why?
3. What did the Greeks believe about Earth? How did their ideas change over time?

Introducing the Sun-Earth-Moon System

Earth from above the Moon's horizon as seen by astronaut Michael Collins in the Apollo 11 Moon orbiter Columbia.

NATIONAL AERONAUTICS AND SPACE ADMINISTRATION

INTRODUCTION

You probably have witnessed the beauty of the Sun as it appears to rise over the horizon. You may have noticed that the Moon appears to change shape each night of the month. These events and others can tell us much about the Sun-Earth-Moon system.

In this lesson, you will examine the relative sizes and distances of the Sun, Earth, and Moon, and how these three bodies interact within our solar system. First, you will work with your group to demonstrate what you know about the Sun-Earth-Moon system using model spheres. Then you will compare your group's ideas with those of other groups. In the second inquiry, you will compare the size of the Sun, Earth, and Moon and their distances from one another. This helps you prepare for later lessons in this module.

OBJECTIVES FOR THIS LESSON

Demonstrate what you know about the Sun-Earth-Moon system using simple models.

Examine the diameters of the Sun, Earth, and Moon, and their relative distances from each other.

Compare the relative distances between two objects based on their apparent and true diameters.

Record the times at which the Moon rises and sets, and observe its appearance over a one- to two-week period.

Getting Started

1. How many stars do you think are in our solar system? Discuss your ideas with the class.

2. Read "Folklore: Making Sense of the Skies." Share with the class your thoughts on the reading selection and your answers to the questions at the end of the reader.

MATERIALS FOR LESSON 2

For your group
- 1 transparency
- 1 set of fine-point transparency markers
- 1 white sphere, 7.5 centimeters (cm)
- 1 white sphere, 3.5 cm
- 1 marble, 1 cm
- 1 globe of Earth, 12 cm
- 1 flashlight
- 2 D-cell batteries
- 1 metric measuring tape

Inquiry 2.1
Demonstrating What We Know About the Sun-Earth-Moon System

PROCEDURE

1. Divide a page in your science notebook into four sections (quadrants). Use both words and labeled pictures in each section to record four things you know about the Sun-Earth-Moon system. For example, you may want to illustrate how these three solar system bodies are positioned, or describe how they move relative to one another.

2. Use the materials in the plastic box as models of the Sun, Earth, and Moon to demonstrate to your group one thing that you recorded about the Sun-Earth-Moon system. One member of your group will record your idea on the transparency. Have each member of your group contribute one idea.

REFLECTING ON WHAT YOU'VE DONE

1. Use the transparency and models to demonstrate to the class one thing that your group knows about the Sun, Earth, and Moon.

2. In your science notebook, write about something new that you learned in this lesson.

3. On the basis of your class discussions, record in your science notebook the difference between the terms "rotation" and "revolution." Which word means the same as "orbit?" Feel free to use examples. Record your responses in both words and pictures, and label your diagrams. You will return to the meanings of these terms in Lessons 3 and 4.

Inquiry 2.2
Scaling the
Sun-Earth-Moon System

PROCEDURE

1. Do you think that the size of the sphere that you selected for your Moon was to scale with the size of the 12-cm globe of Earth? How big would a model Sun have to be in order to be to scale with your 12-cm Earth? Share your ideas with the class and explain your answers.

2. Read "Scaling the Sun-Earth-Moon System" in this lesson. As you read, answer the following questions in your notebook:

A. What is the diameter of Earth at the equator?

B. What is the diameter of the Moon?

C. What mathematical equation describes how many times smaller in diameter the Moon is than Earth?

D. What is the distance from Earth to the Moon?

E. What mathematical equation describes how to measure the distance from Earth to the Moon using Earth's diameter as a unit of measure?

F. What is the diameter of the Sun?

G. What mathematical equation describes how many Earth diameters equal the Sun's diameter?

H. Why does the Sun appear to be the same size as the Moon in the sky? What mathematical equation would you use to explain why the Sun and the Moon appear to be the same size?

I. Why is there a leap year every four years?

J. Use the reading selection to help you decide if the diameter of the model Moon you used in Inquiry 2.1 is to scale with your 12-cm globe of Earth.

K. How large would your model Sun be if scaled to your 12-cm Earth?

REFLECTING ON WHAT YOU'VE DONE

1. Share with the class what you learned about the Sun, Earth, and Moon from the reading selection.

2. How far away would your model Sun be if scaled to your model Moon and Earth? Watch as someone in your class demonstrates this.

3. Return to your notebook entries showing the four quadrants. Is there anything that you want to change or add to reflect your new thinking? Add that information now.

FOLKLORE
Making Sense of the Skies

How did ancient people explain the apparent changes in the shape of the Moon or the rising and setting Sun? They didn't have all the scientific information we have today, yet they wanted to make sense of the mysteries around them.

The ancient Greeks, for example, wondered about the strange light that fell on Earth at night. They didn't know that it was light from the Sun reflected off the Moon. Instead, they believed that Artemis, their goddess of the Moon, rode her chariot across the sky and shot silver arrows to Earth. Those silver arrows created the mysterious light we know as moonlight.

Phases of the Moon

The moon often appears to change its shape. These "phases" of the Moon confounded the ancients. They didn't understand that the changing positions of the Moon in relation to Earth caused different parts of the illuminated Moon to be visible from Earth. They didn't know that the Moon never really changes shape.

To make sense of this mystery, ancient Hindus believed that the Moon held a special drink that only gods could consume. As the gods drank the special liquid, the Moon shrank. When the gods refilled the Moon with their special drink, it became full again.

An old story that is still recounted by the Inuits of Greenland explains the Moon's phases this way: The Moon god, Anningan, continually chases his sister, the Sun goddess Malina, across the sky. During the chase, he forgets to eat and grows thinner and thinner. To satisfy his hunger, he disappears for three days each month (during the new moon) and then returns to chase his sister again.

The Day-Night Cycle

The continuous cycle of day and night spawned many fascinating tales. The Mamaiurans, an Amazon tribe in Brazil, say that at the beginning of time so many birds lived in the sky that their wings blocked the Sun's light, making it always nighttime. Because of that, the people feared attacks from wild animals.

Tired of the darkness, Mamaiuran brothers Iae and Kuat decided to force the king of the birds, Urubutsin, to share some of the daylight. The two brothers hid inside a dead animal and waited for Urubutsin. When the Bird King came close, Kuat grabbed his leg and held him until he agreed to share daylight with the people of the Amazon. That, according to Mamaiuran legend, is why day alternates with night.

An ancient Japanese legend explained sunlight another way. The Sun goddess, Amaterasu, had

In this painting of Father Sky and Mother Earth, the Navajo included patterns of constellations.

SMITHSONIAN INSTITUTION, NATIONAL ANTHROPOLOGICAL ARCHIVES

a younger brother, Sunsanoo, who was a mischievous god of storms. One day he destroyed Amaterasu's beautiful garden. Deeply saddened, Amaterasu hid in a dark cave, plunging the world into darkness and causing all life to wither and die. Amaterasu was eventually drawn out of the cave by the music and dancing of another goddess. The other gods hung a mirror that reflected to Amaterasu her own dazzling beauty and light. She returned to her throne to warm and light the world and nurture life. ☐

QUESTIONS

1. Why did people tell tales like these?
2. According to Chinese mythology, a white hare is believed to live on the Moon, which is carried by a dragon. Write a creative story to explain this myth.

Legend has it that so many birds lived in the sky, their wings blocked the Sun's light.

This woodcut shows Amaterasu, the Japanese Sun goddess.

Scaling the Sun-Earth-Moon System

Earth's Moon

The Moon's age is estimated to be between 4.3 billion and 4.5 billion years. There are many theories about how the Moon was formed. Some astronomers think the Moon may have been formed when a Mars-sized asteroid collided with Earth about 100 million to 200 million years after Earth was formed approximately 4.5 billion years ago. The debris from that collision was thrown out into space, and that debris eventually joined together to form the Moon. The newly formed Moon traveled at just the right speed so that it remained within the control of Earth's gravitational field.

Now the Moon is Earth's natural satellite. This means that the Moon revolves around, or orbits, Earth. If the Moon were to travel too quickly, it could escape Earth's gravity and zoom out into space. If the Moon were to travel too slowly, Earth's gravity could overcome it and the Moon could fall to Earth.

Since the Moon is our nearest neighbor in the sky—about 384,000 kilometers away—it was the first object that humans visited when space travel became possible. Because the Moon has no atmosphere, it has no weather patterns. Because the Moon has no weather—no wind, rain, ice, or snow—it is still in its near-original state. This makes the Moon a perfect object for scientists to study the history and origin of the solar system.

The Moon is about 3500 kilometers in diameter. The Earth is 12,756 kilometers in diameter at the equator. (The Earth is not an exact sphere. It is slightly flattened at the poles, where its diameter is only 12,720 kilometers.)

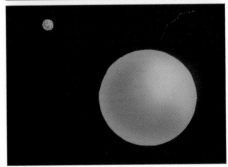

One theory of how the Moon formed

This means that the Moon is slightly more than one-fourth (0.27) the size of Earth. See Table 1 for a summary of this information.

Natural Calendars

Earth rotates, or spins, on its axis. It also revolves, or orbits, around the Sun. Like Earth, the Moon also rotates on its axis. But the Moon rotates much more slowly than Earth, taking approximately 27.3 days to turn once on its axis. The Moon also takes 27.3 days to orbit Earth.

The relative motions of the Sun, Earth, and Moon spurred ancient cultures to develop natural

Table 1 Size and Distance Comparison Sun-Earth-Moon Data

Solar System Body	Distance from Earth (km)	Earths Away	Diameter (km)	Earths Across
Sun	150,000,000	~12,000	1,392,000	109
Moon	384,000	30	3500	0.27
Earth			Equator = 12,756	1

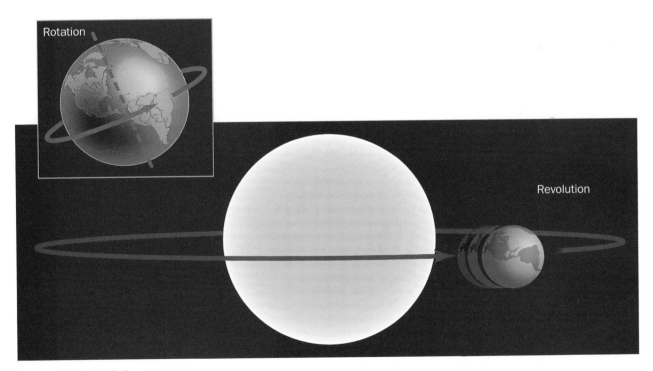

Rotation and revolution

calendars and timekeeping methods that eventually led to the clocks, calendars, and timekeeping devices we use today.

Day and Night Day and night are caused by Earth's rotation on its axis. It takes Earth approximately 24 hours to rotate one time through day and night. This repetitive cycle of light and dark provides a clocklike regularity for measuring our days, and ancient cultures based the measure of a day on this rotation.

Month The Moon takes approximately one month—about 27 days—to orbit Earth. We observe the Moon's orbit by seeing its appearance change shape throughout each month. This repetitive cycle of the Moon's apparent change in shape led ancient cultures to identify this pattern and to measure each month.

Year It takes Earth 365¼ days, or one year, to orbit the Sun one time. Since a calendar year is 365 days long, we have an extra ¼ day every year that needs to be accounted for. So every four years, we have a leap year in which an extra day—February 29—is added to our calendar.

It's easy for us to see the links between the relative motions of the Sun, Earth, and Moon and the calendars and clocks that we use every day. But earlier civilizations had to carefully track these planetary motions to arrive at predictable, measurable results.

Our Sun the Star

Our Sun is the only star in our solar system. Within the Milky Way galaxy—the collection of dust, gas, and stars to which our solar system belongs—the Sun is just one of 100 billion or so stars. There are billions of other galaxies in the universe.

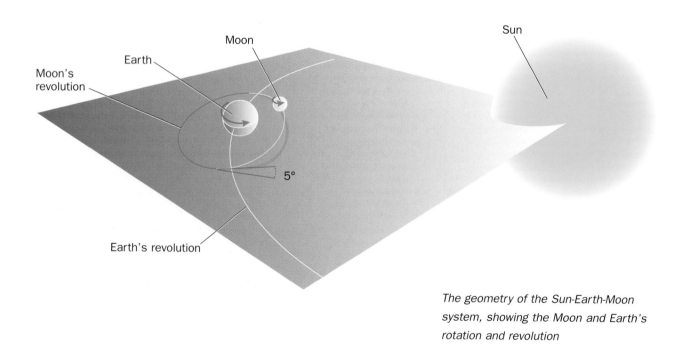

The geometry of the Sun-Earth-Moon system, showing the Moon and Earth's rotation and revolution

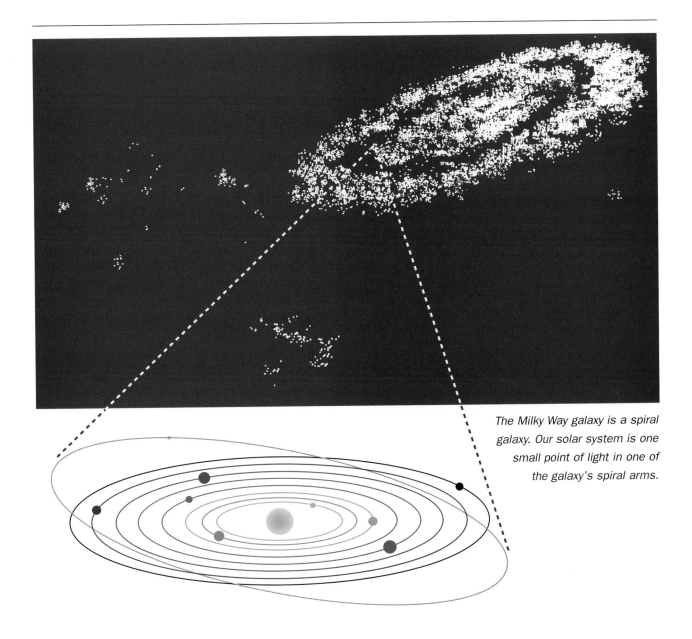

The Milky Way galaxy is a spiral galaxy. Our solar system is one small point of light in one of the galaxy's spiral arms.

The Sun may seem close to Earth, but it is actually about 150 million kilometers (93 million miles) away. With a diameter of 1,392,000 kilometers, the Sun is 400 times larger than the diameter of the Moon. The Sun is also 400 times farther away from Earth than the Moon is. This means that the Moon and Sun appear to be the same size in the sky.

The Sun is bigger in volume than anything we can imagine. One million Earths would fit inside the Sun, and 109 Earths could fit across the Sun's diameter.

Models of the Sun, Earth, and Moon

Sometimes the best way to understand abstract concepts is to use models. Models are smaller representations of an object that might be too large, too complex, or too far away to study firsthand. Look at the facts that you have read here. Use your models and what you know about math to demonstrate what you know about these facts. ☐

3

Tracking Shadows

The Sun sets along the horizon at Stonehenge (which means "hanging stones"). Stonehenge was constructed outside of London from about 2400 B.C. to 1200 B.C.

INTRODUCTION

If you go to Stonehenge during the summer solstice, you will notice that the Sun always rises over a stone called the Heel Stone or Sun Stone. Why does this happen? Some scientists theorize that Stonehenge may have been an ancient astronomical observatory and calendar. Those who built it could tell when Earth arrived at a certain point in its yearly orbit around the Sun. Some scientists think that Stonehenge also may have been used to mark changing seasons and to predict eclipses. Still others believe that it was a temple for Sun worshipers who used the stones to mark significant points in the Sun's journey across the sky.

To begin this lesson, you will share with the class what you know about the Sun and Moon's apparent motion across the sky, as well as what causes day, night, and seasons. During Inquiry 3.1,

OBJECTIVES FOR THIS LESSON

Record the length and angle of shadows cast by a shadow stick at different times during the day.

Relate the length and angle of shadows to the apparent position of the Sun in the sky.

Model winter and summer shadows and compare the Sun's apparent position in the sky during each season.

Simulate Earth's rotation, and relate it to the Sun's apparent daily motion across the sky.

Create a working definition for the term "rotation."

ENGLISH HERITAGE

you will record the Sun's position in the sky throughout the day by marking the location of shadows cast by a shadow stick. During Inquiry 3.2, you will use a computer program to analyze shadows and the path of the Sun throughout the year. During Inquiry 3.3, you will use a flashlight to simulate the rising and setting of the Sun. At the end of the lesson, you will use a small globe and the Sun's natural light to determine what changing shadows tell us about our planet Earth.

Getting Started

1. Be prepared to discuss with your class what you know about day, night, and the seasons.

2. In this lesson you will use a shadow stick to make general observations of shadows throughout the day. Do you know how shadow sticks were used in the past? Discuss your ideas with the class.

3. In a class discussion, describe shadows you have seen at home or school. What patterns did you observe in the shadows throughout the day? How might you study the patterns in shadow data firsthand?

4. You will be collecting shadow data outside. Before you do, read "How To View the Sun Safely." Discuss the Safety Tip with your teacher.

MATERIALS FOR INQUIRY 3.1

For you

- 1 copy of Student Sheet 3.1: Analyzing Shadow Data

For your group

- 1 Sun-Earth-Moon Board™
- 3 sheets of white paper, taped together
- 4 large binder clips
- 1 rod #1
- 1 rod #2
- 1 rod #3
- 1 piece of chalk
- 1 magnetic compass
- 1 student timer (or other timepiece)
- 1 metric ruler, 30 cm (12″)

SAFETY TIP

Never look directly at the Sun! It can cause permanent eye damage, or even blindness.

5. Look at Side A of the Sun-Earth-Moon (SEM) Board™. How might you use it to record shadows throughout the day? What would you need to keep constant to compare shadow patterns? How will you record your data? Discuss your ideas with the class.

Inquiry 3.1
Analyzing Shadows

PROCEDURE

1. Set your group's timer to the correct time of day.

2. Use Figure 3.1 and your teachers' guidance to position the board to get the best shadow data. If a class before yours used this board, keep it in the same location. Listen to find out which rod to use.

Figure 3.1 *Put the Sun-Earth-Moon Board in a flat, sunny place so that Side A is facing up. Turn the board so that the stick is in the middle of the southern edge of the board. Use your compass to find north. Use chalk to outline your board's position on the ground.*

3. Trace the shadow cast by the stick directly onto your SEM Board paper. Then write the time above, near, or inside the shadow, as shown in Figure 3.2.

4. Discuss what you think will happen to the shadow throughout the day.

5. Wait 10–15 minutes to record your next shadow. While you wait, read "Solar Noon." If you have time, read "The Anasazi: Ancient Skywatchers" as well. Discuss these readers with your group or class.

6. Record your second and final shadow. Do not take your board apart. Other classes may continue to add shadows to your board. During your next class you will analyze a full day's worth of shadows.

Figure 3.2 *Trace the shadow, then write the time.*

SOLAR NOON

Have you ever noticed that light from the Sun feels more intense when the Sun is high in the sky? The point at which the Sun is highest in the sky (and when shadows are shortest) is called "solar noon."

When the Sun first becomes visible in the morning, a given point on Earth receives sunshine at an extremely small angle. This means that the relative intensity of the Sun's radiation is small at this point. The more the light spreads out (or diffuses), the less intense the Sun's radiation is at a given point. By solar noon, however, when the Sun is highest in the sky, the sunshine is slanted the least, or is closest to being vertical. At the close of the day, the Sun's rays again strike Earth at a lesser angle.

But sometimes it is hotter at 3:00 P.M. than at solar noon. Why? A given point at the top of Earth's atmosphere receives more energy from the Sun at solar noon than at 3:00 P.M. or 4:00 P.M. Nonetheless, heat energy from the Sun collects in the atmosphere, on the surface of Earth, and in man-made objects on Earth's surface from the time the Sun rises until it sets. Earth's surface sends this heat energy back into the atmosphere. The amount of heat energy sent (radiated) by Earth's surface determines air temperature. This means that the afternoon—and not solar noon—is often the hottest part of the day.

REFLECTING ON WHAT YOU'VE DONE

1. Get one copy of Student Sheet 3.1. For your group, get a full day's worth of shadow data.

2. Use your metric ruler to measure each shadow tracing. Record the times and shadow lengths on Table 1 on Student Sheet 3.1.

3. Plot your time and length data on Graph 1 on the student sheet. Connect the dots on your graph so that they form a curve.

4. Answer the following questions in your notebook:

A. What shadow patterns did you observe?

B. At what time of day did the shortest shadow occur? Where is the Sun in the sky at this time of day?

C. At what times of day did the longest shadows occur? Where is the Sun in the sky at these times of day?

D. If solar noon were the lowest point on your curve, how would you define the term "solar noon"?

E. How could you use your graph to predict the length and location of a shadow for a particular time not plotted on the graph? Give an example and explain.

A. It carved opposite the sun.

B. Noon, the sun is directly overhead

C. The earliest time, the sun is almost flush with the ground

D. 1:45 pm

E. At any time I could correspond any point to a specific length.

**MATERIALS FOR
INQUIRY 3.2**

**For you and your
computer partners**

1 transparency
1 set of fine-point
   transparency
   markers

Inquiry 3.2
Collecting Computerized Shadow Data

PROCEDURE

1. Open the program *Starry Night Enthusiast* on your computer. Practice using the program and explore what you can find out about the Sun, Moon, and planets using this program.

2. If necessary, open the *Starry Night* program from <Options> on the main menu and select <Viewing Location>. On the list of cities, select the city closest to your home location. Click on <Go to Location>. If a grassy field is not already showing, select <Home> on the tool bar.

3. Check the time on your program to make certain it is the same time as your watch or classroom clock. If it is not, click on <NOW> and the time will change to your current time.

4. If objects are labeled on the screen, go to <Labels> on the main menu and select <Hide All Labels>.

5. Find the Sun in the sky. If you can't find it, left-click and drag your cursor around the screen until you find the Sun.

6. What does the Sun look like in the sky on your screen? In which direction are you looking? Discuss your observations with your partner.

7. Now set the date and time to June 1 at 4:00 A.M. To do this, perform the following operations using the functions on the tool bar:

A. Set the <Time Flow Rate> to 3000X, then click on the red <Stop Time> button.

B. Click on the month and use the up and down arrows on your keyboard to change the month to June. (The down arrow takes you back in time, the up arrow takes you forward in time.)

C. Click on the day of the month and enter "1."

D. Make sure the year is the current year. If it is not the current year, click on the year and change it to the current year.

E. Set the time to 4:00 A.M. by clicking on the hour and entering "4," then clicking on the minute display and entering "0." If the time is set to "PM," click on "PM" and the time will change to "AM."

8. Run the program using the <Run Time Forward> button and find the time when the Sun is at its highest point in the sky during the day. You may need to use both the <Run Time Forward> button and the <Run Time Backward> button to determine when the sun is the highest in the sky during the day. When you have found the highest point in the sky that the Sun reaches during the day, do the following:

A. Click on the <Stop Time> button to stop motion when the Sun is at its highest point. Then click on the Sun, changing the cursor to an arrow. Drag the arrow down to the horizon.

B. Observe the angle of separation displayed on the screen. What is the angle of separation (the measurement between the Sun's position in the sky and Earth's horizon)? See Figure 3.3 for an example. Tell this number to your partners and record this information.

Figure 3.3 *The angle of separation can be thought of as the Sun's apparent position in the sky relative to the horizon, as viewed by an observer on Earth.*

9. Click on the <Favourites> tab and then select <Horizon Shadows>. The screen will change to a simulation of a landscape with trees. Set the date and time to June 1 at 8:00 A.M. of the current year.

10. Divide your transparency in half as shown in Figure 3.4, and write 06/01 on the top half of the transparency.

11. Use the cursor to click and drag the scene up, so that half of your screen is grass. Focus on the taller tree to the right of the "S" (South) compass mark.

12. Place the transparency on the computer screen. (Use masking tape to secure it if you are allowed.) Trace the taller tree onto the top half of the transparency.

13. On the transparency, draw the tree's shadow. Mark 8:00 A.M. next to the shadow, as shown in Figure 3.4. In your notebook, draw the tree and its shadow and indicate the date and time as well.

14. Click on the down arrow on the <Time Flow Rate> button and then on "hours" in the <Discreet Time Steps> menu. The <Time Flow Rate> will display "1 hours."

15. Click on the <Step Time Forward> button. On the same tree on the transparency, trace the shadow for 9:00 A.M. Draw the shadow in your notebook.

16. Click the <Step Time Forward> button again. Trace the shadow of the tree at 10:00 A.M. Repeat this procedure until you have traced all of the shadows for the full day. Label the time for each shadow. When the shadow is the shortest, measure the Sun's angle of separation.

Figure 3.4 *In the top half of your drawing, trace the taller tree and its 8:00 A.M. shadow. Label the shadow 8:00 A.M.*

17. Move your transparency up so the bottom half is now over the "S" tree. Set the date on the screen to 12/01 (December 1) of this year. Set the time to 8:00 A.M. Then repeat Steps 13–16. Record all your new shadows on the bottom half of the transparency. Keep a record of your shadows in your notebook as well.

REFLECTING ON WHAT YOU'VE DONE

1. Discuss your observations with the class.

2. Discuss the following questions:

What patterns do you observe in the shadow data overall? What do you think causes these patterns?

What differences do you observe between the summer and winter shadow data? What patterns do you observe in the Sun's angle of separation? What do you think causes these patterns?

MATERIALS FOR INQUIRY 3.3

For you

1 copy of Student Sheet 3.3: Graphing the Sun's Path in Winter and Summer

2 markers, pens, or pencils (different colors)

For your group

1 Sun-Earth-Moon Board™

1 "Modeling Shadows" sheet

4 large binder clips

1 rod #1

1 Mini Maglite®

2 AA batteries

1 piece of string, 50 cm

1 super jumbo plastic straw

1 metric measuring tape

1 foam sleeve (optional)

Inquiry 3.3
Modeling Winter and Summer Shadows

PROCEDURE

1. Use binder clips to attach the two-sided "Modeling Shadows" sheet to Side A of your SEM Board so that the Winter side faces up.

2. Place rod #1 in the hole.

3. Tie one end of the string to the hook on your board. Tie the other end to your Mini Maglite®, as shown in Figure 3.5. There should be 30 cm from the hook to the head of the Mini Maglite when the string is pulled tight.

Figure 3.5 *Tie the Mini Maglite® to the string. Attach the string to the hook on the board. Keep the string pulled tight at all times, so that your Mini Maglite® travels in an arc across the "sky."*

Figure 3.6 *Measure the height of the Mini Maglite® at each of the nine points.*

4. Move the Mini Maglite to recreate the Sun's motion in the winter sky in the Northern Hemisphere. Pull the string so that it is tight at all times. If you need help keeping the string straight, thread the string through the plastic straw.

5. For each shadow, record on Table 1 of Student Sheet 3.3 how high your Mini Maglite is from the table at each of the nine points for Winter (see Figure 3.6).

6. What do you notice about the Sun's path in relation to the horizon? Discuss your observations with your group.

7. Now attach the "Modeling Shadows: Summer" sheet face up on Side A of the SEM Board. Repeat Procedure Steps 4–6. Remember that the string must be pulled tight at all times. What do you notice about the Sun's path in the summer compared to winter? Discuss your observations as a group.

8. Graph the data that you recorded in Table 1 onto Graph 1 of Student Sheet 3.3. Connect each set of points on the graph with a curved line. Use the color key to label each set of points.

REFLECTING ON WHAT YOU'VE DONE

1. Share your data and graph with the class. Where would the winter shadow fall between points 6 and 7? Mark your prediction on your graph of Student Sheet 3.3.

2. With your teacher, use a planning sheet to summarize your investigation from Inquiry 3.3.

3. Answer the following questions in your notebook:

A. What shadow patterns did you observe for summer?

B. What shadow patterns did you observe for winter?

C. During which season and at what time of day might a post cast little or no shadow? Why?

D. At which locations did the longest shadows occur? Where is the "Sun" at these times of day?

E. Compare the path of the "Sun" in the winter sky to the path of the "Sun" in the summer sky. How are the paths alike or different?

**MATERIALS FOR
INQUIRY 3.4**

For your group
- 1 globe of Earth,
  12 cm
- 1 rod labeled "E"
- 1 toothpick, 1 cm
  of the tip
  Modeling clay,
  bead-sized
  amount

Inquiry 3.4
Analyzing the Effects of Earth's Rotation

PROCEDURE

1. Help your teacher identify your local region on the class globe. How can you use the shadow stick to determine the effects of Earth's rotation on shadow data? Share your ideas with the class.

2. Make an axis for your group's small globe by placing the rod labeled "E" through the globe's holes.

3. Using modeling clay and the tip of a toothpick, mark your home location on the globe, as shown in Figure 3.7.

Figure 3.7 *Stick the toothpick on the globe at the location of your school. Hold the rod so the toothpick faces up.*

4. Work either outside with the Sun or inside with a clamp lamp. Find a shadow on your globe cast by the toothpick. What needs to happen to make the shadow change length and direction? Discuss your hypotheses with your group.

5. Test your predictions. Rotate your globe on the rod in all directions. How does the shadow of the toothpick change as the globe rotates? Record your observations in your notebook. Set the globe aside.

6. Now stand with the light (Sun or lamp) behind your left shoulder. Simulate the rotating Earth and apparent "rising Sun" by slowly rotating your body counter-clockwise. Watch how the Sun seems to move relative to your body. Discuss your observations with your group. Record them in your notebook.

REFLECTING ON WHAT YOU'VE DONE

1. Discuss your observations with the class. You may be asked to demonstrate your observations.

2. In collecting shadow data outside, you might describe the Sun's path as the "apparent path of the Sun across the sky." Why is the word "apparent" used in that description? Record your ideas in your science notebook.

3. Write the following statements in your notebook. After each statement, indicate whether it is true or false and describe why.

A. The Sun rises.

B. The rotation of Earth makes it look as if the Sun is moving above the horizon.

4. In your own words, define the term "rotation." Record your working definition in your notebook. Compare this to the definition you wrote during Lesson 2.

5. With your class, return to the Lesson 1 folder for Question A. Is there anything you would now change or add? Discuss your ideas with the class.

NATIONAL OCEANIC AND ATMOSPHERIC ADMINISTRATION (NOAA) PHOTO LIBRARY/NOAA CENTRAL LIBRARY

How To
View the Sun Safely

The Sun, our neighborhood star

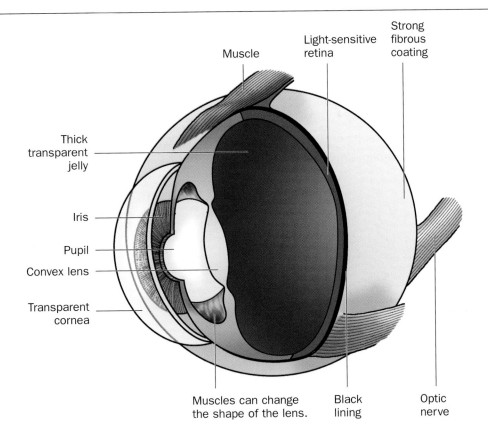

Muscle

Light-sensitive retina

Strong fibrous coating

Thick transparent jelly

Iris

Pupil

Convex lens

Transparent cornea

Muscles can change the shape of the lens.

Black lining

Optic nerve

Cross-section of the eye

Much of our progress in understanding stars comes from studying our "neighborhood star," the Sun. Although we usually associate the study of astronomy with the night, studying the Sun during the day can help us learn more about Earth as a planet.

You will study the Sun in this module. Before you begin, keep an important warning in mind: *Never look directly at the Sun*. Never use binoculars or a telescope to view the Sun directly, even when you have on safe solar viewing glasses. Looking directly at the Sun will cause *permanent eye damage* in seconds. Because you cannot feel the injury, you will not know that your eyes have been damaged until it is too late! This damage is permanent and it can even cause blindness.

How the Eye Is Damaged

Immediate eye damage occurs if you directly observe the Sun without adequate eye protection. The retina of the eye burns from the solar exposure. Over time, exposure to high levels of ultraviolet radiation from the Sun can cause rapid aging of the outer layers of the eye, as well as the skin. Solar ultraviolet radiation eventually can lead to the development of cataracts, which cloud the lens of the eye.

How does exposure to the Sun damage the eye? The dark pigment behind the retina absorbs visible light and near-infrared radiation. The light energy is converted into heat that can literally cook the exposed tissue. This destroys the nerve endings and light-sensitive cells of the eye, leaving a permanently blind area in the retina.

Safe Viewing

The best way to view the Sun and avoid eye damage is with projection—that is, by looking at a projected image of the Sun rather than at the Sun itself. You can project an image of the Sun onto the ground or a screen using a pinhole projection. You can make a pinhole projection by poking a very small hole into a piece of cardboard or other material so that the Sun's light travels through the pinhole onto the screen. You can even project the image of the Sun onto the ground using a small telescope or a pair of binoculars with low magnification. (You will do this in Lesson 8.)

If your telescope is equipped with a special filter, you can also view the Sun through the telescope. The only reliable filters are those that fit over the front of the telescope and reflect away most of the light. Unless you are working with an adult and are *absolutely sure* of what you are doing, do not use a sun filter or telescope to view the Sun.

You also can view the Sun directly using solar viewing glasses, which are designed specifically for viewing the Sun. Keep in mind that regular sunglasses or 3-D tinted glasses

A pinhole projects the image of the Sun onto the screen.

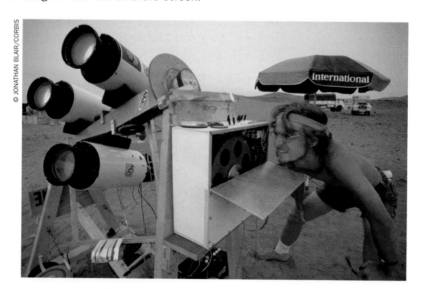

U.S. scientists from Hopkins Observatory check a telescope in Ramnicu Valcea. The August 1999 eclipse lasted for 2 hours and 23 minutes, casting a 113-kilometer strip of darkness across Romania.

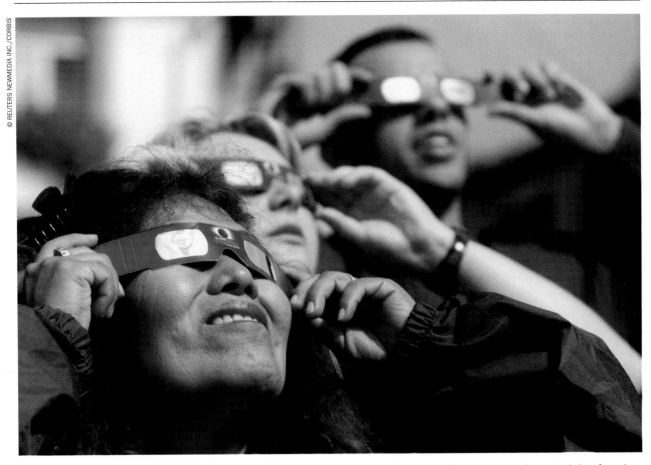

© REUTERS NEWMEDIA INC./CORBIS

Watching total solar eclipse in southern Belgium, August 1999. The people shown here are wearing special safe solar viewing glasses.

cannot protect your eyes from solar radiation while you are observing the Sun!

In this module, you will use projection and safe solar viewing glasses to view the Sun. Do not use any other methods unless you have adult supervision.

Remember, even though there are safe ways to view the Sun, there is always a chance that someone may not take the necessary precautions, or may disobey instructions, and an accident may result. So stay safe. *Never* look directly at the Sun! ☐

THE ANASAZI: Ancient Skywatchers

You only have to look at a calendar to know what month it is. The Anasazi, who lived in the Southwest about a thousand years ago, had no calendars. Their lives depended on knowing precisely the time of year.

These ancient people made their home in a desert valley in Arizona called Chaco Canyon. Temperatures there can sink as low as –39 °Celsius (C) in the winter and soar to 38 °C in the summer. Because the Anasazi had a short growing season, they needed to plant crops at just the right time. If they planted too early, the plants would freeze; too late, and the plants wouldn't have time to mature or bear fruit.

How could the Anasazi determine the best time to plant their crops? They created their own calendar—based on the movements of the Sun.

Tracking the Sun

The Anasazi tracked the Sun and other celestial bodies in several ways. They etched spirals on rocks throughout Chaco Canyon. Sunlight would strike certain points of these spirals and act like a seasonal clock to tell the Anasazi what they needed to know about the season, time of year, or time of day.

One of the most famous Anasazi spirals, the "Sun dagger," was carefully placed behind three upright slabs of rock on a butte. A dagger of light sliced through the spiral during the change of each season—at the winter solstice (around December 21), the spring equinox (around March 21), the summer solstice (around June 21), and at the fall equinox (around September 21).

The Anasazi also used natural markers to track the Sun. When sunrise and sunset occurred at certain places against the peaks and valleys of a distant mountain range, skilled observers would know that it was time to plant crops or to expect the arrival of the rainy season.

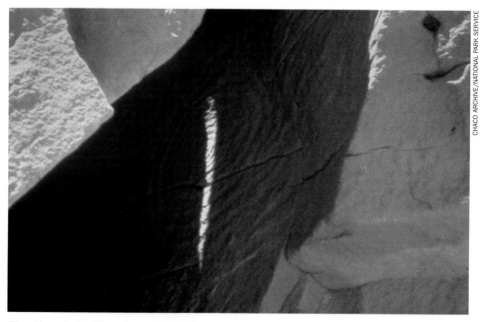

CHACO ARCHIVE/NATIONAL PARK SERVICE

The "Sun dagger" marks various solar events.

The time of year and the time of day make all the difference in what you see. These are support beams whose shadows indicate the Sun's position in the sky.

Petrograph of supernova 1054. Notice the large star blazing next to the hand and crescent moon.

Recording the Great Events

The Anasazi civilization was at its peak in 1054. That same year, light from an exploding star, or supernova, reached Earth. The gas, dust, and other matter that blew out of the exploding star burned six times brighter than Venus! Visible even in the middle of the day, the supernova could be seen for 23 days before it disappeared.

Before the supernova left their sight, the Anasazi did something that may never have been done before. They recorded the first image of a supernova—a large star blazing next to a hand and crescent moon. This record is called a petrograph.

Just a few years after the supernova, Halley's comet streaked across the southwest sky. Below the petrograph of the supernova, the Anasazi added three circles with flames trailing from them. Scientists believe that these ancient drawings represent Halley's comet.

The Skywatchers Burn Out

Just two hundred years after their desert civilization began, the Anasazi abandoned Chaco Canyon. Many scientists believe they left after years of drought. Others aren't so sure. Perhaps the sky signs became unreliable, and the Anasazi lost faith in their calendar system. Whatever the reasons, these ancient astronomers left their homeland, leaving behind only their stories in stone. ☐

QUESTIONS

1. Why did the Anasazi need a calendar?
2. What did the Anasazi use to create their own calendars?
3. What is one astronomical event, besides the apparent motion of the Sun and Moon, which the Anasazi recorded in stone?

4

Seasons on Earth

On Earth, orange and red autumn leaves stand out against the blue sky.

NATIONAL OCEANIC AND ATMOSPHERIC ADMINISTRATION (NOAA) PHOTO LIBRARY/NOAA CENTRAL LIBRARY

INTRODUCTION

Nearly every place on Earth has four distinct seasons: winter, spring, summer, and fall. Both the Northern and Southern Hemispheres experience seasons, but they experience different seasons at the same time. When it is summer in the Northern Hemisphere, it is winter in the Southern Hemisphere, and vice versa. The shape and tilt of Earth on its axis affects the angle at which the Sun's rays pass through the atmosphere, and the length of daylight that an area experiences.

In this lesson, you will read about seasons and observe how the relative positions of the Sun and Earth change throughout the year. You will investigate the tilt of Earth's axis as it orbits the Sun, and you will see how the tilted Earth's orbit relates to seasons and changing shadows. You also will return to the software program you used in Lesson 3 to analyze the position of the North Star, as well as sunrise and sunset data over the year at different latitudes. You will

OBJECTIVES FOR THIS LESSON

Model Earth's orbit.

Identify Polaris as the current North Star.

Compare sunrise and sunset times at different latitudes throughout the year.

Relate changes in the apparent path of the Sun and the length of daylight to Earth's orbit on its tilted axis.

Create a working definition of the term "revolution." Identify "orbit" as its synonym.

explore what the apparent path of the Sun at different latitudes tells us about Earth's position relative to the Sun. Why does Earth's revolution around the Sun cause seasons? Let's find out.

Getting Started

1. Examine the shadow data from Lesson 3. Why do you think winter and summer shadows are different? Do you think that the shadows in June are the same everywhere on Earth? Discuss your ideas with the class.

2. What do you already know about seasons? What questions do you have about seasons? Share your ideas with the class.

3. Look at the two mounted globes. What observations can you make about the globes? Discuss your ideas as a class.

MATERIALS FOR LESSON 4

For you
- 1 copy of Student Sheet 4.3a: Sunrise and Sunset Data for Different Latitudes
- 1 copy of Student Sheet 4.3b: Graphing the Ecliptic at Different Latitudes
- 1 copy of Student Sheet 4: Review: Lessons 1-4

For your group
- 1 transparency copy of Student Sheet 4.3a: Sunrise and Sunset Data for Different Latitudes
- 1 transparency copy of Student Sheet 4.3b: Graphing the Ecliptic at Different Latitudes
- 1 set of fine-point transparency markers
- 1 Sun-Earth-Moon Board™
- 1 globe of Earth, 12 cm
- 1 rod labeled "E"
- 1 toothpick, 1 cm of tip
  Modeling clay, bead-sized amount
- 1 Mini Maglite®
- 2 AA batteries
- 5 removable dots
- 1 protractor
- 1 foam sleeve (optional)

4. Watch as your teacher demonstrates how Earth's axis can be "fixed" on one star as it orbits the Sun, as shown in Figure 4.1.

5. Read "The Reasons for Seasons" in this lesson. Discuss the questions with the class.

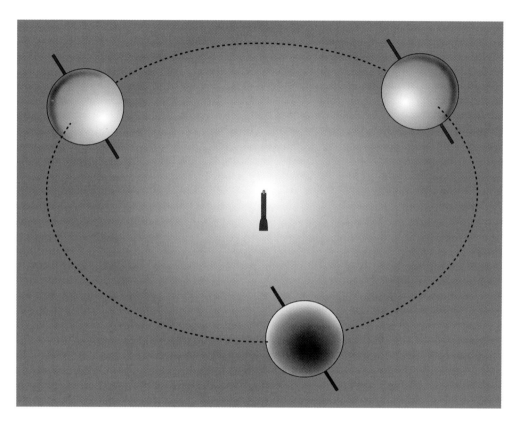

Figure 4.1 *The axis of this globe is "fixed" on the same point in the room as it orbits the Mini Maglite®.*

Inquiry 4.1
Investigating Seasons on Earth

PROCEDURE

1. Insert the rod labeled "E" through your globe to form an axis.

2. Stick the rod of your globe into the center hole of Side B of the SEM Board. If you have a protractor, measure the degree to which the axis is tilted. It should tilt approximately 23.5 degrees, as shown in Figure 4.2.

3. Mark your home location on the globe using a small bead-sized amount of modeling clay and the tip of your toothpick, as in Lesson 3 (see Figure 3.7). This will serve as a miniature shadow stick.

4. How can you use these materials to recreate winter and summer shadows on your globe? Discuss your ideas with your group.

Figure 4.2 *Setting up the Sun-Earth-Moon Board*

5. Place a removable dot in the center of your workspace. Place four additional removable dots approximately 30 cm from that dot to form a cross. Label the center dot "S." Label the outside dots "A," "B," "C," and "D" for the four seasons, as shown in Figure 4.3.

6. Position the SEM Board so that the rod of your globe is approximately over the dot labeled "A." Position the board so that the hole on the board marked "1" is closest to your "S" dot, as shown in Figure 4.4.

Figure 4.3 *Place the removable dots on your table, floor, or desk. Position and label them as shown. If the dots were a compass, the "A" would be north, the "B" would be west, the "C" would be south, and the "D" would be east. The "S" would be the center of the compass.*

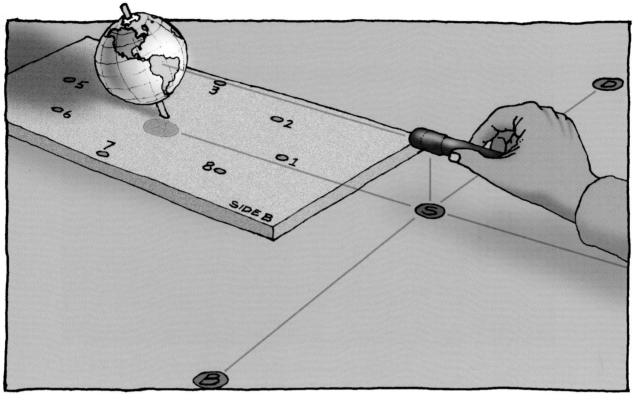

Figure 4.4 *Set up your model as shown. Shine the Mini Maglite® on the equator of your globe. Keep the head of the light over the "S" at all times.*

7. Hold the Mini Maglite over the "S" so that the light shines on the equator of your globe. Slowly rotate the globe counterclockwise so that your toothpick experiences day and then night. Observe the shadows that form near the toothpick. Do this several times. Discuss your observations with your group.

8. Record a description of your observations in your notebook. Label your observations "A." You may want to draw a picture as well.

Figure 4.5 *Move your Sun-Earth-Moon Board counterclockwise around your Mini Maglite® to dot "B." Keep the axis of the globe pointing in the same direction each time.*

9. Now slide your SEM board counterclockwise around your Mini Maglite until the axis of your globe rests approximately over the dot labeled "B," as shown in Figure 4.5. Keep the axis of your globe facing the same direction as it was in Step 6. This means that the hole on the board marked "3" should now be closest to your "S" dot and your globe is still leaning toward the hole marked "5."

10. Examine the new position of your board. How many months would it take Earth to move one-fourth of its orbit around the Sun (from dot "A" to "B")? Discuss your ideas with your group.

11. Keep your Mini Maglite over the dot labeled "S," but shine it on your globe. Rotate your globe counterclockwise on its axis. What shadows does the toothpick cast as your globe rotates on its axis? Discuss your

observations. Record them in your notebook. Label your observations "B."

12. Repeat Step 11 with the dot labeled "C." Keep the axis of your globe facing the hole on the board marked "5," which should now be closest to the "S" dot. Keep the Mini Maglite over the dot labeled "S" but face it toward the globe. Discuss, record, and label your observations.

13. Repeat Step 11 with the dot labeled "D." The hole on the board marked "7" should now be closest to your "S" dot.

14. Now move your clay and miniature shadow stick to a place in the Southern Hemisphere (such as South Africa). Repeat Steps 6–13. Record your observations in both words and pictures. Label your observations (for example, "Southern Hemisphere").

REFLECTING ON WHAT YOU'VE DONE

1. Share your group's results. Your teacher may ask you to demonstrate what you did.

2. Answer the following questions in your science notebooks, and then discuss them with your class:

A. Describe and draw the position of the Sun and Earth during winter in the Northern Hemisphere.

B. Describe and draw the position of the Sun and Earth during summer in the Northern Hemisphere.

C. Why are summer and winter 6 months apart?

D. What is happening in the Southern Hemisphere when it is winter in the Northern Hemisphere?

E. Earth travels in a slightly elliptical orbit around the Sun. Therefore, Earth is closer to the Sun in December than it is in June. If Earth is closer to the Sun in December, why is December in the Northern Hemisphere colder than June?

F. What did you learn in this lab that helps you to describe one reason why winter is colder than summer?

Inquiry 4.2
Observing the North Star

PROCEDURE

1. Read "Steering by the Stars." Discuss the questions at the end of the reading selection.

2. Review the steps of the inquiry, in which you will observe the North Star during four different times of the year. Create a table in your notebook to record your observations.

3. Using *Starry Night Enthusiast™*, set the computer program to your <Viewing Location> (use today's date and your nearest city). Record the latitude of your <Viewing Location>. Use the <Status> tab to find latitude and longitude.

4. Select <Celestial Poles> from <View> on the menu bar. Set the <Time Flow Rate> to 3000X.

5. Click and drag the cursor around the screen until you find the labeled North Celestial Pole.

6. Put the screen in motion by clicking on the <Run Time Forward> button. Stop it when you see the night sky. Move your cursor over the North Celestial Pole to see the name of the star nearest the pole. You should find the North Star, which is currently Polaris. Use this name in the title of your table.

7. Measure the angle of separation between the North Star and the horizon. Do this by moving the cursor over the North Star, turning the cursor into an arrow. Then click and drag the arrow to the horizon. Record the date and the angle of separation in your observation table.

8. Set the sky in motion again by clicking on the <Run Time Forward> arrow. What observations can you make about the apparent motion of the stars? Record your observations in your table. Explain what you see and why you think it is happening.

9. Change the date on the screen to 3 months from the date of the lesson. Repeat Steps 6–8. Do this for all four seasons by advancing the dates in 3-month intervals. What observations can you make about the North Star and the motion of the other stars throughout the year? What observations can you make about the star's angle of separation each time? Record the date, angle of separation, and your observations in your table each time.

10. Visit another location (latitude) in the Northern Hemisphere. What observations can you make about the relationship between latitude and the location of the North Celestial Pole? What does the apparent motion of the stars tell you about Earth? In your notebook, write a short paragraph describing the conclusions you can make from this inquiry.

11. Visit a country in the Southern Hemisphere. Find the South Celestial Pole. Find the "South Star." What do you observe? Discuss your ideas with your group.

Inquiry 4.3
Investigating Seasonal Variations at Different Latitudes

PROCEDURE

1. How can you use *Starry Night Enthusiast* to learn more about sunrise and sunset and seasons at various latitudes? Your group will be assigned one of the following places to investigate using the computer:

- Viewing location (nearest city)
- Anchorage, Alaska
- Quito, Ecuador
- Antarctica (anywhere along 75° S latitude)

2. Record your assigned location on both Student Sheets 4.3a and 4.3b.

3. Using *Starry Night Enthusiast*, find the <Favourites> tab, and choose <Horizon Shadows>. Then find <Options> on the main menu and set <Viewing Location> to the place to which your group was assigned. Record the longitude and latitude of that place onto Student Sheets 4.3a and 4.3b, then click on <Go to Location>.

4. Set the date on the computer program to March 21 of this year.

5. Set the time on the program to 4:00 A.M.

6. Set the <Time Flow Rate> to 3000X and watch the screen. Stop the screen when the Sun begins to rise (that is, the first moment you see a shadow appear). You may have to use both the <Run Time Forward> button and the <Run Time Backward> button to stop the screen at the exact time of sunrise.

7. Record the sunrise time in Table 1 of Student Sheet 4.3a. (If you do not see the Sun rise at all on March 21, record "0" in Table 1.) Where along the horizon is the Sun rising? Record the compass direction of the rising Sun in Table 1. What is the altitude of the Sun (angle of separation between the Sun and the horizon) when it is rising? Remember, to find the angle of separation between the Sun and the horizon, put your cursor on the Sun, turn the cursor to an arrow, click, and drag the arrow down to the horizon.

8. Put the screen in motion again. At solar noon (when the shadows are the shortest for that day), stop the screen. Find the Sun in the sky. What is the Sun's altitude? Record the Sun's alttitude and the time in Table 1. (Record "0" if the Sun does not rise.)

9. Put the screen in play again. Stop the screen when the Sun begins to set (the minute you see the shadow disappear). Record the sunset time. Record the compass direction and the altitude of the Sun.

10. How many hours elapsed from the time of sunrise until the time of sunset? Calculate the total daylight hours and minutes. Record the total daylight hours in Table 1.

11. Reset your date to June 21. Repeat Steps 5–10 and record your data in Table 1. Then do the same for September 21 and December 21.

12. Use the data in Table 1 to complete the graph on Student Sheet 4.3b. Connect the sunrise, sunset, and angle of separation points using an arc (curved line). Use your key to color code each month's curve. A sample graph of what the ecliptic looks like in June at the equator is shown in Figure 4.6.

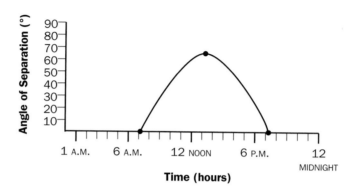

Figure 4.6 *Sample graph of the ecliptic for Quito, Ecuador, on June 21*

REFLECTING ON WHAT YOU'VE DONE

1. Be prepared to share your group's data from Table 1 on Student Sheet 4.3a and Graph 1 on Student Sheet 4.3b with the class.

2. Answer the following questions in your science notebook, and be prepared to discuss your answers with the class:

A. Describe the pattern of sunrise and sunset times for the equator. Why do you think this is so?

B. How do sunrise and sunset times at the Antarctic compare to those in Alaska?

C. How does the apparent path of the Sun across the sky during summer change as you move closer to the North Pole?

D. How might the apparent height of the Sun in the sky and the length of daylight affect the temperature for a particular latitude?

E. What do you think is responsible for the differences in the path of the Sun and in the sunrise and sunset times for different latitudes throughout the year?

3. In your own words, record a working definition for the term "revolution" in your notebook. Compare your definition to the definition of the term "orbit" in the glossary.

4. With your class, return to the Question B folder (from Lesson 1) and its accompanying photo card. Review the self-stick responses about what causes seasons. As a class, remove any postings that now seem incorrect. Add any new ideas you may have to the folder.

The Reasons for Seasons

Like all the planets in our solar system, Earth orbits around the Sun. Earth also rotates on its axis, which is currently tilted 23.5 degrees to the plane of its orbit. While the tilt of Earth's axis will change very little over your lifetime, the part of Earth that is exposed to the most solar energy—energy from the Sun—does change, and on a regular basis. This is because the tilted Earth orbits the Sun.

What do you think causes the seasons? Many people believe that seasons depend on the distance between Earth and the Sun. That might seem logical, but consider this: Earth travels in an ellipse, or oval, around the Sun. Due to this ellipse, Earth is slightly closer to the Sun in December than in June. If the distance from the Sun were responsible for how warm Earth is, it would mean that everyone on Earth would have summer in December. You know this is not true if you live in the Northern Hemisphere.

It is Earth's atmosphere and the tilt of its axis that are responsible for the changes in seasons. These factors affect the amount of solar energy that reaches each part of Earth at any time. The tilt of Earth on its axis affects the angle at which the Sun's rays pass through the atmosphere and strike Earth's surface. The higher the Sun's angle, the more intense the solar radiation and the less atmosphere the rays must pass through. The lower the Sun's angle, the less intense the solar radiation and the more atmosphere the rays must pass through (see the illustrations).

(continued)

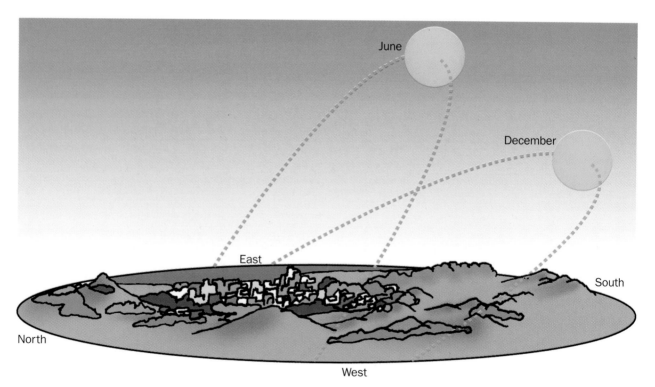

The angle of the Sun above the horizon is much greater in the summer than in the winter.

The higher the angle, the more intense the solar radiation.

Because of the curvature of Earth, sunlight strikes the poles at a low angle. Rays striking Earth at a low angle must pass through more atmosphere. Earth's atmosphere absorbs and reflects solar energy. The more atmosphere the rays have to pass through, the less solar energy reaches Earth's surface. This is one reason the poles are colder than other parts of Earth.

The tilt of Earth also affects the length of daylight in any particular area. Between March 21 and September 21 on average, the Northern Hemisphere tilts toward the Sun. During this period the surface of Earth in the Northern Hemisphere receives longer periods of daylight than the surface of Earth in the Southern Hemisphere. More direct sunlight for longer periods causes warmer weather. However, between September 21 and March 21, the Southern Hemisphere tilts toward the Sun and has warmer weather. On December 21 (or December 22, depending on the year), the Southern Hemisphere celebrates the first day of summer—called the summer solstice; on that same day, the Northern Hemisphere experiences its first day of winter—the winter solstice!

On two days of the year (somewhere around March 21 and September 21), the Sun is over Earth's equator and neither hemisphere tilts toward the Sun. On those two days, the surface of Earth in both hemispheres receives equal amounts of energy from the Sun. Night and day are almost equal in length all over the world except at the poles. These two days are called the equinox. (To remember this term, think of "equal night.") Equinoxes occur midway between the solstices.

On average, December 21 has the shortest period of daylight in the Northern Hemisphere. But December 21 is not usually the coldest day of the year because it takes several weeks in fall and early winter before the atmosphere and oceans cool off. There is a lag, or delay, in seasonal temperatures, and the coldest period in

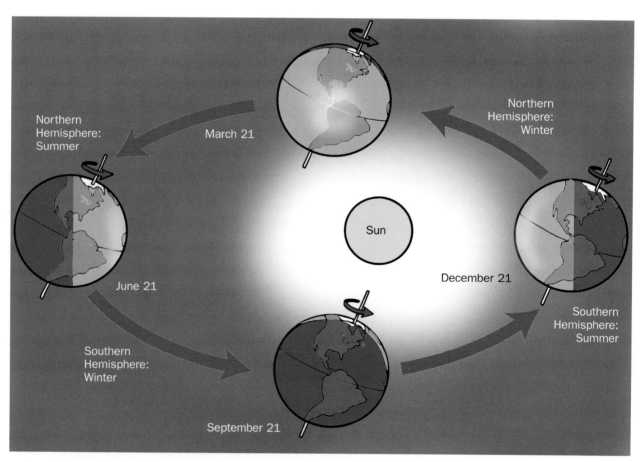

Between March 21 and September 21, the Northern Hemisphere tilts toward the Sun and has spring and summer. During that same time, the Southern Hemisphere tilts away from the Sun and has fall and winter. The equator is warm all year round. (Diagram is not drawn to scale.)

the Northern Hemisphere therefore may not arrive until early February. The same seasonal temperature delay occurs in spring and summer.

The amount of solar energy that reaches each hemisphere affects the temperature of the Earth's surface. Even though the Sun is closer to Earth in winter than in summer in the Northern Hemisphere, the Sun's rays do not hit Earth directly. The rays hit it at an angle after passing through the atmosphere. During winter, there are also fewer hours of daylight, which accounts for some of the chill of winter.

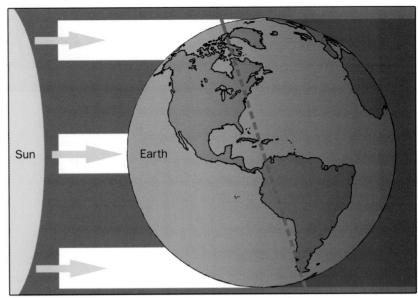

Seasons are the result of uneven heating of Earth's surfaces.

Seasons on Other Planets

Did you know that other planets also have different seasons? The spin axis of Uranus, for example, points to the Sun. That means that Uranus is tilted about 98 degrees to the plane of the ecliptic (the plane along which the Sun exists), compared to Earth's current tilt of 23.5 degrees. With Uranus completely on its side, one hemisphere always has summer during half of Uranus's 84-year orbit around the Sun, while the other hemisphere doesn't experience summer until the second half of its 84-year orbit! This pattern creates 42-year seasons of warmth and cold on each end of Uranus. Other planets also have interesting relationships to the Sun that cause different seasonal characteristics. You will learn about them in Part 2 of this module. ☐

QUESTIONS

1. What is the winter solstice, and when does it occur in the Northern Hemisphere?
2. Draw a picture of Earth's position relative to the Sun when the Southern Hemisphere is experiencing summer.
3. How long is winter on Uranus? Why?

| Mercury 0.1° | Venus 177° | Earth 23° | Mars 25° | Jupiter 3° | Saturn 27° | Uranus 98° | Neptune 30° | Pluto 120° |

Obliquity of the Nine Planets

Each planet is tilted slightly differently. Notice how Uranus is tilted 98 degrees on its axis as it revolves around the Sun. What other planet might have an unusual pattern of seasons?

Steering by the Stars

How did sailors of centuries past find their way across the seas before the invention of the compass and the sextant? The earliest sailors followed the coastline as far as they could, using features on land to mark their location. But when their journey took them far from land, they relied on the sky.

Early sailors knew that the Sun rises in the east and sets in the west, and they used that knowledge to guide them. So if they sailed into the rising Sun, they knew they were heading east. If they turned to the right, putting the rising Sun on their left side, they knew that they were heading south.

At night, these ancient mariners steered by the stars. The North Star proved a stable marker in the Northern Hemisphere because Earth's northern axis points to the North Celestial Pole (*celestial* means "dealing with the sky; heavenly"). The North Star, Polaris, is the star currently closest to the North Celestial Pole. As Earth rotates on its axis, the stars in the night sky seem to move in a circle, because they are fixed relative to Earth. But the North Star remains in one spot in the Northern Hemisphere sky at all times, and all the other stars seem to rotate around it. The farther north a sailor traveled in the Northern Hemisphere, the higher the North Star appeared in the sky. The farther south one sailed in the Northern Hemisphere, the lower the star appeared in the sky.

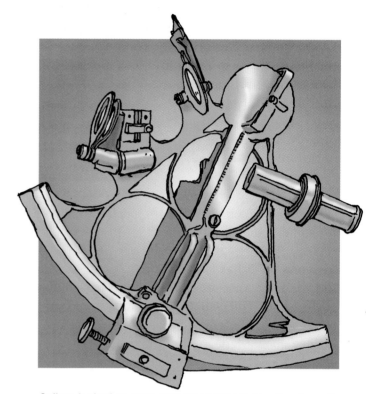

Sailors looked at stars and other celestial bodies through the telescope of this sextant. The angular distance of a star above the horizon was read off the sextant's scale. This way, sailors could calculate their positions.

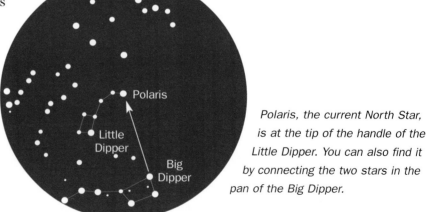

Polaris

Little
Dipper

Big
Dipper

Polaris, the current North Star, is at the tip of the handle of the Little Dipper. You can also find it by connecting the two stars in the pan of the Big Dipper.

Many sailors of old used a handy tool to help measure precisely how high or low a star was in the sky: their fingers! By holding his arms straight out in front of him, a mariner laid his fingers on top of each other to measure the "height" of a star such as the North Star from the horizon. Because the height of Polaris above the horizon is equal to the latitude at a particular location, sailors could use the star to estimate their location. They would, for example, turn west or east once a particular star selected for navigation was two finger-widths above the horizon. Very clever!

Although the skies are still important in guiding ships, today's sailors use computer and satellite technology—such as the Global Positioning System—to guide their travels. Navigators have come a long way since the days of steering by the stars. ☐

NATIONAL OPTICAL ASTRONOMY OBSERVATORY/ASSOCIATION OF UNIVERSITIES FOR RESEARCH IN ASTRONOMY/NATIONAL SCIENCE FOUNDATION

This time exposure shows star trails that mirror Earth's rotation. It was taken with a camera aimed at the North Star over Kitt Peak National Observatory in Arizona.

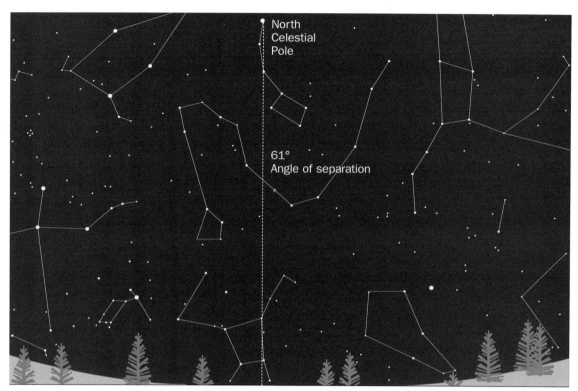

This illustration shows what the North Star looks like from Anchorage, Alaska (latitude 61° N).

This illustration shows what the North Star looks like from Mexico City, Mexico (latitude 19° N).

Constant as the North Star

As constant as it seems, Polaris, the North Star that we see in our night sky, has not always been our North Star. This is because Earth wobbles on its axis as it rotates, like a spinning top. While a top can make one complete wobble in a second, it takes Earth 26,000 years to complete one wobble—or precession. This means that Earth's axis points to different stars over the centuries. For example, around 3000 B.C., the North Celestial Pole pointed to Thuban, not Polaris.

QUESTIONS

1. Before the invention of the compass, how did sailors determine if they were sailing east or west?
2. Why is Polaris called the North Star?
3. Why is Polaris a stable sky marker today?
4. What handy tool did sailors use to help them navigate? How did this tool work?
5. What is the relationship between the position of the North Star and latitude?

Investigating Lunar Phases

The waning crescent Moon shines down on the landscape as the Sun begins to rise.

CORBIS/ROYALTY-FREE

INTRODUCTION

At certain times of the month, the Moon seems to rise over the horizon right before the Sun appears. When this apparent chase begins, the Moon usually looks like a sliver of light in the early morning sky. This "waning crescent," as it is called, is just one of many phases the Moon goes through as it journeys around Earth.

What causes the Moon's different phases, and what do these phases tell us about the Sun-Earth-Moon system? In this lesson, you will investigate how these three bodies interact to create lunar phases. You will model the phases of the Moon as it makes its way around Earth and examine the factors that affect these phase changes.

OBJECTIVES FOR THIS LESSON

Demonstrate that the Moon reflects the Sun's light as it orbits Earth.

Track, model, and illustrate the phases of the Moon as seen from Earth.

Create working definitions of the terms "waxing" and "waning."

Make predictions about the Moon's appearance on the basis of observed patterns.

Getting Started

1. Go over your homework from Lesson 2 with your class. Discuss any patterns that you observed in the Moon's rising and setting times and in its appearance.

2. Why do the rising and setting times and appearance of the Moon change over time? Share your ideas with the class.

3. Your teacher will set up a lamp in the center of your classroom. When do objects reflect light? When are objects in their own shadows? Test your ideas with your class.

MATERIALS FOR LESSON 5

For you

1 copy of Student Sheet 5.1: Investigating the Moon's Reflected Light

1 copy of Student Sheet 5.2: Modeling Phases of the Moon

1 copy of Student Sheet 5: Recording Lunar Phases Over Time

For your group

1 copy of Inquiry Master 5: Assessment: Identifying Lunar Phases

1 Sun-Earth-Moon Board™

1 set of 8 rods, labeled #1–#8

1 rod labeled "E"

1 globe of Earth, 12 cm

1 Mini Maglite®

2 AA batteries

1 large black-and-white sphere, 7.5 cm

1 white sphere, 3.5 cm

1 set of wide-tipped markers

1 sheet of newsprint

1 fine-point black marker

1 pair of scissors

Glue

1 foam sleeve (optional)

Inquiry 5.1
Investigating the Moon's Reflected Light

PROCEDURE

1. Look at one set of materials. How can you use the Sun-Earth-Moon (SEM) Board and a Mini Maglite to investigate how much of the Moon is illuminated by the Sun at any one time as the Moon orbits Earth? Discuss your ideas with your group. Then discuss the procedures of the inquiry with your teacher.

2. Set up Side B of your SEM Board as shown in Figure 5.1. Make sure that you match the number on each rod with the numbered holes on the board. Attach the globe of Earth to the center rod labeled "E." Each numbered rod represents a different position of the Moon along its orbit around Earth.

3. Push the smaller sphere onto rod #1 through the predrilled hole. If your sphere

Figure 5.1 *Set up Side B of the Sun-Earth-Moon Board™ as shown. Push each rod into its corresponding hole. Attach the globe of Earth to the center rod labeled "E." Attach the 3.5-cm sphere to the rod labeled "1." (Note that this model is not to scale and that the tilt of the Moon's orbit is exaggerated for the purposes of the inquiry.)*

does not have a hole, make one with your pen tip. This sphere will represent the Moon in its orbit around Earth.

4. Reexamine the illustration in Figure 5.2, which is from Lesson 2. What do you notice about Earth, the Moon's orbital plane, and the Sun? Discuss your ideas with your group.

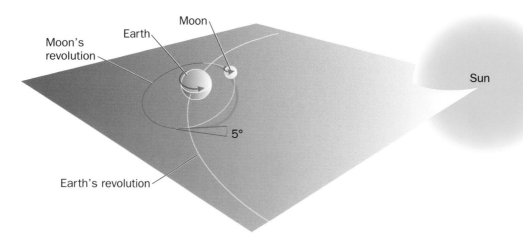

Figure 5.2 *Geometry of the Sun-Earth-Moon system showing the Moon's rotation and revolution (orbit). Note that the Moon's orbit is tilted approximately 5 degrees to Earth's orbital plane. This means that in most cases (except for two times each month), the Moon is either higher or lower than Earth, not level with it, as Earth orbits the Sun.*

5. Now compare Figure 5.2 to your SEM Board. What do you think the rods on your board represent? Why are the rods different heights? Why does the rod go through the globe at an angle? Discuss your ideas with your group.

6. Shine the Mini Maglite directly on the sphere on rod #1. Keep the Mini Maglite steady. Look at the sphere from all directions as if you are looking down at the Moon from space. How much of the sphere reflects light at any one time? Discuss your observations with your group. Color circle #1 on Student Sheet 5.1 to show how much of the Moon is dark and how much of it reflects light. Make sure that the student sheet is facing the same direction as your SEM Board.

7. Move the sphere to rod #2. Shine the Mini Maglite directly on your white sphere as you did with rod #1 (see Figure 5.3). Discuss your observations with your group. Record what you see in circle #2 on Student Sheet 5.1.

8. Repeat Step 7 with rods #3–#8. Record your observations on Student Sheet 5.1 each time.

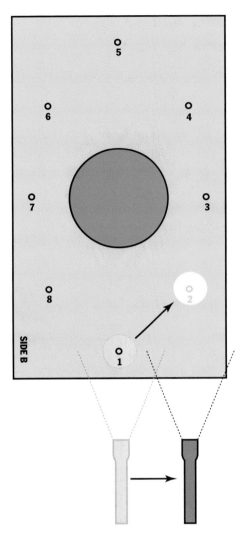

Figure 5.3 *Try to shine the light directly on the sphere each time you move the sphere.*

REFLECTING ON WHAT YOU'VE DONE

1. Answer the following questions in your science notebook, and then discuss them with your class:

A. As seen from space, how much of the Moon is illuminated by the Sun at each position as the Moon orbits Earth?

B. Given your results from Inquiry 5.1, why do you think the Moon appears to change its shape when viewed from Earth?

2. Draw a 360-degree circle that connects all eight of your completed Moons on Student Sheet 5.1. Then cut along that circle (see Figure 5.4).

3. Analyze the circle that you have cut out. What part of the Moon's lighted side can we see from Earth at each position in the Moon's orbit around Earth? On the back of your circle, write a paragraph summarizing your observations from this inquiry.

Figure 5.4 *Draw a circle to connect the eight Moons. Cut out the circle.*

Inquiry 5.2
Modeling Lunar Phases

PROCEDURE

1. Place the large black-and-white sphere on the end of a pencil. This will represent the Moon.

2. Face the cloth Sun. Hold the Moon out in front of you so that the white half of the Moon is facing the Sun, as shown in Figure 5.5. Your head represents Earth. What part of the Moon can you see from Earth?

3. Orbit the Moon around you. Stop at each of its 8 positions along its orbit. Remember to keep the white half of the Moon facing the cloth Sun at all times. How does the Moon look from Earth during each phase as it orbits Earth?

4. Record your observations on Student Sheet 5.2. Make sure that the Sun on your sheet is facing the same direction as the cloth Sun in your lab setup.

5. Switch roles within your group. Have another student hold the Moon, and repeat Steps 2–4. Do this until everyone has had a turn.

Figure 5.5 *If your head represents Earth, what part of the Moon's illuminated side can you see when the Moon is in this position?*

REFLECTING ON WHAT YOU'VE DONE

1. Share your results from Student Sheet 5.2 with the class.

2. Answer these questions in your science notebook, and then discuss them with the class:

A. As seen from Earth, what causes the Moon to change its apparent shape throughout the month?

B. Approximately how long does it take for the Moon to go through one set of phases? How many days does each phase last?

C. Is the Moon visible only in the nighttime sky? Why or why not? (Think about what you saw when you were facing the Sun— which represents daytime on Earth.)

D. Does everyone on Earth see the same phase of the Moon on any given day? Why or why not?

3. Is the same side of the Moon always dark? Discuss your ideas with the class.

4. Use Inquiry Master 5: Assessment: Identifying Lunar Phases to create a poster that shows the lunar phases in the correct order around Earth. Use Table 5.1: Lunar Phases to label each lunar phase on your poster.

5. Share your completed poster with the class. Create working definitions of the terms "waxing" and "waning."

6. With your class, return to the Question C folder (from Lesson 1) and its accompanying photo card. Review the self-stick responses from Lesson 1 about why the Moon appears to change its shape. As a class, work together to remove any notes that now seem incorrect. Add any new ideas you have to the folder.

Table 5.1 Lunar Phases

Photo	Phase name	Description	Visibility, Location, and Time
	New Moon	Cannot be seen	
	Waxing crescent	A narrow strip of the Moon's lighted hemisphere is visible from Earth. Shaped like a crescent. The light is on the right.	Visible late afternoon and just after sunset in the southwestern sky.
	First quarter	Half of the lighted hemisphere is visible from Earth. Shaped like a semicircle. The light is on the right.	Visible afternoon and evening, until it sets about midnight.
	Waxing gibbous	Three-quarters of the lighted hemisphere is visible from Earth. Shaped like an upended football. The light is on the right.	Visible in the eastern portion of the sky in the late afternoon. After sunset, the Moon moves across the southern part of the sky and sets sometime after midnight.

(continued)

Table 5.1 Lunar Phases (continued)

Photo	Phase name	Description	Visibility, Location, and Time
	Full Moon	The Moon's entire lighted hemisphere is visible from Earth. Shaped like a full circle.	The full moon rises when the Sun sets, is up all night, and sets when the Sun rises.
	Waning gibbous	Three-quarters of the Moon's lighted hemisphere is visible from Earth. Shaped like an upended football. The light is on the left. In this phase, the Moon wanes, or turns away from Earth.	Rises after sunset (as much as 5 or 6 hours later). Best seen in the southwest sky during the morning after sunrise.
	Third (or last) quarter	Half of the Moon's lighted hemisphere is visible from Earth. Shaped like a semi-circle. The light is on the left.	Rises at midnight, sets at noon, much like the waning gibbous Moon.
	Waning crescent	A narrow strip of the Moon's lighted hemisphere is visible from Earth. Shaped like a crescent. The light is on the left.	Can only be seen in the early morning.

COURTESY UCO/LICK OBSERVATORY

Apollo 11 Lands On the Moon:
A NASA Log

On July 20, 1969, a very famous day in American history, *Apollo 11* and two of its three crew members landed on the Moon. Michael Collins piloted the Command Module as it continued to orbit the Moon. Shortly thereafter, Neil Armstrong and Edwin (Buzz) Aldrin descended from the Lunar Module and explored the Moon's surface for more than two hours.

People from around the world watched the Moon landing on TV. The three crew members were instant heroes.

The following account traces some highlights of this famous journey, based primarily on a log from NASA.

July 16

Around 1100 Universal Time Coordinated (UTC), or 7 A.M. Eastern Daylight Time (EDT), the crew arrive at Launch Pad 39A at Kennedy Space Center in Florida. The weather is clear and

calm—a good day for a liftoff. The Saturn V rocket, which will send the crew and spacecraft toward the Moon, is ready to go. It is 111 meters high and produces more than 3.4 million kilograms of thrust at liftoff. It is the largest, most powerful rocket ever flown.

The crew of three includes Mission Commander Neil Armstrong; Michael Collins, pilot of *Apollo;* and Edwin (Buzz) Aldrin, who will pilot *Eagle,* the Moon landing craft.

Hundreds of kilometers west at the Johnson Space Center in Houston, the staff of Mission Control prepare to monitor the space trip. Flight Director Clifford E. Charlesworth is in charge.

At 9:32 A.M. EDT, *Apollo* lifts off successfully.

By noon, *Apollo* is in the middle of its second orbit around Earth. The astronauts fire the engine that puts *Apollo* out of Earth's orbit and head toward the Moon. Its speed is around 39,000 kilometers per hour.

The crew of Apollo 11 *(left to right): Commander Neil A. Armstrong, Command Module pilot Michael Collins, and Lunar Module pilot Edwin E. "Buzz" Aldrin*

July 19

After three days of travel, *Apollo 11* passes behind the Moon. It is out of radio contact with Mission Control for the first time. While the spacecraft is behind the Moon, the crew fires the thrust engine to slow the spacecraft enough that lunar gravity can capture it.

The crew sends photos of their landing site back to Earth. The site they have chosen is called *Mare Tranquillitas*. Although this name means the "Sea of Tranquility," it is not really a sea. It is a large, dark plain on the Moon's surface, called *maria*. It was chosen as a landing spot because it is flat and relatively free of large craters.

July 20

Astronauts Armstrong and Aldrin board the mooncraft *Eagle* to prepare it for landing. As they hover about 101 kilometers above the Moon's surface, the *Eagle* unlocks from the *Columbia*. Michael Collins, now alone in the *Columbia,* continues to orbit the Moon. Soon the *Eagle* begins its descent. Collins looks out his window at the *Eagle:* "I think you've got a fine-looking machine," he radios to his fellow crew members, "despite the fact you're upside-down."

When the *Eagle* is about 16 kilometers from the Moon, some computer alarms go off. The astronauts realize it's just a minor problem and will not affect the spacecraft. There is one problem, though: The *Eagle* overshoots its original landing site. Aldrin has to find a new place to land.

At 2018 UTC (or 4:18 P.M. EDT), with only 40 seconds of fuel remaining, the *Eagle* touches the surface of the Moon. Armstrong radios Mission Control with the long-awaited news: "The *Eagle* has landed." Aldrin describes the scenery as "magnificent desolation."

Aldrin and Armstrong spend a few hours preparing to leave the *Eagle* and explore the Moon. Their spacesuits are well padded to protect them from the jagged rocks and high-speed micrometeoroids that constantly bombard the Moon's surface. The suits weigh 83 kilograms on Earth. Because the Moon's gravity is much less than that of Earth, however, the suits feel as if they weigh only about 14 kilograms.

Armstrong, as commander, is the first to descend. He makes a footprint on the powdery soil. "That's one small step for a man, one giant leap for mankind," he radios to Earth.

The mooncraft Eagle *hovers above the lunar surface as Earth shines in the background.*

First footprint on the Moon left by Commander Neil Armstrong in the Sea of Tranquility. This footprint (barring any meteorite impacts) will probably last on the lunar surface for millions of years.

NATIONAL AERONAUTICS AND SPACE ADMINISTRATION

The astronauts plant a United States flag in the lunar soil.

Aldrin climbs down the *Eagle*'s ladder. "Now I want to back up and partially close the hatch—making sure not to lock it on my way out," he jokes.

The next two hours are busy ones. Aldrin sets up a solar wind experiment to catch particles from the Sun on a sheet of aluminum foil. He sets up a seismometer to record "moonquakes" and mirrors to reflect laser beams from Earth. These beams will enable astronomers on Earth to more precisely measure the distance between the Earth and Moon. Using tongs and a scoop, Armstrong collects rocks and soil samples.

The astronauts also plant a United States flag in the lunar soil. They take time for an important phone call—from President Richard Nixon. He tells them that he hopes that the mission will bring peace and tranquility to all of Earth.

About two hours and fifteen minutes after they first stepped on the Moon, the two men climb back into the *Eagle*. After a much-needed nap, they start the engine and begin their vertical ascent. Within a few hours, they redock with *Columbia*.

The astronauts abandon *Eagle*, which crashes into the Moon.

NATIONAL AERONAUTICS AND SPACE ADMINISTRATION

On July 24, 1969, the Columbia splashed down about 812 nautical miles southwest of Hawaii, returning the three crew members safely to Earth. Here they are shown in a life raft with a Navy frogman.

July 24

After several days of testing and observation, the crew heads home. On July 24, 1969, at 1650 UTC (12:50 P.M. EDT), they splash down in the Pacific Ocean approximately 195 hours (eight days and three hours) after liftoff. They are retrieved by a helicopter and welcomed aboard the recovery ship, *USS Hornet.* ☐

QUESTIONS

1. When did the *Apollo 11* crew land on the Moon?
2. Where on the Moon did the *Eagle* land, and why was this spot selected?
3. What did Neil Armstrong say when he set foot on the Moon? What do you think he meant by this?
4. What experiments did the astronauts conduct while on the Moon? Why is it important to conduct experiments such as these?

Solar and Lunar Eclipses

The "diamond ring" effect occurs when only the barest sliver of the Sun is visible around the Moon during a total solar eclipse.

INTRODUCTION

In Lesson 5, you investigated how relative positions of the Sun, Earth, and Moon affect our view of the Moon and its changing phases. Sunlight reflects off the lunar surface, and when the Moon is full, nighttime on Earth can look almost like day. But what happens when Earth's shadow falls on the full moon? A lunar eclipse occurs. At other times, the new moon may move in front of the Sun and block its light. It's a solar eclipse! In this lesson, you will determine why eclipses can occur during each of these phases. You also will analyze the Moon's orbital plane and Earth's revolution to determine why solar and lunar eclipses do not occur each month.

OBJECTIVES FOR THIS LESSON

Model shadows cast by the Moon and Earth.

Analyze the conditions under which the Moon and Earth's shadows cause eclipses.

Describe the phases during which lunar and solar eclipses occur.

Analyze solar and lunar eclipse data and compare it to phase data.

Develop working definitions for the terms "umbra" and "penumbra."

Getting Started

1. What do you already know about eclipses? What do you want to know about eclipses? Discuss these questions with the class. Your teacher may record your ideas.

2. Your teacher will set up a lamp in the center of the room. Stand with a partner so that you can see your shadow. Work with your class to examine how you and your 7.5-cm sphere can cast shadows and can block, or *eclipse*, light.

3. Relate what happened with the sphere to what happens to the Moon and Earth during an eclipse. Record in your notebook what you think the terms "lunar eclipse" and "solar eclipse" mean.

MATERIALS FOR LESSON 6

For you
1 copy of Student Sheet 6.2a: Geometry of Eclipses

For you and your partner
1 white sphere, 7.5 cm
1 pencil (to support the sphere)

For your group
1 Sun-Earth-Moon Board™
1 set of 8 rods, labeled #1–#8
1 rod labeled "E"
1 globe of Earth, 12 cm
1 Mini Maglite®
2 AA batteries
1 white sphere, 3.5 cm
5 removable dots
1 toothpick, 1 cm of the tip Modeling clay, bead-sized amount
1 foam sleeve (optional)

Inquiry 6.1
Investigating Lunar and Solar Eclipses

PROCEDURE

1. Model a full moon using the large white 7.5-cm sphere (the Moon), a Mini Maglite (the Sun), and yourself (Earth).

2. Model the conditions under which a full moon is totally eclipsed (or its light is blocked), as shown in Figure 6.1. Share roles with your group so that everyone has a chance to model Earth. What is casting the shadow on the Moon? Draw this type of eclipse in your notebook. Label the Moon, Sun, and Earth in your drawing. Draw the shadow. Write a sentence that describes your drawing.

3. Now model the conditions under which a full moon is partially eclipsed (its light is only partially blocked). Where does the shadow fall on the Moon? Draw this type of eclipse in your notebook. Label your drawing. Write a sentence that describes your drawing.

4. Model a new moon using your sphere (Moon), Mini Maglite (Sun), and yourself (Earth).

5. Model the conditions under which a new moon can totally eclipse the Sun's light. Have your partner examine the shadow cast by the new moon. Where does the shadow fall? Draw this type of eclipse in your notebook. Label and describe your drawing.

6. Again model a new moon eclipsing the Sun's light, but this time increase the distance between your head (Earth) and the sphere (new moon). What happens to the eclipsed light? Have your partner examine the shadow cast by the new moon. Where does it fall? Draw your results in your notebook and label them.

7. Model a new moon eclipsing the Sun's light again, but this time, lower the sphere (new moon) so that it is only partially in line with your head (Earth) and the Mini Maglite (Sun). What happens to the eclipsed light? Have your partner examine the shadow cast by the new moon. Where does it fall? Draw your results and label them.

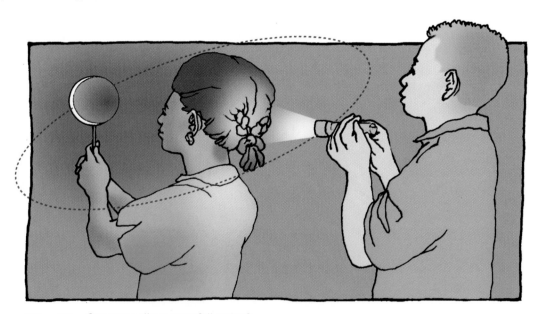

Figure 6.1 *Can you eclipse your full moon?*

REFLECTING ON WHAT YOU'VE DONE

1. Read "Eclipses."

2. Return to each of your drawings from Inquiry 6.1. Give each drawing one of the following titles: "Total Lunar Eclipse," "Total Solar Eclipse," "Partial Lunar Eclipse," "Partial Solar Eclipse," or "Annular Solar Eclipse."

3. Use the information in Table 6.1: Solar and Lunar Eclipses 2001, Table 6.2: Full and New Moon Dates 2001, and your observations from Inquiry 6.1 to answer the following questions in your notebook:

A. During what phase does a lunar eclipse occur? Give one date as an example.

B. During what phase does a solar eclipse occur? Give one date as an example.

C. How many lunar eclipses occurred during the year 2001?

D. How many solar eclipses occurred during the year 2001?

E. Did an eclipse occur with each full and new moon? Explain.

F. Under what conditions does a total solar eclipse occur?

G. Under what conditions can a partial solar eclipse occur?

H. Under what conditions does an annular solar eclipse occur?

Table 6.1 Solar and Lunar Eclipses 2001

Month	Type of Eclipse	Description
Jan 9	Lunar	Total
June 21	Solar	Total
July 5	Lunar	Partial
Dec 14	Solar	Annular
Dec 30	Lunar	Penumbral

Table 6.2 Full and New Moon Dates 2001

Date	Lunar Phase	Date	Lunar Phase
Jan 9	Full	July 20	New
Jan 24	New	Aug 3	Full
Feb 8	Full	Aug 18	New
Feb 23	New	Sept 2	Full
Mar 9	Full	Sept 17	New
Mar 24	New	Oct 2	Full
April 7	Full	Oct 16	New
April 23	New	Oct 31*	Full
May 7	Full	Nov 15	New
May 22	New	Nov 30	Full
June 5	Full	Dec 14	New
June 21	New	Dec 30	Full
July 5	Full		

* When two full moons occur in one calendar month, we call the second full moon a "blue moon." The expression "once in a blue moon" refers to rare occurrences such as this.

Inquiry 6.2
Analyzing the Geometry of Eclipses

PROCEDURE

1. Set up your SEM Board as you did in Lesson 5. Put your small sphere on rod #1 and your globe of Earth on the rod labeled "E."

2. Place a removable dot in the center of your workspace, and add four additional removable dots approximately 30 cm from that dot, forming a cross, as you did in Lesson 4. Label the center dot "S." Working counterclockwise, label the outside dots A, B, C, and D, as you did in Lesson 4 (see Figure 4.3). Each dot will represent a position of the Earth-Moon system as it orbits the Sun.

3. Position the SEM Board so that the rod of your globe is approximately over the dot labeled "A." Position the board so that rod #1 is closest to your "S" dot, as shown in Figure 6.2.

4. Hold the Mini Maglite parallel to the table and over the "S" so that it shines on the small sphere. Move the small sphere (your Moon) from rod #1 through to rod #8. Shine the Mini Maglite on the sphere each time. Which rod holds the new moon (N)? Which rod holds the full moon (F)? Mark an "N" inside the Moon in Box A of Student Sheet 6.2 that shows a new moon. Mark an "F" inside the Moon in Box A of Student Sheet 6.2 that shows a full moon.

5. Put the sphere on the rod that holds the new moon. With the Mini Maglite parallel to the tabletop and shining on the small sphere, examine Earth. Does the new moon cast a shadow on Earth? Discuss your observations with your group.

6. Put the sphere on the rod that holds the full moon. With the Mini Maglite parallel to the tabletop and shining on the small sphere, examine Earth. Does Earth cast a shadow on the full moon? Discuss your observations with your group.

Figure 6.2 *Set up your model as shown. Shine the Mini Maglite® on the small sphere, keeping the head of the Mini Maglite® over the "S" and facing rod #1. Hold the Mini Maglite® parallel to the table.*

7. Now slide your SEM Board counterclockwise around your Mini Maglite until the axis of your globe rests approximately over the dot labeled "B," as shown in Figure 6.3. This models Earth's orbit around the Sun. How many months later does dot "B" represent? Record this time on Student Sheet 6.2.

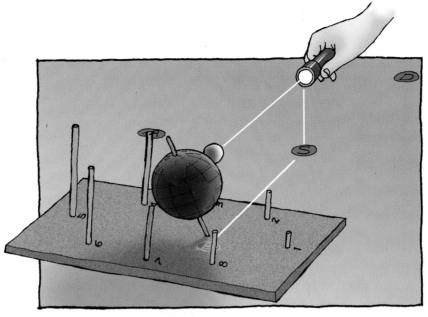

Figure 6.3 *Move your SEM board counterclockwise around your Mini Maglite® to dot "B." Hold the Mini Maglite® parallel to the table, over the dot marked "S." Shine the light on the sphere.*

8. Put the small sphere on rod #3. Keep the Mini Maglite over the dot labeled "S," but turn the light so that it shines on the sphere in its new position.

9. Move the small sphere (the Moon) from rod to rod. Shine the Mini Maglite on the sphere each time. Which rod now holds the new moon? Mark an "N" inside the new moon in Box B on Student Sheet 6.2. Can you create a solar eclipse (cast a shadow on Earth) with your new moon? Which rod now holds the full moon? Mark an "F" inside the full moon in Box B on Student Sheet 6.2. Can you create a lunar eclipse (cast a shadow on your full moon)? Discuss your observations.

10. Repeat Steps 7–9 with the dots labeled "C" and "D." Keep the Mini Maglite over the dot labeled "S" but face it toward the sphere each time. Discuss your observations each time. Record the "N" and "F" in Boxes C and D on Student Sheet 6.2 each time.

11. Keep your SEM Board over dot "D." Place the tip of the toothpick on your globe to show where your city or town is located. Shine the Mini Maglite on your globe. Move the small white sphere from rod to rod. Examine the umbra and penumbra of a shadow cone in Figure 6.4. Can you see the umbra and penumbra of the Moon's shadow on the globe? Is your city experiencing a total solar eclipse, partial solar eclipse, or no eclipse? What countries are experiencing a total solar eclipse? Rotate your globe to examine the "path of totality." Is your city in this path? Discuss your findings with your group.

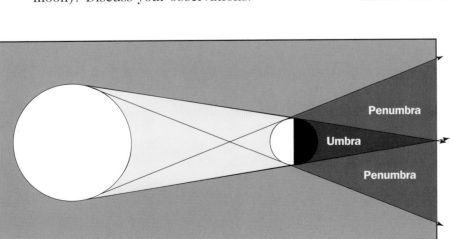

Figure 6.4 *Umbra and penumbra of a shadow cone*

REFLECTING ON WHAT YOU'VE DONE

1. Discuss your results of Inquiry 6.2 with your class. Then, in your notebook write one paragraph summarizing your observations of the Inquiry.

2. Examine the data in Table 6.3 Solar and Lunar Eclipses 2002, Table 6.4 Solar and Lunar Eclipses 2003, and Table 6.5 Solar and Lunar Eclipses 2004. Use these data and your observations from Inquiry 6.2 to answer the following questions in your notebook:

A. About how often do lunar and solar eclipses occur each year?

B. Why don't solar and lunar eclipses occur every month?

C. Count the number of days between each solar and lunar eclipse. Is there a pattern? What do you notice? Why do you think this is?

D. What would have to happen for lunar and solar eclipses to occur every month?

3. Create your own working definitions of the terms "umbra" and "penumbra." Record them in your notebook.

4. With your class, return to the Question D folder (from Lesson 1). Is there anything you would now change or add? Discuss your ideas with the class.

Table 6.3 Solar and Lunar Eclipses 2002

Date	Type of Eclipse	Description
May 26	Lunar	Penumbral
June 10	Solar	Annular
Nov 20	Lunar	Penumbral
Dec 4	Solar	Total

Table 6.4 Solar and Lunar Eclipses 2003

Date	Type of Eclipse	Description
May 16	Lunar	Total
May 31	Solar	Annular
Nov 8–9	Lunar	Total
Nov 23	Solar	Total

Table 6.5 Solar and Lunar Eclipses 2004

Date	Type of Eclipse	Description
Apr 19	Solar	Partial
May 4	Lunar	Total
Oct 14	Solar	Partial
Oct 28	Lunar	Total

ECLIPSES

True or False?

Which of the following statements is true?

- An eclipse of the Sun occurs when an invisible dragon eats the Sun.
- During eclipses, poisons drop from the sky.
- An eclipse is a sign that the world is coming to an end.

The answer? None of these statements is true. But people from cultures all over the world created these and other stories to explain the mysterious disappearance of the Sun and Moon from the sky.

Today, we know how and why eclipses take place. While eclipses have nothing to do with dragons, poisons, or the end of time, they are amazing celestial spectacles.

Solar Eclipse

A solar eclipse occurs when the Moon comes directly between Earth and the Sun. The key word is *directly*, because the Moon orbits Earth every month, and every month the Moon casts

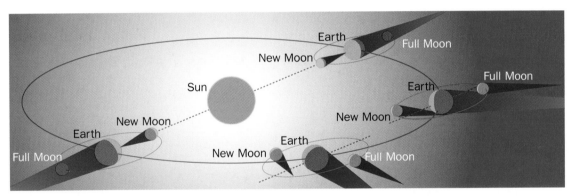

Eclipses can happen only when the Sun and Earth are in line with the full moon or new moon.
At all other times, the shadows of the Moon and Earth fall into space.

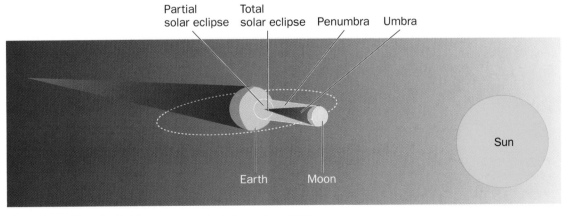

Geometry of Sun-Earth-Moon system during a solar eclipse

a shadow. We don't have a solar eclipse every month because the Moon's shadow falls either above or below Earth during most months. But on rare occasions, when the Sun, Earth, and Moon are aligned just right, the Moon's shadow falls directly on Earth.

During a solar eclipse, the darkest part of the Moon's shadow cone, called the "umbra," is often only about 250 kilometers in diameter. As the Earth spins, different parts of it fall within the umbra. People who happen to be in the umbra can see a total blocking of the Sun, or a total solar eclipse. During a total solar eclipse, the air cools and daylight disappears. It becomes dark enough to see stars! For a few breathless minutes, we can see what it's like to live in a sunless world.

Outside the narrow path of the umbra, the Moon blocks only part of the Sun and creates a partial solar eclipse. A shadow is cast, but it isn't as dark as the umbra. This lighter part of the shadow cone is called the "penumbra." Because the penumbra is much larger than the umbra, a greater area of Earth experiences a partial eclipse than a total eclipse.

Annular Eclipse

In an annular eclipse, most of the Sun is covered, but an annulus (which means "ring" in Latin) of light surrounds the darkened Moon. To understand an annular eclipse, remember that the Moon's orbit around Earth is an ellipse, not a circle. As a result, the Moon's

Total solar eclipse of June 21, 2001—path of totality. The path forms as Earth rotates on its axis beneath the Moon's shadow.

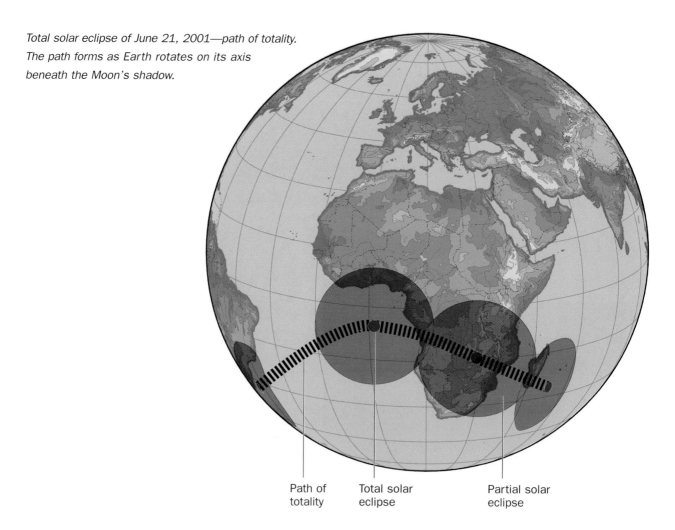

Path of totality   Total solar eclipse   Partial solar eclipse

distance from Earth varies. When the Moon is closer to Earth, it covers the Sun completely, creating a total solar eclipse. When the Moon is farther away, it appears smaller and cannot completely cover the Sun.

Lunar Eclipse

In a lunar eclipse, Earth comes directly between the Sun and Moon—an alignment that puts the Moon in Earth's shadow. When the entire full moon falls within the center of Earth's shadow, or umbra, we have a total lunar eclipse. Everyone on the night side of the Moon (half the globe!) can see such an eclipse. Depending on how much dust and how many clouds are in Earth's atmosphere, the Moon will appear dark brown, red, orange, or yellow.

This is because light bounces off Earth, passes through Earth's atmosphere, and creates a glow on the Moon.

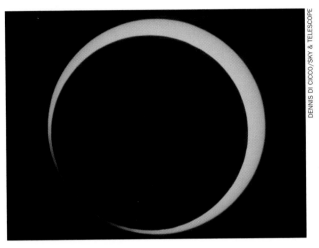

Annular eclipse of the Sun. Annulus means "ring."

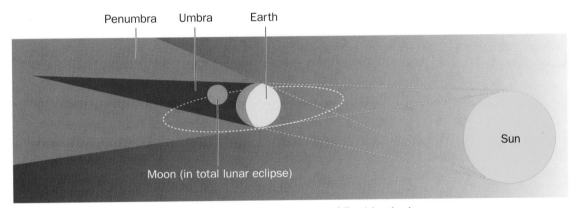

A total lunar eclipse occurs when the Moon is in the umbra of Earth's shadow.

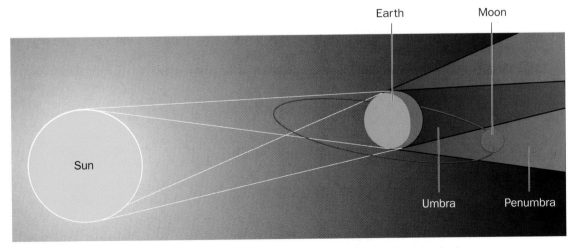

A penumbral lunar eclipse occurs when the Moon is in the penumbra of Earth's shadow.

A partial lunar eclipse occurs when only part of the Moon passes through the Earth's umbra. A penumbral lunar eclipse occurs when the Moon passes through only the lighter part of Earth's shadow cone—the penumbra. Neither of these lunar eclipses is as colorful as a total eclipse.

Look in astronomy field guides for the dates and locations of future eclipses. The next time that you have an opportunity to view a solar or lunar eclipse, don't pass it up. Whether you watch the disappearance of the Sun as the Moon passes in front of it in the middle of the day, or if you watch the transformation of a full moon into an orange-red disk, it is a worthwhile experience. ☐

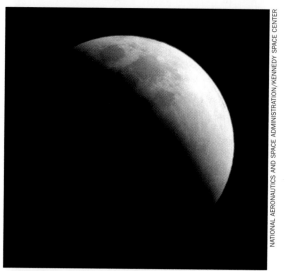

An eclipse of the Moon. When the Moon is totally eclipsed, it appears dark brown, red, orange, or yellow.

Pinhole Projectors

Solar eclipses are beautiful events, but watching a solar eclipse can damage your eyes even if only a small part of the Sun is visible. How can you watch a solar eclipse safely? One way is with a pinhole projector.

You can turn your bedroom into a pinhole projector that can be used as a solar eclipse viewing area. On a sunny day, make your room very dark. Cover your windows using newspaper, butcher paper, or cardboard. Make a small hole in the window cover, and sunlight will stream through the hole. On the wall opposite your window, you will see the view outside your window—upside down!

It sounds like magic, but it's not. It's physics.

Pinhole History

A Chinese philosopher named Mo Ti wrote about the physics of pinholes 2500 years ago! Mo Ti knew that light travels in straight lines, and that when rays pass through a hole, they cross (see the illustration). The top of an object forms the bottom of an image, and vice versa.

One hundred years after Mo Ti, Aristotle observed that the openings between the leaves of a tree worked like tiny pinholes to cast images of the Sun on the ground during a partial eclipse of the Sun. He recognized that the smaller the hole, the sharper the image. But many more centuries would go by before people understood how to use pinholes in their work.

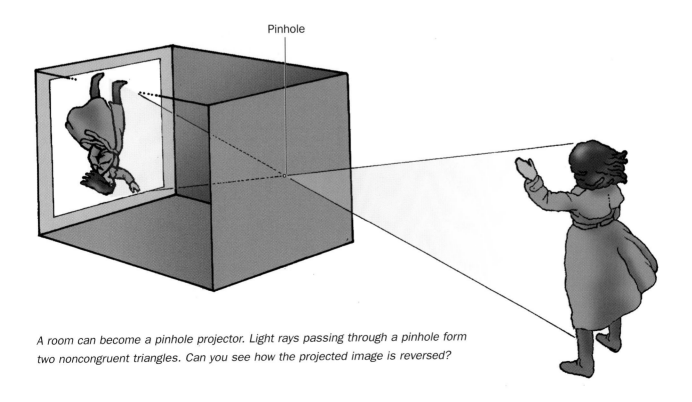

Pinhole

A room can become a pinhole projector. Light rays passing through a pinhole form two noncongruent triangles. Can you see how the projected image is reversed?

Pinholes were especially helpful in the study of astronomy. In 1544, a German astronomer, Gemma Frisius, used a pinhole in his darkened room to study a solar eclipse. The image of the Sun was projected on the wall so that he could view it safely.

You don't need to use an entire room to make a pinhole projector. Any box with a tiny hole in one end will do. Remember that your image will not be as sharp as an image that passes through a lens. A lens focuses and directs light rays; a hole only lets them in. ☐

The openings between the holes of a straw hat work like tiny pinholes. This photo shows hundreds of projected images of the annular eclipse seen in the United States on May 10, 1994.

Making a Pinhole Projector

How can you make a small pinhole projector? Follow the steps outlined below:

1. Collect a box (a shoebox with a lid works well), ruler, clear tape, scissors, foil, and white or black paper.
2. Cut out a 2.5-cm square opening at one end of the box.
3. Cut out a 2.5- × 10-cm opening on the side of the box (see the illustration).
4. Tape a piece of foil over the square opening at the end of the box.
5. Make a pinhole right in the center of the foil over the opening.
6. Tape or glue a piece of white (or black) paper on the inside of the box. This paper should be placed opposite the pinhole and serves as a projection screen.
7. Tape the lid onto the box, and make certain there are no areas where light can get in other than through your cut openings.
8. Stand with your back to the Sun and look through the side opening at the white paper. You should see the Sun's image projected onto the screen. You can use this projector to view a solar eclipse.

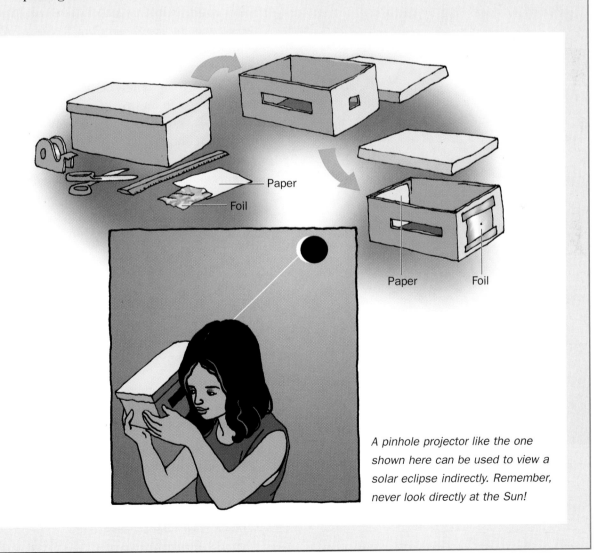

Paper

Foil

Paper   Foil

A pinhole projector like the one shown here can be used to view a solar eclipse indirectly. Remember, never look directly at the Sun!

The Sun as an Energy Source

Sun, water, and the air we breathe are ingredients for life on Earth.

NATIONAL OCEANOGRAPHIC AND ATMOSPHERIC ADMINISTRATION (NOAA)/NOAA CENTRAL LIBRARY

INTRODUCTION

In Lesson 6, you investigated solar and lunar eclipses. You saw that the Sun's light can be temporarily blocked by a particular alignment of the Sun, Earth, and Moon. But what if the Sun's light were not available to us on a daily basis? How much do our lives depend on the Sun's energy? In this lesson, you will learn about the Sun as an energy source. To begin, you will conduct an investigation to determine how the distance from a light source to an "energy detector" affects the amount of energy received. You then will design an investigation to test how other variables, such as the angle of light, affect the amount of energy received from the light source. You then will compare your results to what you know about the Sun. This lesson prepares you for Lesson 8, in which you will track sunspots and analyze how changes in the Sun's energy output affect Earth.

OBJECTIVES FOR THIS LESSON

Investigate the effects of distance on the amount of energy received from a light source.

Design an investigation to observe the effects of different variables on the amount of energy received from a light source.

Use a radiometer to observe the effects of solar energy.

Read to learn more about the Sun.

Getting Started

1. Read "Using Eclipses To Study Solar Wind." What do you know about solar energy? Discuss your ideas with the class.

2. Review the Safety Tips with your teacher. Then carefully unwrap the radiometer.

3. The radiometer is an "energy detector." Test how it works, first under your classroom lights and then with your clamp lamp. Observe the lamp and radiometer when they are set up at different distances. Discuss your observations with your group by answering questions such as the following:

How does the light affect the radiometer?

What causes the radiometer to behave as it does?

Why are the panels inside the radiometer black and white?

4. Discuss the following question as a class: *How does the distance from the clamp lamp to the radiometer affect the length of time the radiometer vane spins?* You will investigate this question further in Inquiry 7.1.

MATERIALS FOR LESSON 7

For you

- 2 copies of Planning Sheet
- 1 copy of Student Sheet 7.1: Collecting Radiant Energy Data
- 1 sheet of graph paper

For your group

- 1 transparency copy of Student Sheet 7.1: Collecting Radiant Energy Data
- 1 transparency
- 1 transparency copy of graph paper
- 1 set of fine-point transparency markers
- 1 clamp lamp with reflector
- 1 50-W lightbulb
- 1 100-W lightbulb
- 1 150-W lightbulb
- 2 bookends
- 1 radiometer
- 1 removable dot
- 1 student timer (or other timepiece)
- 1 protractor
- 1 pair of heat-resistant KEVLAR® gloves
- 1 metric measuring tape or ½-meter stick
     Access to electrical outlet

SAFETY TIPS

The radiometer will shatter on impact. Keep it away from the table's edge.

Avoid touching the metal reflector or lightbulb on the clamp lamp while it is on or cooling.

Inquiry 7.1
Investigating the Effects of Radiant Energy

PROCEDURE

1. Record the question you will try to answer in this investigation on your planning sheet. Consider what you are testing (the distance from the clamp lamp to the radiometer) and its effect (the length of time the radiometer vane spins).

2. What do you think will happen if you change the distance between the lamp and the radiometer? Record your prediction on your planning sheet.

3. On your planning sheet, list the materials you will use and the procedures you will follow.

4. How will you control your experiment? Record what you will change. Record what you will keep the same.

5. What will you look for? What you will measure? Record these on your planning sheet.

6. Use the removable dot to mark a spot in your workspace away from any edges. Keep the radiometer on that dot at all times. This may help prevent your radiometer from being knocked to the floor.

7. Read the directions on Student Sheet 7.1. Record the power (in watts) of the lightbulb your group will use. (Remember not to change the lightbulb once you start. Change only the distance.) Record the number of seconds you will keep the clamp lamp on during each trial. Examine Table 1 on the student sheet. On Table 1, list the three different distances you will test. You will conduct three trials for each distance and then average your results.

8. Set up your equipment as outlined on your planning sheet (see Figure 7.1.) (Use either a metric measuring tape or a ½-meterstick).

9. Conduct your investigation. Complete Table 1 on the student sheet as you work.

10. Graph your data on Student Sheet 7.1. Use your data to determine the scale of your *x*- and *y*-axes. Record your independent variable (distance) on the *x*-axis. Record your dependent variable (average time the radiometer vane spins after shutting off the clamp lamp) on the *y*-axis.

REFLECTING ON WHAT YOU'VE DONE

1. Share your results with the class. You may want to show your data table and graph to the class.

2. Answer the following questions in your science notebooks, and then discuss them with your class:

A. Do you see a general pattern in your data? What is the pattern?

B. What do the patterns in the data tell you?

C. Why might different groups get different results?

D. If the conditions on all planets were the same, except for their distance from the Sun, how would distance affect the amount of energy a planet receives from the Sun?

E. Why do you think distance from the Sun affects how much energy a planet receives?

3. Read "Distance and Light." Review your answers to Questions D and E. Is there anything you want to change or add to your answers on the basis of this new information?

Figure 7.1 *One suggestion for setting up the investigation. Between trials, what variables would you change in this investigation? What variables would you keep the same?*

DISTANCE AND LIGHT

Light spreads out spherically from a source. As light gets farther from its source, it covers an ever-widening area. The size of the surface area of light is related to its distance. If you double the distance from the light source, the light spreads out more than four times the area (2 x 2 = 4). The surface area of light is "squared" ($2^2 = 4$). (See the illustration.) If you make the distance three times as great, the light spreads out more than nine times the area ($3 \times 3 = 3^2 = 9$). We can describe this relationship by saying: The larger the area over which light is spread, the smaller the amount of energy that passes through any unit area of that sphere. Less light means less energy. This is why the farther you are from the clamp lamp, the more the light spreads and the less energy the radiometer receives.

How does this apply to our solar system? When light from the Sun reaches Earth, it is spread over a sphere that is equal to the radius of one Earth-distance to the Sun.

When light from the Sun has gone twice as far as Earth, that light is spread out over an area four times larger than Earth's distance from the Sun. By the time the Sun's light reaches Saturn, which is 10 Earth-distances from the Sun, the Sun's light is spread out over an area 100 times larger than one Earth-distance. The fact that energy decreases with increasing distance from the source is sometimes called the inverse square law. "Inverse" means that the relationship is reversed. You might think that if you increase one factor, another factor related to it also would increase. (For example, increase the food you feed your dog and his weight also may increase.) But the relationship between light and energy is inverse—or reversed. Energy decreases as the distance from the light source increases.

The inverse square law explains why the inner planets closer to the Sun are hotter than the outer planets farther away from the Sun. Of course, other factors—such as the tilt of a planet on its axis, surface composition, and atmosphere—also affect the temperature of a planet. But overall, the farther a planet is from the Sun, the less solar energy it receives.

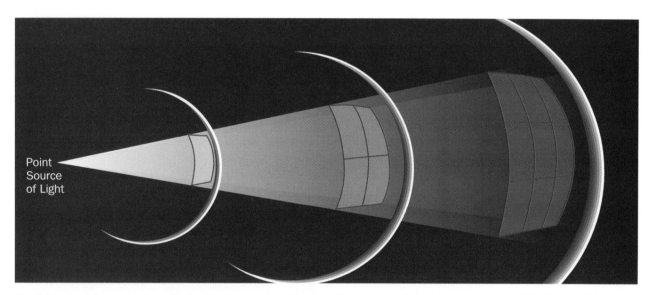

Point Source of Light

Sunlight spreads out spherically. The farther a planet is from the Sun, the larger the area over which the sunlight spreads and the smaller the amount of energy the planet receives.

Inquiry 7.2
Designing an Energy Investigation

PROCEDURE

1. What other questions would you like to explore using this equipment? Discuss possible ideas with your group. Then decide with your group which question you will test. Complete your group's planning sheet.

2. Review your group's plan with your teacher.

3. Discuss with your group how to record your results. Set up a data table in your notebook similar to the one you used during Inquiry 7.1.

4. Review the Safety Tips that relate to your investigation. Then complete your investigation.

5. Graph your results. You may be asked to graph your results on a transparency as well so that you can share your data with the class.

SAFETY TIPS

Turn off your clamp lamp and unplug it before changing lightbulbs.

Use heat-resistant KEVLAR gloves when changing hot lightbulbs.

REFLECTING ON WHAT YOU'VE DONE

1. Share your results with the class.

2. Answer the following in your notebook, and then discuss them as a class:

A. Do you see a general pattern in your data? If so, what is it?

B. How are your data like those of other groups?

C. Why do you think different groups that tested the same thing may have gotten different results?

D. Draw some conclusions from your investigation. For example, how does changing the wattage of the lightbulb affect the amount of energy received by the radiometer?

E. Make a prediction: How do you think the Sun will affect the radiometer?

F. What characteristics of the Sun will affect how the radiometer spins?

G. What characteristics of Earth will affect how much solar energy the radiometer receives?

3. You might be able to take your radiometer outside, or work near a sunlit window, to see how it responds to the Sun's light. If so, how do your observations compare to your predictions? What explanation can you give for your observations?

4. How many radiometers do you think the Sun could "power" compared to a clamp lamp? Discuss your ideas with the class. If possible, test your ideas in the lab.

5. With your class, return to the Question E folder (from Lesson 1) with its accompanying photo card. Review the self-stick responses from Lesson 1 about the points of light in the night sky. As a class, work together to remove any postings that may now prove incorrect. Add any new ideas you may have to the folder.

Using Eclipses To Study Solar Wind

Physicist Shadia Habbal does not have an easy job. At the Smithsonian Astrophysical Observatory, she studies the solar wind. The best time to observe the solar wind is during total solar eclipses—which occur only once every year or two and last only for a few minutes.

"Not only are total solar eclipses rare and short-lived, but if one occurs during cloudy weather—well, it can be frustrating," says Dr. Habbal. An additional difficulty is that each total solar eclipse can be seen only along a narrow stretch of Earth—and that narrow stretch may occur on the other side of the planet.

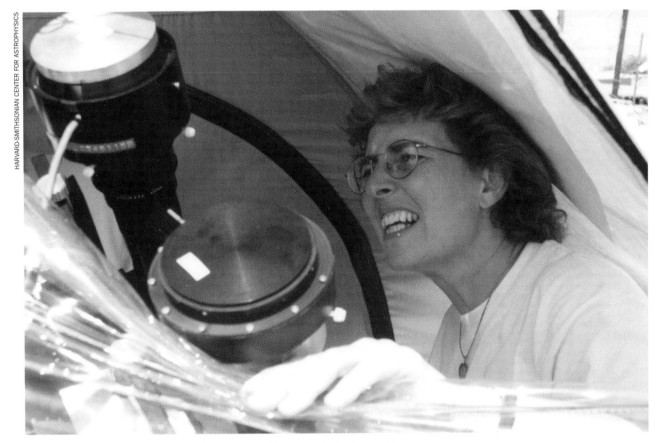

HARVARD-SMITHSONIAN CENTER FOR ASTROPHYSICS

Dr. Shadia Habbal working at the Smithsonian Astrophysical Observatory

Solar eclipses occur when the Moon, aligned perfectly between Earth and the Sun, blocks the bright solar disk. For just a few minutes, the Sun's outer layer, or corona, becomes visible—and so does the path of solar wind. "It shows up as bright streaks in the Sun's corona," says Dr. Habbal.

What Is Solar Wind?

Solar wind is a flow of particles out of the Sun's corona. The particles may be few and far between, but they are speedy! Some particles that escape from the Sun's poles travel as fast as 800 kilometers per second. Particles that blow out from other regions of the Sun move at a slower rate—about 300 kilometers per second. But even at this slower speed, solar wind could travel around the Earth's equator in less than 2½ minutes! Some winds can even travel beyond Pluto!

Is solar wind really a wind? "Not one you will ever feel," explains Dr. Habbal. "The flow of particles is much less dense than in wind on Earth, so you wouldn't even feel it if you stood in its way." Not that you could. Earth's magnetic field shields the planet from solar wind as it moves throughout the solar system.

NATIONAL CENTER FOR ATMOSPHERIC RESEARCH/UNIVERSITY CORPORATION FOR ATMOSPHERIC RESEARCH/NATIONAL SCIENCE FOUNDATION

During "totality," when the bright solar disk is covered, the Sun's outer layer—the corona—becomes visible.

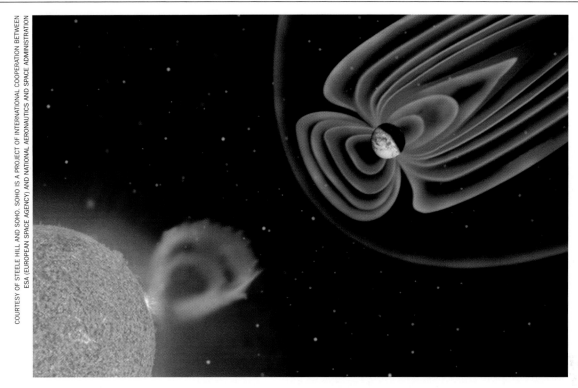

COURTESY OF STEELE HILL AND SOHO. SOHO IS A PROJECT OF INTERNATIONAL COOPERATION BETWEEN ESA (EUROPEAN SPACE AGENCY) AND NATIONAL AERONAUTICS AND SPACE ADMINISTRATION

This NASA illustration shows Earth's magnetosphere and its interaction with the solar winds.

What Exactly Is Blowing?

As it turns out, the Sun sheds—that is, it gives off particles. The particles making up solar wind are mainly electrons and protons coming from the Sun itself. These particles are electrically charged, and according to Dr. Habbal, they are super-hot, measuring more than a million degrees! The hotter something is, the more energy it has. Solar wind particles have so much energy that the Sun's gravity cannot hold them back. "It's this heat that enables these particles to escape solar gravity and flow out to space," she explains.

Why Study Solar Winds During an Eclipse?

A total solar eclipse is a perfect opportunity for scientists like Dr. Habbal to study the Sun. The eclipse blocks the Sun's bright light, making it easier to see solar winds, flares, and other flamelike eruptions. In her 20-year career, Dr. Habbal has traveled to many continents to witness solar eclipses. "The beauty of the total eclipse is that it offers terrific resolution and details of the corona all the way to the solar surface," she says. A coronagraph is a tool that attaches to a telescope and blocks out most of the Sun and creates an artificial eclipse. But according to Dr. Habbal, it doesn't give the same sharp, complete picture as a total solar eclipse. And partial eclipses, says Dr. Habbal, "do not block the solar disk enough to be able to study the corona."

Find out when the next total solar eclipse will occur and where. You can bet that Dr. Habbal and other solar scientists will have a front-row seat. ☐

OUR SUN'S ENERGY

The Sun is a star—a huge nuclear reactor.

The Sun may be only one star among billions of other stars in the universe, but it's the one that makes our life on Earth possible. How? The Sun provides us with energy that gives us solar power, fossil fuels, waves, and surface wind. Without heat and light from the Sun, Earth would be just another dark, cold planet in space where life as we know it could not exist.

Where does the Sun get all its energy? It all starts with its size. The Sun's mass is enormous— approximately 300,000 times greater than Earth's. The more mass an object has, the greater the pressure at its center due to the force of gravity. And when gas is squeezed, or compressed, it becomes hot. Most of the Sun's mass is composed of hydrogen gas atoms. Physicists came up with the hypothesis that the Sun's tremendous mass squeezed the hydrogen atoms until they fused and released the heat and light energy that reaches Earth.

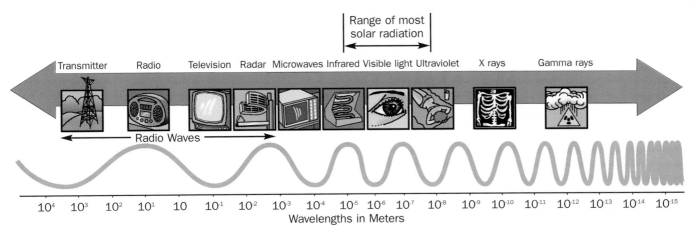

Solar energy travels through space in the form of electromagnetic waves. Along the electromagnetic spectrum, solar energy is mostly visible energy, infrared energy, and ultraviolet energy.

Think about the hottest oven you can imagine—and then turn up the temperature to about 14,000,000 °C (or 1.4×10^7). That's how hot it gets in the center of the Sun. At that temperature, the hydrogen nuclei—or centers of each hydrogen atom—are moving so fast that when they crash into each other, they stick together to form helium.

The result of the crash of hydrogen nuclei is a tremendous amount of energy, released mainly in the form of heat and light. This reaction is called nuclear fusion. Scientists calculate that there is enough hydrogen in the Sun to continue the fusion reaction and provide heat and light energy for at least another 5 billion years or so.

Solar Energy

Energy from the Sun is called solar energy. Solar energy is the source of most of the heat on Earth's land, in its oceans, and in its atmosphere. This energy makes its way through the vacuum of space to Earth by a process known as radiation. Radiation is often identified by the effect it produces when it interacts with an object. Some solar radiation is visible as light (43 percent), but not all solar radiation can be detected by the human eye. Infrared radiation (49 percent) cannot been seen at all, but we can detect it as heat. Another type of radiation is responsible for the sunburn that can occur after exposure to the Sun (scientists call that ultraviolet radiation, which makes up 7 percent). Gamma rays, X rays, microwaves, TV waves, and radio waves make up the remaining 1 percent.

Solar energy is important to life on Earth. But surprisingly, most of the Sun's energy does not reach Earth at all; it travels out through space in all directions. Earth's land and oceans absorb about half of the small amount of solar energy that reaches us. The rest is reflected back into space or absorbed by the thin blanket of air—the atmosphere—that surrounds Earth. The interaction of solar energy with air, soil, and water on Earth creates our weather. The uneven heating of Earth causes wind, rain, and other elements of weather, and makes our planet unique and habitable.

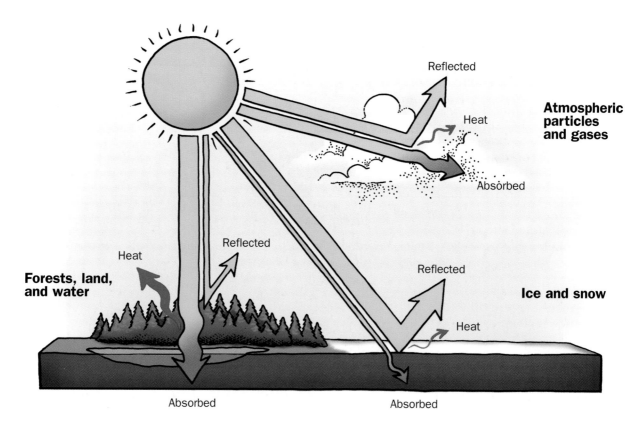

Earth's atmosphere and surfaces absorb and reflect the Sun's energy.
Some of the absorbed energy is given off as heat.

Our Atmosphere and Life on Earth

Earth's atmosphere protects our planet. How? The atmosphere keeps us from receiving too much solar energy. The tilt of Earth on its axis and Earth's rotation help vary the amount of solar energy that reaches any one place on our planet at any time. Too much of the Sun's energy—too much ultraviolet radiation, for example—would be harmful to life on Earth. Like a blanket, Earth's atmosphere also helps keep our planet warm at night. And most meteors and other rocks from space burn in the atmosphere before they reach Earth's surface.

Our planet receives just the right amount of solar energy to sustain life. If Earth were just a little farther away from the Sun, or just a little closer, life as we know it probably could not exist. ☐

Solar Energy on Other Planets

Planets get most of their energy from sunlight. If all conditions were the same, the closer a planet is to the Sun, the warmer that planet should be. But this is not always the case. The temperature of each planet depends not only on the amount of sunlight that strikes it but also on the way that planet's surface returns infrared radiation into space.

The way a particular planet absorbs the Sun's radiant energy depends on its atmosphere. For example, Earth's atmosphere reflects part of the radiation back into space and distributes heat from the sunlit regions to the cooler poles and to the side facing away from the Sun. Without its atmosphere, which is made up mostly of nitrogen and oxygen, the temperature of Earth would be nearer to –260 °C and the oceans would freeze.

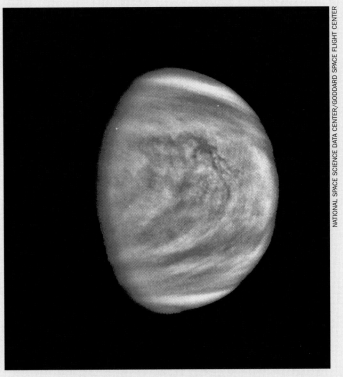

NATIONAL SPACE SCIENCE DATA CENTER/GODDARD SPACE FLIGHT CENTER

Venus is covered by a hot, cloud-filled atmosphere made up mostly of carbon dioxide.

The climate of Venus is very different from Earth's even though Venus is similar to Earth in size, mass, density, and distance from the Sun. Its atmosphere is made up of 95 percent carbon dioxide and trace amounts of water vapor. This mixture lets in visible light from the Sun but does not release the infrared radiation generated by its hot rocky surface. This "greenhouse effect" makes Venus extremely hot, with surface temperatures that can reach 482 °C.

Mars also has an atmosphere that is made up of 95 percent carbon dioxide. But because Mars' temperature is always below freezing, its water vapor is frozen in the planet's polar ice caps and soil. Without water in the atmosphere, most of the Sun's energy that reaches Mars returns to space. In addition, the Martian atmosphere is so thin that it cannot block the deadly ultraviolet rays of the Sun, greatly reducing the greenhouse effect as compared to Earth or Venus.

Sunspots and Space Weather

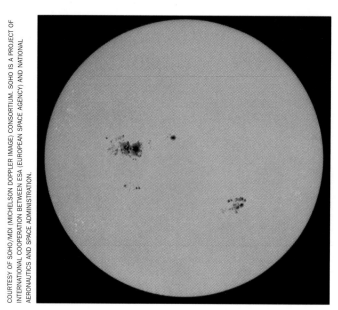

Visible-light image of the Sun, showing spots on its surface

INTRODUCTION

In ancient China around 28 B.C., astronomers recorded their observations of what looked like small, changing, dark patches on the surface of the Sun. Some early references to the spots also occur in the writings of Greek philosophers from the fourth century B.C. However, none of those early observers could explain what they saw.

Galileo was one of the first scientists to observe sunspots through a telescope. He made drawings of the changing shapes and watched the spots cross the visible surface of the Sun. These drawings represent the first steps of science toward understanding sunspots. In this lesson, you will observe projected sunspots and track patterns in their movements and occurrences. You also will read about Galileo and his discoveries.

What are sunspots? What do they tell us about the Sun and "weather" in space? In this lesson, you will discover these things for yourself. You also will prepare for Lesson 9, in which you will be assessed on your skills and knowledge about the Sun-Earth-Moon system.

OBJECTIVES FOR THIS LESSON

Examine projected images of the Sun for changes in its surface features.

Analyze patterns in the locations of sunspots.

Graph sunspot data and identify sunspot maximums and minimums.

Read about the effects of sunspots and space weather on Earth.

Getting Started

1. Discuss what you know about the Sun's energy and how it affects Earth as a planet.

2. What do you know about sunspots? How do you think sunspots affect Earth? Share your ideas with the class.

3. Spend a few minutes working with your group's binoculars. Discuss how the binoculars can be used to study the Sun.

4. Look back at the reading selection in Lesson 3, "How To View the Sun Safely." Review the section on safe viewing and projection. How can the binoculars be used to project the Sun's image? Discuss your ideas with your class. Then review the Safety Tips.

MATERIALS FOR LESSON 8

For you
- 1 small square transparency of the Sun
- 1 copy of Student Sheet 8: Sun-Earth-Moon System Review
- 1 colored transparency marker
- 1 sheet of graph paper
- 1 box of colored pencils
- 1 metric ruler, 30 cm (12″)
- 1 pair of solar viewing glasses

For your group
- 1 pair of binoculars
- 1 sheet of fine cardboard
- 1 pair of scissors
  Masking tape
- 1 sheet of white paper
- 1 Sun-Earth-Moon Board™ Side A (from Lesson 3)
- 4 large binder clips
- 1 flashlight (optional)
- 2 D-cell batteries (optional)

Inquiry 8.1
Projecting Images of the Sun

PROCEDURE

1. Trace the size of your large binocular lenses onto your sheet of cardboard. Cut out the two circles in your sheet of cardboard (see Figure 8.1).

2. Tape the sheet of cardboard to the front of the binoculars with the larger lenses sticking through the holes.

3. You only want light to show through one lens. Use one of the cut-out circles to cover one of the larger lenses of the binoculars or tape over the front of the lens with masking tape.

Figure 8.1 *(A) Cut out the two circles from your cardboard sheet. (B) Tape the cardboard sheet to the large lenses of the binoculars. The cardboard will help you to create a shadow around the light's image. (C) Cover one lens with cardboard or tape so that light comes through only one opening.*

4. Use the four binder clips to attach the sheet of white paper to your Sun-Earth-Moon (SEM) Board to keep it in place.

5. With your class, go outside or to a sunny window. Take a pencil, the binoculars, and your SEM Board.

6. Find a sunny location. Have one member of your group hold the SEM Board at an angle against the ground. Face the white paper up, as shown in Figure 8.2.

7. Have another member of your group hold the binoculars about 60 cm from the SEM Board. Point the larger lenses of the binoculars toward the Sun. Try to project the Sun's image onto the board. It will take a little effort to find the Sun.

8. Slowly move the binoculars away from the board. Try to keep the image of the Sun on the board.

Figure 8.2 *Hold the Sun-Earth-Moon Board™ at an angle with the white side facing up. Use the binoculars to project the image of the Sun onto the paper.*

9. Once the binoculars are about 1.5 m from the SEM Board, focus the binoculars to sharpen the Sun's image. (You may want to hold the binoculars on top of your head to keep them steady. See Figure 8.3.) Keep the Sun's image on the board.

10. Examine the projected image of the Sun. What do you observe? Are any spots visible inside the image? If you see sunspots, how many are there? Where are they?

Write your observations in your notebook. (Keep in mind that a sunspot on the Sun's surface that is visible by projection can be 200,000 km in diameter—more than 15 times the diameter of Earth! If you can see a spot on your solar image, it is probably a sunspot much larger than Earth.)

11. Put away your binoculars. Do not remove the cardboard sheet.

Figure 8.3 *Hold the binoculars about 1.5 m from the board. Steady the binoculars by holding them on top of your head. Keep your image in place on your paper.*

12. Review the Safety Tips. Watch as your teacher demonstrates how to use the solar viewing glasses (see Figure 8.4).

13. Obtain one pair of solar viewing glasses. Can you see sunspots on the Sun's surface?

Figure 8.4 *Students viewing the Sun safely using solar viewing glasses*

Inquiry 8.2
Tracking Sunspots

PROCEDURE

1. Place the small square transparency of the Sun over Figure 8.5 (Day 1). Use your marker(s) to trace the sunspots onto the transparency. Label each group of sunspots with a different capital letter, different color, or different shape, and then create a key.

2. Lift up the transparency and place it over Figure 8.6 (Day 2). Trace the sunspot groups again and label them.

3. Repeat Step 2 with Figure 8.7 (Day 3) and Figure 8.8 (Day 4).

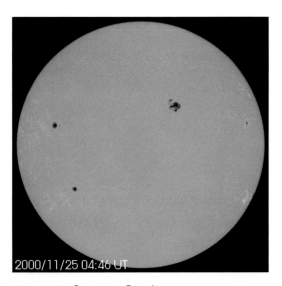

Figure 8.5 *Sunspots Day 1*

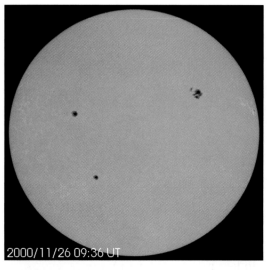

Figure 8.6 *Sunspots Day 2*

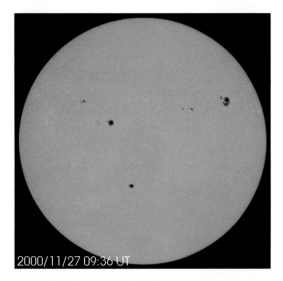

Figure 8.7 *Sunspots Day 3*

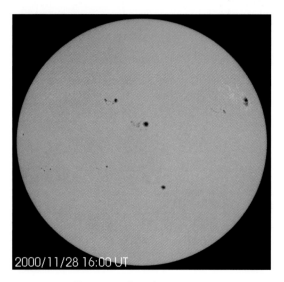

Figure 8.8 *Sunspots Day 4*

ALL PHOTOS COURTESY OF SOHO/MDI (MICHELSON DOPPLER IMAGE) CONSORTIUM. SOHO IS A PROJECT OF INTERNATIONAL COOPERATION BETWEEN ESA (EUROPEAN SPACE AGENCY) AND NATIONAL AERONAUTICS AND SPACE ADMINISTRATION.

4. Create a data table in your notebook. An example is shown in Table 8.1.

5. Select one sunspot group to track. Record that group's longitude and latitude over 4 days.

Table 8.1 Sunspot Data

Sunspot Group: _____

Day	Longitude	Latitude
1		
2		
3		
4		

REFLECTING ON WHAT YOU'VE DONE

1. Share your transparency data with the class.

2. Analyze your sunspot data by answering the following questions in your notebook:

   A. How does the position of the sunspot group change over the 4-day period?

   B. What might be happening to cause these results?

3. Read "Galileo's Discoveries." Can you use the movement of sunspots to determine where the rotational axis of the Sun on your transparency is located?

4. Clean off your transparency. Then complete Student Sheet 8 as a review for Lesson 9, which is an assessment for Part 1.

Inquiry 8.3
Analyzing Long-Term Sunspot Data

PROCEDURE

1. What does the term "space weather" mean to you? How do you think it is related to the Sun? How is it related to sunspots? Brainstorm with the class.

2. Read "Space Weather." In your own words, write a definition of "space weather" in your notebook.

SPACE WEATHER

The term "space weather" refers to conditions on the surface of the Sun that ultimately affect Earth and its atmosphere. The Sun emits radiative and particle emissions that flow into space. These emissions and their flow are called "solar wind." Solar wind explodes continuously from the outer region of the Sun's dense atmosphere, called the solar corona.

Space is filled with low-energy charged particles, photons, electric and magnetic fields, dust, and cosmic rays. Solar wind energizes these particles, which affect spacecraft, humans in space, and occasionally human activities on Earth. Solar wind also causes changes in the space environment, which we see as auroras. (See the reading selection "Auroras.")

The radiation from space weather can endanger human life and health. In addition, radiation surges energize particles in the atmosphere and can damage electrical power systems, interfere with telecommunications, ruin high-tech ship navigation systems, and harm astronauts in space. Residents of Quebec, Canada, for example, suffered a blackout in 1989 when many electrical transformers were destroyed by the charged particles from a solar flare. Many of the risks from space weather can be avoided with reliable space weather forecasts and by taking precautions.

3. Examine Table 8.2: Space Weather Report and Forecast. This information was reported for October 15, 2000, on the NOAA Space Environment Center (SEC) Web site.

Table 8.2 Space Weather Report and Forecast

Solar Data	Solar Forecast
The sunspot number for today [October 15, 2000] is 99. Today's solar wind velocity is 582.9 kilometers per second, and its density is 1.6 protons per cubic centimeter.	Solar activity is expected to be predominantly low for the next 3 days, though there is a chance for isolated moderate-level flare activity from three separate sunspot groups.

4. Use Table 8.2 to answer the following questions:

How many sunspots were reported?

How fast was the solar wind traveling?

How dense was the solar wind?

On the basis of this forecast, do you think the number of sunspots remains the same each day? What evidence do you have to support your answer?

If the number of sunspots changes each day, do you think these changes are predictable? Explain why you think this.

5. Discuss Table 8.3 with your teacher. Your teacher will assign each student a set of data points to graph. Before beginning, discuss with the class how you should standardize the graphing. With your teacher, use the data provided to determine the scale for each axis. Discuss how to label the maximum points (Max or "M") and minimum points (min or "m").

Table 8.3 Sunspot Data (1750–1999)

Year	No. of sunspots	Year	No. of sunspots	Year	No. of sunspots
1750	83	1779	125	1808	8
1751	47	1780	84	1809	2
1752	47	1781	68	1810	0
1753	30	1782	38	1811	1
1754	12	1783	22	1812	5
1755	9	1784	10	1813	12
1756	10	1785	24	1814	13
1757	32	1786	82	1815	35
1758	47	1787	132	1816	45
1759	54	1788	130	1817	41
1760	62	1789	118	1818	30
1761	85	1790	89	1819	23
1762	61	1791	66	1820	15
1763	45	1792	60	1821	6
1764	36	1793	46	1822	4
1765	20	1794	41	1823	1
1766	11	1795	21	1824	8
1767	37	1796	16	1825	16
1768	69	1797	6	1826	36
1769	106	1798	4	1827	49
1770	100	1799	6	1828	62
1771	81	1800	14	1829	67
1772	66	1801	34	1830	71
1773	34	1802	45	1831	47
1774	30	1803	43	1832	27
1775	7	1804	47	1833	8
1776	19	1805	42	1834	13
1777	92	1806	28	1835	56
1778	154	1807	10	1836	121

Year	No. of sunspots	Year	No. of sunspots	Year	No. of sunspots	Year	No. of sunspots	Year	No. of sunspots	Year	No. of sunspots
1837	138	1866	16	1895	64	1924	16	1953	13	1982	116
1838	103	1867	7	1896	41	1925	44	1954	4	1983	67
1839	85	1868	37	1897	26	1926	63	1955	38	1984	46
1840	63	1869	73	1898	26	1927	69	1956	141	1985	118
1841	36	1870	139	1899	12	1928	77	1957	189	1986	13
1842	24	1871	111	1900	9	1929	65	1958	184	1987	29
1843	10	1872	101	1901	2	1930	35	1959	158	1988	100
1844	15	1873	66	1902	5	1931	21	1960	112	1989	148
1845	40	1874	44	1903	24	1932	11	1961	53	1990	143
1846	61	1875	17	1904	42	1933	5	1962	37	1991	149
1847	98	1876	11	1905	63	1934	8	1963	27	1992	94
1848	124	1877	12	1906	53	1935	36	1964	10	1993	55
1849	95	1878	3	1907	62	1936	79	1965	15	1994	30
1850	66	1879	6	1908	48	1937	114	1966	47	1995	18
1851	64	1880	32	1909	43	1938	109	1967	94	1996	9
1852	54	1881	54	1910	18	1939	88	1968	106	1997	22
1853	39	1882	59	1911	5	1940	67	1969	106	1998	64
1854	20	1883	63	1912	3	1941	47	1970	105	1999	93
1855	6	1884	63	1913	1	1942	30	1971	67		
1856	4	1885	52	1914	9	1943	16	1972	69		
1857	22	1886	25	1915	47	1944	11	1973	89		
1858	54	1887	13	1916	57	1945	33	1974	34		
1859	93	1888	6	1917	103	1946	92	1975	16		
1860	95	1889	6	1918	80	1947	151	1976	13		
1861	77	1890	7	1919	63	1948	136	1977	27		
1862	59	1891	35	1920	37	1949	134	1978	93		
1863	44	1892	72	1921	26	1950	83	1979	155		
1864	47	1893	84	1922	14	1951	69	1980	155		
1865	30	1894	78	1923	5	1952	31	1981	140		

SOURCE: NOAA SPACE ENVIRONMENTAL CENTER

6. Graph your assigned data points.

REFLECTING ON WHAT YOU'VE DONE

1. Tape together all four graphs from your group to form a single graph. Analyze the graph. Then answer the following questions in your notebook:

A. What patterns can you see in the sunspot data?

B. How many years apart (on average) are the sunspot maximums?

C. How many years apart (on average) are the sunspot minimums?

D. Using the graph, predict when you think the next sunspot maximum should have occurred?

E. On your graph, when might it have been relatively cold on Earth? Explain your answer.

F. Why might it be important for scientists to determine patterns in sunspot data?

2. Now all groups' graphs will be taped together to form one 200-year graph. What additional observations can you make? Discuss your ideas with the class.

3. Read "Little Ice Age" and "Tree Rings Hold Solar Secrets." Discuss the readings with your class.

4. Are there any questions from the class brainstorming sheet of Lesson 1 that you can now answer? Are there any questions that you want to add? Work with your teacher to do that now.

GALILEO'S DISCOVERIES

Until about 1600, people believed that the universe was a very small place. They thought that Earth was the center of the universe, and that the Sun, Moon, and stars were small, flat disks.

One of the original telescopes

People also believed that the other five planets known at that time—Mercury, Venus, Mars, Jupiter, and Saturn—were also flat disks and that all planets and stars moved across the sky while Earth stood still below. This concept of the universe was perfect and precise. People called it "the clockwork universe."

Today, such beliefs seem silly, but centuries ago, many people held those beliefs so strongly that anyone who challenged them could get into terrible trouble. New discoveries that threatened the old, orderly beliefs were considered dangerous.

Discovering Through a Telescope

Dutch craftsmen invented the telescope about 1608. The invention of the telescope—which uses lenses and mirrors to make distant objects appear larger and nearer—changed astronomy forever. Suddenly, European astronomers could peer into space and see previously unimagined details on objects such as the Moon, Sun, and planets. They also were able to discover planets and stars that had never been visible.

In 1610, an Italian astronomer named Galileo Galilei aimed one of the first telescopes at the sky. What Galileo saw through the telescope was very different from what could be seen with the naked eye.

One of the things that Galileo discovered was that four small moons

Composite of four of Jupiter's largest moons, known as the Galilean satellites. From top to bottom, the moons shown are Io, Europa, Ganymede, and Callisto. Jupiter's Great Red Spot is in the background. (You would not see the four moons together like this.)

orbit Jupiter. Today, we know that those moons are among the biggest in the solar system. More important to Galileo was that those moons weren't orbiting Earth. If everything orbited Earth, he asked, how could Jupiter have its own moons?

Then Galileo looked at our Moon. Instead of a flat disk, he saw mountains, valleys, and the strange features we now call craters.

Sunspots

Galileo, along with other scientists, made another discovery. When he trained his telescope on the Sun, he saw small, dark spots on its surface. He also observed that the spots appeared to move across the Sun's surface from west to east. Again, Galileo was puzzled. If the universe was perfect, as people claimed,

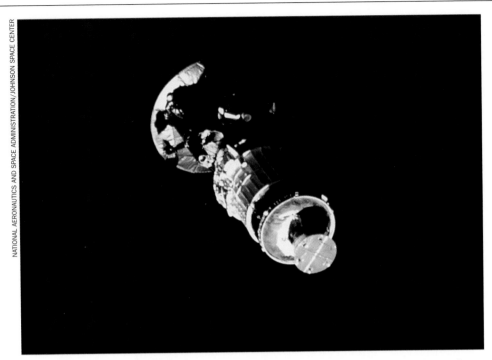

The Galileo *space probe was launched in 1989. It sent back pictures of Jupiter and four of its moons, which Galileo first saw in 1609.*

why would the Sun have spots? And if the Sun was a flat disk, why were these spots moving?

Galileo could not explain why these spots existed, but he believed they were part of the Sun itself. Other scientists argued that the spots they were seeing must be planets or moons in front of the Sun.

Galileo noted that all the spots moved at the same speed. They raced across the surface, disappeared, and reappeared. In fact, every spot that Galileo observed took exactly the same amount of time to disappear and reappear in the same place on the Sun's surface. He also noticed that the spots flattened as they neared the Sun's edge, which meant that they had to be a part of the Sun's surface. Galileo concluded that the Sun must rotate. And if it was rotating, it couldn't be a flat disk. It had to be a sphere just like Earth!

New Discoveries Can Be Dangerous

Galileo's discoveries about Jupiter, the Moon, and the Sun were very controversial, especially to leaders of the Church. They put him on trial for heresy (beliefs that were different from accepted beliefs) and threatened him with torture. To keep Galileo from expressing new ideas that contradicted currently held ideas, the Church leaders put him under house arrest. Galileo could not talk or write about his discoveries for the rest of his life, but he remained convinced that his ideas about the solar system were correct.

Other scientists at the time also were threatened whenever they announced discoveries that challenged accepted ideas. But over the years, as more and more telescopes were pointed at the skies, scientists realized that Galileo's ideas were true. Eventually Galileo's theories were accepted. Today we honor him for his contributions to science. ☐

Who Saw Them First?

The Aztec Empire existed from about the 14th to the 16th centuries. One Aztec myth of creation tells about a brave god with a scabby, pock-marked face who sacrificed himself by fire to become the Sun.

Observers of long ago could not explain what they were seeing. Today, however, scientists and historians deduce that the blemishes mentioned in these myths must have been the ancients' first observation and record of sunspots.

There is some debate over which European was the first to formally discover sunspots. The credit is usually shared by Galileo Galilei of Italy, Johann Goldsmid (known as Johannes Fabricius) of Holland, Christopher Schiener of Germany, and Thomas Herriot of England, all of whom claimed to have discovered sunspots

sometime in 1611. All four men observed sunspots through telescopes. They made drawings of the changing shapes and watched the spots move across the visible surface of the Sun. These drawings were the first steps toward understanding sunspots.

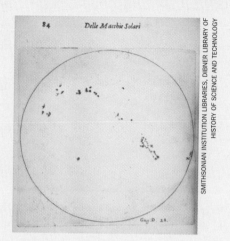

Sunspot drawing by Christopher Schiener of Germany

The Aztec myth suggests they had seen spots on the Sun.

What Are Sunspots?

Careful observation from Earth reveals a surprisingly large number of visible features on the Sun. The most obvious and best known is the sunspot. A sunspot is a region in the Sun's photosphere—the visible surface of the Sun—that is relatively cooler than its surroundings and which therefore appears darker. Sunspots are different sizes. They vary in diameter from around 10,000 to 50,000 kilometers. (Earth's diameter is 12,756 kilometers.) Occasionally, sunspots are as wide as about 200,000 km. Planet-sized sunspots can last from a few hours (for the smallest) to a few weeks or months (for the biggest).

Sunspots appear to move across the face of the Sun. In reality, they are moving with the Sun as the Sun rotates on its axis. The rate at which sunspots move indicates the rotational period of the Sun. At the Sun's equator, the rotational period is approximately 25 days.

At latitudes around 75 degrees, the rotational period of the Sun is approximately 35 days. The fact that sunspots move at different rates at different latitudes demonstrates that the Sun is not a solid body.

Some scientists theorize that sunspots form because of a process that occurs below the surface of the Sun, in a layer called the convection zone. Convection is the circular movement of a gas or liquid caused by differences in heat. Some scientists think that strong convection in the Sun's convection zone may strengthen the Sun's magnetic field. As an example, think about an electromagnet formed by a wire wrapped around a nail. The more coils in the wire, the stronger the magnetic field around the nail. A stronger magnetic field in the convection zone reduces the convection—or rising—of hotter gases from lower levels. This cools the solar surface area above it. These relatively cooler areas on the Sun's surface are sunspots.

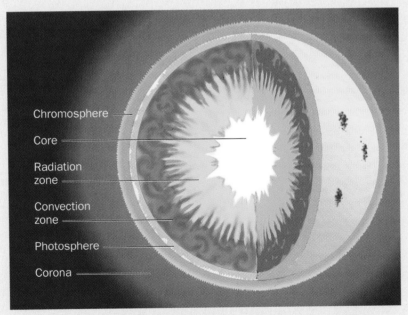

Chromosphere

Core

Radiation zone

Convection zone

Photosphere

Corona

Like Earth, the Sun is made up of layers, including the core, radiation zone, convection zone, photosphere, and chromosphere. The corona is the outer region of the Sun's dense atmosphere.

Little Ice Age

Even if you love winter sports, you may have tired of the cold during the period known as the "Little Ice Age." For about 70 years, from about 1645 to 1715, a severe cold spell gripped Earth. Temperatures dipped and caused glaciers to spread in Greenland, Iceland, Scandinavia, and the Alps. Many springs and summers were cold and wet. As a result, the growing season was shortened, many crops failed, and some people died of starvation.

For many of those 70 cold years, snow covered the northeastern United States from November through mid-April. Many harbors froze. People could even walk or ride sleighs from Staten Island to Manhattan.

What was happening? During the coldest part of this time, astronomers noticed that almost no sunspots appeared on the Sun. Sunspots trigger solar activity that increases the Sun's brightness.

Could Earth experience another Little Ice Age? The answer is—keep your ice skates handy! ☐

ERICH LESSING, ART RESOURCE, NEW YORK

Can you imagine if winter lasted year round?

TREE RINGS HOLD SOLAR SECRETS

Did you know that trees add a ring of new wood each year? Maybe you've seen those rings—light- and dark-colored bands—in a tree stump. And maybe you've heard that you can count the rings to determine a tree's age. But the rings tell us more than a tree's age. They also tell us about the brightness of the Sun!

You might think that the Sun's light is always the same, but it's not. For years at a time, the Sun may shine with a certain degree of brightness, and then it may become somewhat dimmer—or brighter. Sunspots may be the cause. What does this have to do with tree rings?

Scientists know that when the Sun is very active, its magnetic field makes it harder for cosmic rays to reach Earth. Cosmic rays help form a special carbon element in Earth's atmosphere. When the Sun is at its brightest and most active, less carbon is produced. Trees are able to absorb this natural element from the atmosphere. So when there is less carbon in the air, trees absorb less; when there is more carbon in the air, trees absorb more. And the difference shows up in their rings. Scientists measure the amount of carbon in each tree ring. By dating the tree ring, they can tell how bright the Sun was that year! □

IMAGE 235116,
1929, FOREST SERVICE
PHOTOGRAPH COLLECTION,
SPECIAL COLLECTIONS,
NATIONAL AGRICULTURAL LIBRARY

Can this tree's rings tell you how old it is?

AURORAS

Do you like light shows? One of the best shows you could ever see is free, courtesy of nature. It's called an aurora, which is Latin for *dawn*. The aurora—usually red or green—lights up the night sky near the North and South poles. If conditions are right, these auroral storms can be seen thousands of miles away.

In the Northern Hemisphere, this light show is called the aurora borealis. In the Southern Hemisphere, it is called the aurora australis.

Sun Storms Cause Auroras

What causes these beautiful light shows? Scientists have been debating that issue for many years. They have known that there is a connection between activity on the Sun and the appearance of auroras in Earth's atmosphere since 1859. That's when English astronomer Richard Carrington first noticed that auroras often appeared several days after solar storms erupted on the Sun's surface. Now, with advanced space exploration and special space cameras, people are starting to develop a better understanding of this pattern.

How does a solar storm cause a light show on Earth? When a solar storm occurs on the Sun's surface, a very hot, gaseous mixture called "plasma" explodes. Plasma is a mixture of electrons, protons, and ions— very small particles that release tremendous energy.

Streams of this plasma blast through space at very high speeds. The traveling plasma is known as solar wind. The slower solar winds travel at approxi-mately 300 kilometers a second. Faster winds can travel at nearly 800 kilometers a second!

Fortunately, these solar winds never make it to Earth's surface. Earth has a magnetic field that shields it from harm. Most of the solar winds bounce off this magnetic shield. Sometimes, however, solar winds do penetrate the magnetic shield, especially where the magnetic field bends

This aurora borealis was seen over Alaska in April 2000, during some of the most intense auroral storms of the decade.

JAN CURTIS, GEOPHYSICAL INSTITUTE, UNIVERSITY OF ALASKA FAIRBANKS inward toward the poles. At the poles, the charged particles from the Sun become trapped, spiral toward Earth's magnetic poles, and collide with the gases in Earth's atmosphere. These collisions give off energy that we see as colored light in the sky.

More Sun Storms Mean More Auroras

Scientists know that an increase in the number of solar storms—often associated with high sunspot activity—results in more auroras. And the stronger the solar storms, the brighter the auroras.

Sun activity seems to occur in 22-year cycles. The period of greatest solar activity in a 22-year cycle is called the solar maximum. During the solar maximum, we tend to see the most auroras, as well as the brightest ones. This is also when people who live many thousands of miles from the poles get to see auroras.

What Do Auroras Look Like?

Auroras can have many shapes. Some look like flags waving. Others look like arcs or ribbons in the sky. Most auroras are green, although many are red.

The best time to see an aurora is between sunset and midnight. If you live in North America, you have the best chance of seeing an aurora if you live in Canada or Alaska. During a period of solar maximum, however, people in almost every state can view nature's own light show. ☐

This NASA illustration shows Earth's magnetosphere and its interaction with the Sun. Auroras occur most often where the field curves inward at the poles.

COURTESY OF SOHO. SOHO IS A PROJECT OF INTERNATIONAL COOPERATION BETWEEN ESA (EUROPEAN SPACE AGENCY) AND NATIONAL AERONAUTICS AND SPACE ADMINISTRATION.

This aurora was seen over Alaska in the middle of winter.

© DICK HUTCHINSON

Red aurora australis seen over southern Australia.

COURTESY OF DAVID MILLER, NATIONAL GEOPHYSICAL DATA CENTER

Sun-Earth-Moon System Assessment

How does the distance from the thermometer to the clamp lamp affect temperature?

JEFF MCADAMS, PHOTOGRAPHER, COURTESY OF CAROLINA BIOLOGICAL SUPPLY COMPANY

INTRODUCTION

After Parts 1 and 3 of this module, you will be assessed on your ability to show what you know and what you can do as it relates to your study of the solar system. You have now completed Part 1: Sun-Earth-Moon System of *Earth in Space,* and this lesson will assess your grasp of the concepts and skills in Lessons 1–8.

This assessment is divided into three parts. During Part A, you will conduct an investigation and record your observations and conclusions. You also will be asked to describe how the investigation relates to the Sun-Earth-Moon system. For Part B, you will complete multiple-choice and short-answer questions about the Sun, Earth, and Moon. You also will review diagrams and interpret data plotted on a graph. In Part C, you will revisit an activity from Lesson 2 to see how much you have learned.

OBJECTIVES FOR THIS LESSON

Review and reinforce concepts and skills from Part 1: Sun-Earth-Moon System.

Complete a three-part assessment of the concepts and skills addressed in Part 1.

Getting Started

1. Examine the parts of the digital thermometer. Read the Safety Tip.

2. Read the temperature using the Celsius scale. Place the metal rod of the thermometer between your finger and thumb. Which part of the metal on the thermometer registers the temperature? How can you get the temperature to change? How can you get it to return to room temperature? Discuss your ideas with your group and class.

MATERIALS FOR LESSON 9

For you

- 1 copy of the planning sheet
- 1 copy of Inquiry Master 9.1a: Sun-Earth-Moon Performance Task (Part A)
- 1 copy of Student Sheet 9.1a: Sun-Earth-Moon Performance-Based Assessment (Part A)
- 1 copy of Inquiry Master 9.1b: Sun-Earth-Moon Written Assessment (Part B)
- 1 copy of Student Sheet 9.1b: Sun-Earth-Moon Assessment Answer Sheet (Part B)
- 1 copy of Student Sheet 9.1c: What We Now Know About the Sun-Earth-Moon System (Part C)

For your group

- 2 bookends
- 1 clamp lamp with reflector
- 1 100-W lightbulb
- 1 digital thermometer
- 1 student timer (or other timepiece)
- 1 metric measuring tape, or ½-meter stick
- 1 protractor
- 1 white foil square
- 1 black foil square

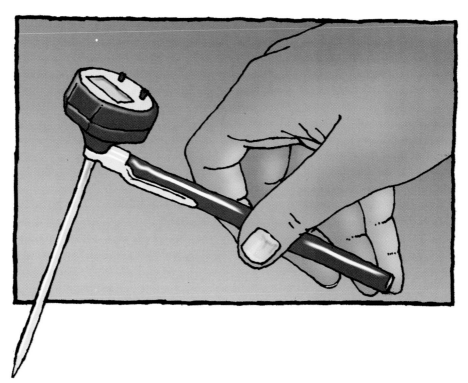

Figure 9.1
Holding the thermometer

3. To keep results consistent among groups, discuss with your class how to hold the thermometer. See Figure 9.1, which shows one method.

4. How will a clamp lamp affect the temperature of the thermometer at different distances from the lamp? Discuss your ideas with the class. You will formally test your ideas in this lesson.

PROCEDURE

Part A

1. Collect one copy of the planning sheet, one copy of Student Sheet 9.1a, and one copy of Inquiry Master 9.1a.

2. Review the Inquiry Master 9.1a and the planning sheet with your class. Examine the equipment. Note that you will not use all the equipment; the equipment you use depends on the question you test.

3. Discuss with your teacher how you will be assessed in this lesson.

4. Complete your planning sheet. Review it with your teacher.

5. Review the Safety Tip. Then obtain your lab equipment. Although you will share a set of materials with other students, you should complete Student Sheet 9.1a in your own words.

6. Complete your investigation. Turn in Student Sheet 9.1a when you are finished. Shut off all clamp lamps. Your teacher will tell you where to put your equipment.

Part B

Complete Part B. Do not write on the sheet of questions; other classes throughout the day will use it. Write answers on your answer sheet.

Part C

Complete Student Sheet 9.1c.

SAFETY TIP

Do not touch the metal reflector on the clamp lamp while it is turned on or while it is cooling.

REFLECTING ON WHAT YOU'VE DONE

1. After you have reviewed this assessment with your teacher, compare your responses on Student Sheet 9.1c with your science notebook entries from Lesson 2. How have your ideas about the Sun-Earth-Moon system changed since Lesson 2?

2. Read "Fast Plants: Ready for Liftoff!"

FAST PLANTS:
Ready for Liftoff!

Dr. Paul Williams works with the Brassica rapa *in his lab.*

Wisconsin Fast Plants™ were grown aboard the Soviet space station *Mir,* as well as on numerous U.S. space shuttles. In this interview, Dr. Paul Williams, retired university professor at the University of Wisconsin and the creator of Fast Plants, answers several questions about Fast Plants' role in space.

Q: What are Fast Plants?
A: Fast Plants are plants that are specially bred for rapid development. In 5 to 6 weeks, these little relatives of turnip and mustard plants go through an entire life cycle, from seed to seed.

Q: Why take Fast Plants—or any plants—into space?
A: For many reasons. First, it's hoped that on long space missions or on space stations, plants will recycle the air. Carrying the oxygen needed by big crews on long missions would be impossible. So, space scientists hope to use plants to take in expelled carbon dioxide and release necessary oxygen in space, just as they do on Earth.

Another reason we experiment with plants in space is to find out if they can provide food for astronauts. Astronauts get tired of freeze-dried and packaged foods. Fast Plants are small. They don't take up much room, and they grow fast. They also belong to one of the largest and most diverse families of plants, Brassica. From various seeds, we can grow edible and industrial oil and a range of veggies—cabbages, broccoli, lettuce, turnips, cauliflower, and many others.

A third reason to take plants into space is that they remind astronauts of Earth. This can add to a sense of well-being and reduce homesickness. Michael Foale, an American astronaut aboard *Mir,* said that tending the plants helped him and his two cosmonaut companions stay hopeful during some tough days.

Q: Do Fast Plants grow in space the same way they grow on Earth?
A: Until *Mir* in 1997, we didn't know if plants would reproduce successfully in space. That was the first time seeds sown in space grew into plants that flowered and produced more seeds. And to our delight, the Fast Plants took the same amount of time to do all that in space that they take on Earth—about 6 weeks.

Fast Plants™, which were grown in space aboard the Columbia *space shuttle, were kept in a special growth chamber.*

However, in space the plants are kept in a special growth chamber where temperature, air quality, humidity, and light are controlled. We have to give them lots of light, especially at first. We also give them extra carbon dioxide. On Earth, gravity *and* light direct growth in plants. But in space, in microgravity, light alone guides the direction of growth.

Q: What is microgravity?
A: It means "very little gravity." The farther away we travel from Earth, the weaker Earth's gravity becomes. As a spacecraft orbits around Earth, gravity is extremely weak.

Q: How do you water space plants?
A: Astronauts use a syringe to inject a solution of water and nutrients into the foam bed that secures each plant.

Q: How are space plants pollinated?
A: They have to be pollinated by hand because there are—as of yet—no insect pollinators in space. Astronauts use "bee sticks"—toothpicks with dead bees glued on one end that can pick up pollen grains and deposit them on the stigma of plants.

It's not hard, but as you might imagine, it takes time. Astronauts have to mark each plant to make sure each one is included. I'm waiting for someone to experiment with live butterflies and bees as pollinators in space. That would be a terrific next step! ☐

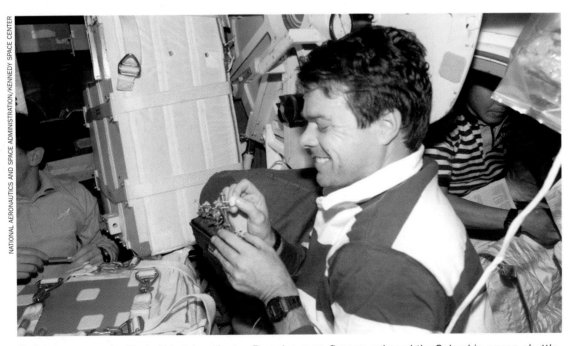

Training commander Kevin Kriegel pollinates Brassica rapa *flowers onboard the* Columbia *space shuttle.*

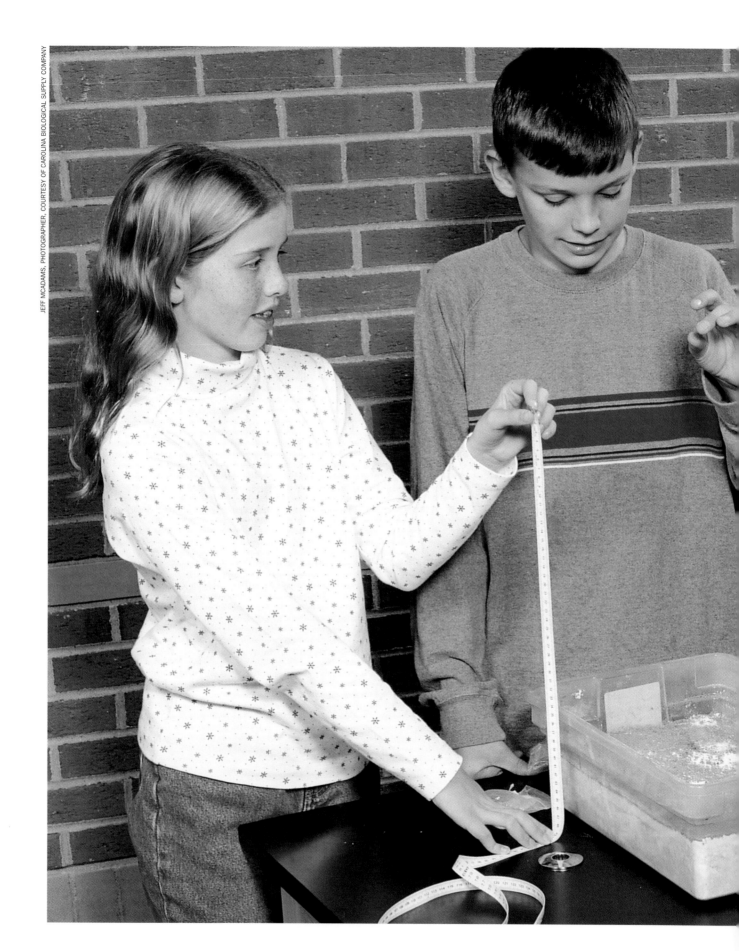

LESSON 10

Anchor Activity: Space Exploration

Astronaut Sally Ride communicates with ground controllers from the flight deck of the Earth-orbiting space shuttle Challenger. Dr. Ride holds a tape recorder.

NATIONAL AERONAUTICS AND SPACE ADMINISTRATION/JOHNSON SPACE CENTER

INTRODUCTION

For much of human history, our knowledge about space has been limited. Information that we obtained about space came either from our own observations or from the observations made by instruments set up on Earth. Only since the 1960s have we been able to leave Earth and experience space firsthand. Since then, space exploration has literally opened up "new worlds."

In this lesson, the first in Part 2: Solar System, you will begin a research project (called an Anchor Activity) to learn more about the planets. First, you will read the introduction to a series about some of the missions and space probes that have helped us learn more about our neighbors in the solar system. Then, after you review the guidelines for the Anchor Activity, you will use different resources over the next few weeks to learn more about a particular planet and probes that have observed it. You will record your research in a planetary travel brochure. Then, with your team members, you will use the information to design a space mission to explore

OBJECTIVES FOR THIS LESSON

Read about the history of the space program.

Discuss how science and technology contribute to the advancement of planetary studies.

Review the Anchor Activity guidelines and the time line for researching a planet.

Plan to design a space mission for exploring your planet in the future.

that planet in the future. During Lesson 19, you will present your brochure to the class and your team will share its future mission design.

Getting Started

1. Read "Mission Introduction: History of Space Exploration."

2. With your group, select one space mission (such as Gemini) or a space probe (such as *Pathfinder*) from the reading selection. Report to the class what you learned or already know about that mission or probe.

3. Discuss the following with your class:

How has space exploration changed since the 1960s?

What have we learned about the solar system from the space program?

What do you think will happen to space exploration in the future?

MATERIALS FOR LESSON 10

For you

1 copy of Student Sheet 10.1a: Anchor Activity Time Line

1 copy of Student Sheet 10.1b: Planetary Brochure Outline

1 copy of Student Sheet 10.1c: Planetary Chart

1 sheet of white or light-colored paper, 8½" × 11"

Access to a computer lab and the Internet or a classroom resource center

Inquiry 10.1
Beginning the Anchor Activity

PROCEDURE

1. Your teacher will show you a sample travel brochure. Discuss its features.

2. Obtain one white or light-colored sheet of paper and practice folding it to make a brochure. See Figure 10.1. You can use this paper for the rough draft of your planetary travel brochure. You are free to use paper or material of your own choosing for your final brochure.

3. Read the Anchor Activity Guidelines in this lesson. Then discuss them with your class.

4. Your teacher will give you a copy of Student Sheet 10.1a: Anchor Activity Time Line. Discuss the due dates with your teacher.

5. Review your copy of Student Sheets 10.1b and 10.1c. Use these sheets as a way to organize your planet research. Record the due date at the top of Student Sheet 10.1c.

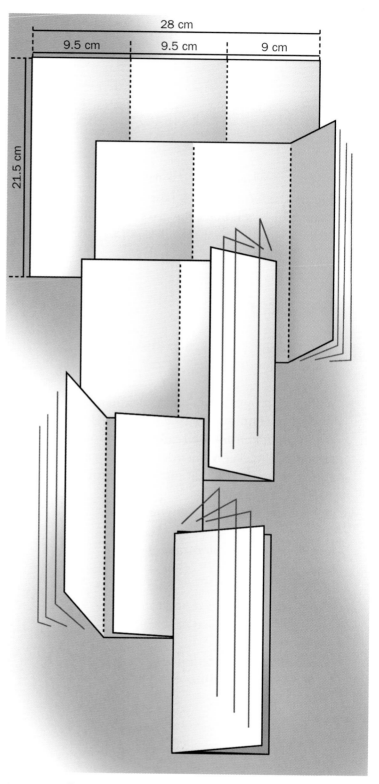

Figure 10.1 *Fold the paper to create a brochure.*

6. Discuss with your teacher how your project will be assessed.

7. Select a specific planet for your Anchor Activity. Record the name of that planet at the top of your student sheets.

REFLECTING ON WHAT YOU'VE DONE

1. Tell the class which planet you have selected.

2. On Student Sheet 10.1a, record the names of one to three other students who will be researching your planet. You will work with these team member(s) to design a mission to explore the planet in the future. You and your team will share your future mission design during Lesson 19.

3. Read "Top 10 Scientific Discoveries Made During Apollo Exploration of the Moon."

Anchor Activity Guidelines

The *Earth in Space* Anchor Activity is a research project that focuses on space exploration and the knowledge gained about the planets from these explorations.

Follow these steps to complete your Anchor Activity:

A. Fill out your time line.

Work with your teacher to decide when each part of the project is due. The time line is on Student Sheet 10.1a.

B. Choose a planet.

Go to the library or the computer lab with your class. Select one planet to research. Your teacher may assign you a specific planet so that your class covers all nine planets.

C. Research the planet.

Conduct research to find out more about your planet. You should use a variety of resources, including those in the classroom, in your school library and other libraries, in newspapers, or on the Internet. You also may conduct personal interviews or use e-mail to ask questions of experts. The Mission reading series in your Student Guide is another excellent resource. Your teacher will tell you how many Internet sources, books, magazines, and newspaper articles you need to use in your research.

Complete Student Sheets 10.1b and 10.1c as you conduct your research. Find out as much as you can about your planet and about space probes and missions that have provided this information. Note that you may not be able to find answers to all of the questions on Student Sheet 10.1b. With your teacher's permission, you may substitute other information about your planet. You also might want to find pictures of your planet to put in your finished brochure.

You should include the following information in your brochure (these items are also listed on Student Sheet 10.1b):

History: The planet's name, who named it, and what the name means

Discovery: When the planet was discovered and who discovered it

Planet structure: The interior of the planet (what it looks like inside) and its surface features (if it is a terrestrial planet)

Atmosphere: The composition and conditions of the planet's atmosphere (for example, does it have storms?), if these are known; if there is no atmosphere, say so

Motion: The planet's orbit (how long it takes to get around the Sun) and rotation (how long it takes to turn one time on its axis)

Missions: A description of probes or missions to the planet; travel times and dates

Data: Complete all of Student Sheet 10.1c. Use the Mission series in your Student Guide to help you. Include each planet's diameter, average distance from the Sun, mass, surface gravity, average temperature, length of sidereal day, length of year, and number of observed moons.

Other: Other interesting information (include pictures and drawings)

D. Create your bibliography.

As you conduct your research, remember to use your school's guidelines for giving credit to your sources, including any images you may be including in your brochure.

E. Make your planetary brochure.

Prepare your planetary travel brochure using the information that you outlined on Student Sheets 10.1b and 10.1c. Include both pictures and text. Try to be original. See Figure 10.2 for examples of completed brochures.

Figure 10.2 *Sample brochures*

Figure 10.3 *Share your travel brochure with your class during Lesson 19.*

F. Work with your team to design a future mission to your planet.

Work as a team with other students in your class who researched the same planet to design a way to explore your planet in the future. You will consider all the knowledge you gained about your planet to determine if there are any travel constraints and to design your exploration to overcome these constraints. Consider questions such as the following:

How does the distance to the planet determine the type of spacecraft you must use to probe the planet firsthand?

Will the probe land on the planet's surface or observe it from space? What if your planet is gaseous?

Can your probe deal with the planet's gravitational forces?

How will the planet's surface conditions and atmospheric composition affect the type of observations you can make of the planet?

G. Present your brochure and future mission design to the class.

During Lesson 19, you will present your brochure to the class and teach others about your planet (see Figure 10.3). Then you and your team will present your future mission design. Be prepared to debate and discuss any issues or topics that arise.

NOTE Remember that Earth is a planet and is observed from space just as other planets are. See Lesson 17 for more information about missions to planet Earth.

MISSION INTRODUCTION:

HISTORY OF SPACE EXPLORATION

The story of space exploration begins in the early 20th century. Before space flight was even physically possible, humans imagined being able to explore space. Human space flight took a giant leap toward reality during World War II, when Germany began to manufacture V2 rockets. The United States captured many of these rockets after the war and used them for testing and further development. In the late 1950s, scientists developed winged rocket planes based on their studies of those earlier V2 rockets. In 1957, the former Soviet Union sent the first satellite, *Sputnik 1,* into orbit. In 1961, the Soviet Union's air force pilot and cosmonaut Yuri Gagarin became the first human to orbit Earth.

Project Mercury

The National Aeronautics and Space Administration (NASA) was formed on October 1, 1958. Six days later, NASA announced that its goal was to place an American in orbit. Building on the groundwork laid by a group working at Langley Air Force Base, NASA began its first high-profile program—Project Mercury. At that time, no human had ever gone into space. No one knew how astronauts would react to weightlessness, the high accelerations of launches and landings, radiation from the Sun, or the psychological stresses of being in space. So NASA first sent chimpanzees, monkeys, and human-like dummies into space. Scientists tested the tracking and recovery systems of various spacecraft. NASA announced that seven astronauts, all military men, would train intensely to prepare for space travel.

Project Mercury flew 13 flights—six of which were piloted. On May 6, 1961, Alan Shephard rocketed 115 miles above Earth in a flawless flight to become America's first man in space, 23 days after Yuri Gagarin's flight. After

© BETTMANN/CORBIS

Yuri Gagarin, a Soviet air force pilot and cosmonaut, was the first human to orbit Earth. His total flight time was 1 hour and 48 minutes.

Shephard's flight, President John F. Kennedy announced NASA's next space program goal: to land a man on the Moon by the end of the decade.

Project Mercury proved that astronauts could control their spacecraft while in space, and that a human could remain in space for more than a day.

NATIONAL AERONAUTICS AND SPACE ADMINISTRATION

Mercury-Atlas *rocket stands on a launch pad at Cape Canaveral awaiting a mission in 1963.*

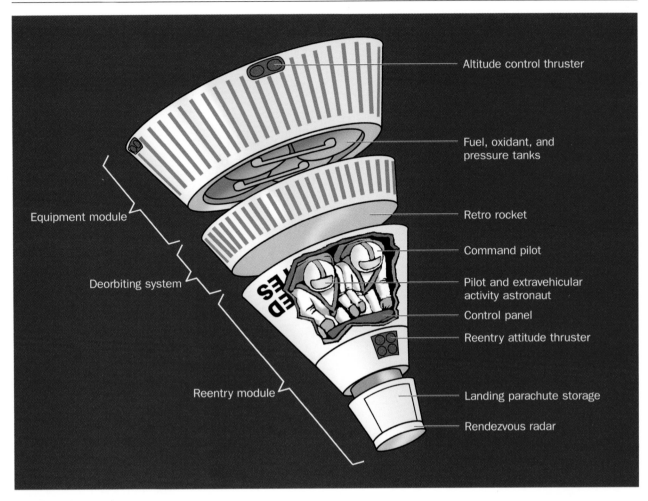

- Altitude control thruster
- Fuel, oxidant, and pressure tanks
- Retro rocket
- Command pilot
- Pilot and extravehicular activity astronaut
- Control panel
- Reentry attitude thruster
- Landing parachute storage
- Rendezvous radar
- Equipment module
- Deorbiting system
- Reentry module

The Gemini *capsule*

Project Gemini

Project Gemini built on Project Mercury's successes and used spacecraft built for two astronauts. The Gemini Project developed the United States' ability to maintain crews on extended space missions and to maneuver and rendezvous, all of which were critical to the later Apollo missions. Gemini astronauts also conducted several scientific experiments and performed the first U.S. "space walks."

A total of 12 Gemini missions flew, two of them unpiloted, carrying 20 astronauts for a total of more than 40 days in space.

Apollo Missions

The Apollo missions were among the most important technological feats in U.S. history. They included 11 piloted missions, six of which ended on the Moon. Twelve Americans walked on the lunar surface, beginning with astronauts on Apollo 11 on July 20, 1969. (See the reading selection "Apollo 11" in Lesson 5 for more information.)

The scientific investigations conducted during the Apollo missions changed our understanding of Earth, as well as our understanding of the origin of the Moon. Astronauts gathered several

hundred pounds of lunar soil and rock from the Moon and brought them back to Earth. These rocks and soils showed that the Moon is rich in resources needed to sustain human life—except for water, a vital ingredient for human existence.

The triumphs of Apollo were paired with tragedy, however. During a training accident in 1967, the first three Apollo astronauts were killed. Apollo 13 suffered a near-disaster, but the program continued with four more successful missions.

Photographs taken by Apollo astronauts, which depicted Earth suspended in space, forever changed the way we view our home planet. The Apollo project demonstrated that humans can live and work in space, and even on other worlds. It also demonstrated that technologies developed for the space program were capable of changing our lives forever. (See the reading selection "Space Spinoffs" in Lesson 20.)

Skylab Project

Skylab was America's first space station. The lab measured about 36 meters long. In building it, scientists adapted elements from the Apollo program. The "lower" level housed the crew's quarters, the toilet, galley and dining area, as well as an experiment area with devices such as a rotating chair and a bicycle ergometer. The "upper" level, or forward compartment, was the storage area for food, water, experimental equipment, and spacesuits. The station had two large solar panels and an unattached airlock at one end. It also had a large, X–shaped structure that consisted of four solar arrays radiating from a central structure known as the Apollo Telescope Mount.

Astronaut Jack Lousma walks in space outside the Skylab *space station during the* Skylab *3 mission. Notice the reflection of* Skylab *and Earth in his helmet.*

NATIONAL AERONAUTICS AND SPACE ADMINISTRATION/JOHNSON SPACE CENTER

Space shuttle Challenger *lifting off*

Skylab was launched on May 14, 1973, and the first crews arrived at the station on May 25. At the lab, astronauts studied and photographed Earth, and conducted experiments such as how extended stays in space affected the human body. In 1979, the space laboratory, emptied of equipment and passengers, burned up in the atmosphere over Australia.

The Apollo–Soyuz Test Project

The Apollo–Soyuz Project demonstrated that the United States and the then-Soviet Union could work together in space. On July 15, 1975, Alexei Leonov—the first human to walk in space—and Valery Kubasov were launched into orbit aboard the *Soyuz* 19. The U.S. Apollo team—Donald Slayton, Vance Brand, and Thomas Stafford—lifted off 7 hours later from the Kennedy Space Center in Florida. The Apollo crew docked with the Soviet craft. On July 17, the two teams shook hands and the crews spoke to the people on Earth via live television. On July 19, the teams went their separate ways. Two days later, the Soviets landed in Siberia. The American crew stayed in orbit until July 24, conducting additional experiments before splashing down in the Pacific Ocean.

Space Shuttle to Space Station

It wasn't until 1981 that NASA resumed its space flight efforts. At that time, it proposed building a space station and space shuttles to service it. The goal was to use the shuttles like airplanes, which could be flown again and again, rather than like rockets, which would be used once and thrown away. NASA built the first shuttle using unmanned solid rocket boosters that fell into the Atlantic Ocean. The boosters were towed back to shore, where they were loaded onto rail cars for a trip back to the factory for rebuilding. The orbiter was completely reusable, but its engines were fed from a huge external tank that had to be thrown away on every mission. In 1993, a completely reusable shuttle was developed.

The shuttle is used to lift heavy payloads into orbit, provide a lab for astronauts to carry out scientific research in space, and provide a platform for retrieving satellites. It has also brought and returned astronauts to the International Space Station—the largest space project in history to date. Through the space station, over 15 nations led by the United States worked to build a laboratory in space. Research on the station will answer basic questions about humans living and working beyond the planet.

Scientific Probes

NASA has launched a number of other significant scientific probes, including *Pioneer, Galileo, Mariner,* and *Voyager.* These spacecraft have explored the moons, planets, and other places in our solar system. NASA sent several spacecraft, including *Viking* and *Mars Pathfinder,* to investigate Mars. The Hubble Space Telescope and other science spacecraft have enabled scientists to make a number of significant astronomy discoveries about our furthest planet, Pluto, and "deep space." (You will read about the discoveries made by these scientific probes in the Mission reading series over the next seven lessons.)

Space exploration has changed the way we live our lives. In addition to the pioneering work that NASA has done on aerodynamics and space applications, satellites have helped change the way we communicate. The history of space exploration has been relatively brief—but the number of changes that it has brought to the way we live on Earth are endless. ☐

Top 10 Scientific Discoveries Made During Apollo Exploration of the Moon

1. The Moon is not in its original state; it has evolved over time and has an internal structure like that of Earth.

Before Apollo, the Moon was a subject of wild speculation. We now know that the Moon is made of rocky material that has been melted, erupted through volcanoes, and crushed by meteorite impacts. The Moon has a thick crust (60 kilometers), a fairly uniform lithosphere (60–1000 kilometers), and a partly liquid upper mantle (1000–1740 kilometers). A small iron core may exist at the bottom of the mantle. Some Moon rocks suggest that there were once ancient magnetic fields, but no magnetic field exists today.

2. The Moon is ancient and preserves an early history (the first billion years) that may be common to all terrestrial planets.

The many meteorite craters on the Moon help scientists understand more about the geologic evolution of Mercury, Venus, and Mars, on the basis of their individual crater records. Our geological understanding of other planets is based mostly on what we have learned from the Moon. Before Apollo, scientists were not sure what caused lunar impact craters, and they did not agree on what caused similar craters on Earth.

3. The youngest Moon rocks are as old as the oldest Earth rocks. Evidence of geologic actions and events that probably affected both planetary bodies can now be found only on the Moon.

Moon rock ranges in age from about 3.2 billion years in the maria (dark, low basins) to nearly 4.6 billion years in the terrae (light, rugged highlands). Geologic forces, including plate tectonics and erosion, continuously change the oldest surfaces on Earth. The old surfaces on the Moon, by contrast, are mostly undisturbed.

4. The Moon and Earth are genetically related. They were formed from different amounts of the same materials.

Similar compositions of Moon rocks and Earth rocks clearly show that they have a common ancestry. Compared with Earth, however, the Moon has little iron and few of the elements needed to form atmospheric gases and water.

5. The Moon is lifeless; it contains no living organisms, fossils, or native organic compounds.

Extensive tests show no evidence for life, past or present, among the lunar samples. Even nonbiological organic compounds are absent. Traces of any organic compounds on the Moon probably came from meteorites hitting the lunar surface.

6. **All Moon rocks originated through high-temperature processes (similar to igneous and metamorphic rocks on Earth) with little or no involvement with water. They can be put into three categories: basalts, anorthosites, and breccias.**

Basalts are dark lava rocks that fill bowl-shaped holes on the Moon. These basalts resemble lavas in the oceanic crust of Earth, but they are much older. Anorthosites are light rocks that form the ancient highlands. They look like the most ancient rocks on Earth, but the Moon's rocks are much older. Even though the Moon is not older than Earth, its surface has not been recycled through plate tectonics, like Earth's surface. Breccias are composite rocks that were formed by crushing and mixing all other rock types during meteorite impacts. The Moon has no sandstone, shale, or limestone, which proves that little or no water was—or is—present on the Moon.

7. **Early in its history, much of the Moon melted to form a "magma ocean." The lunar highlands contain some early, low-density rocks that floated to the surface of the magma ocean.**

The lunar highlands were formed around 4.5 billion years ago. The Moon's early crust floated on an ocean of magma that covered the Moon many kilometers deep. Numerous meteorite impacts through time reduced much of the ancient crust to mountain ranges between basins.

8. **After the lunar magma ocean was formed, a series of huge asteroid impacts created basins that were later filled by lava flows.**

The large, dark basins on the Moon are gigantic impact craters, formed early in lunar history. These craters were filled by lava flows around 3.5 billion years ago. Volcanism on the Moon occurred mostly as lava spread horizontally. Volcanic fire fountains produced deposits of orange and emerald-green glass beads.

9. **The Moon is not symmetrical.**

The mass of the Moon is not distributed evenly, probably because it evolved under Earth's gravitational influence. The Moon's crust is thicker and less dense on the far side, away from Earth, and most dense volcanic basins occur on the near side, closest to Earth. The Moon's core is also leaning, or displaced, toward Earth by several kilometers.

10. **The Moon's surface is covered with rock fragments and dust called the "lunar regolith." This regolith (soil without dead or living organisms) contains a unique radiation history of the Sun that helps us understand climate changes on Earth.**

The regolith was produced by many meteorite impacts through geologic time. Surface rocks and mineral grains on the Moon are marked by chemical elements that come from solar radiation. The Moon has recorded 4 billion years of the Sun's history. □

Adapted courtesy of NASA's Apollo Manned Space Program

The Solar System: Designing a Scale Model

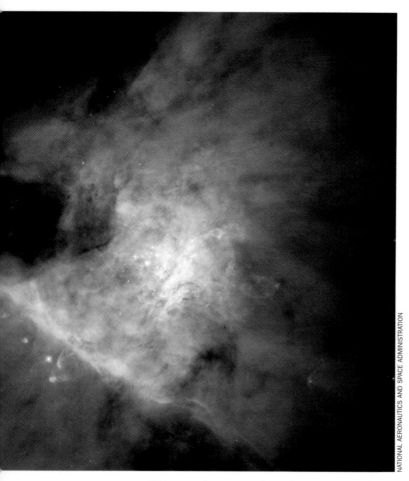

Did our solar system form from a giant cloud of gas and dust like this one—the Orion Nebula?

NATIONAL AERONAUTICS AND SPACE ADMINISTRATION

INTRODUCTION

About 4.6 billion years ago, our solar system evolved from a vast rotating cloud of cold gas and dust. The cloud separated into chunks of matter and collapsed inward. The Sun formed at the center of this matter as the interior started heating up. Near the Sun, rock and metal came together and eventually became the terrestrial (rocky) planets—Mercury, Venus, Earth, and Mars. The giant, gaseous planets—Jupiter, Saturn, Uranus, and Neptune—formed farther away from the Sun. Asteroids and frozen comets were formed from other loose material.

In this lesson, you will begin to investigate the solar system and its planets and asteroids. What do you already know about the solar system? How far apart are the planets? How do the sizes of other planets compare with Earth? You will examine these and other questions as you begin your journey through the solar system.

OBJECTIVES FOR THIS LESSON

Brainstorm what you know and want to learn about the order and sizes of the planets and their distances from each other.

Create a model of the solar system from a set of scaled items.

Use scale models to explore the relative diameters of and distances between the nine planets and the Sun.

Summarize and organize information about Mercury.

Getting Started

1. Record in your science notebook what you already know about the order of, size of, and relative distances between the planets within the solar system. Share your ideas with the class.

2. Discuss with the class what "scale" means when used with maps. Then define the term "model" and give some examples. Why do you think it is important to build models to scale? Discuss with your class what a scale model of the solar system should look like.

Inquiry 11.1
Designing a Model Solar System

MATERIALS FOR INQUIRY 11.1

For you
- 1 copy of Student Sheet 11.1: Our Solar System Model

For your group
- 1 large resealable bag labeled "11.1" containing the following:
  - 2 rubber balls
  - 2 Ping-Pong balls
  - 2 plastic buttons
  - 2 marbles
  - 2 acrylic beads
  - 2 wood barrel beads
  - 2 fishing bobbers
  - 3 split peas
  - 3 pieces of round oat cereal
- 1 strip of adding machine tape
- 1 marker

PROCEDURE

1. Review with your teacher how to convert millimeters to centimeters.

2. Obtain one large resealable bag labeled "11.1." Work with your group to select an object from the bag to represent each planet.

3. Label one end of the strip of adding machine tape "Sun." Position the objects that you have selected along the tape to show the order of, relative sizes of, and relative distances between the planets.

4. Measure the diameter of each planetary model (in centimeters) and record each object's name and diameter on Student Sheet 11.1: Our Solar System Model. Measure and record the distance (in centimeters) between each model planet and your "Sun."

5. Draw a picture of your solar system model on Student Sheet 11.1. Label your drawing. Note any similarities in sizes of or distances between your model planets.

REFLECTING ON WHAT YOU'VE DONE

1. Share your group's solar system model with the class.

2. Answer the following questions in a class discussion. Answer them in your science notebook as well, if instructed to do so by your teacher.

A. What was the largest planet in your model? What was the smallest planet?

B. Do you observe any patterns in the sizes of the planets in your model? If so, what are they?

C. Do you observe any patterns in the distances between your planets in your model? If so, what are they?

D. Do you think the objects in your model are to scale in terms of size? Why or why not?

E. Do you think the objects in your model are to scale in terms of distance? Why or why not?

3. Clean up by returning all your objects to the resealable bag. Save the adding machine tape for another class, if possible.

Inquiry 11.2
Using a Scale Factor

MATERIALS FOR INQUIRY 11.2

For you
1 copy of Student Sheet 11.2: Using a Scale Factor
1 calculator (optional)

PROCEDURE

1. Examine the illustration shown in Figure 11.1. How big would the model of a school bus 10 m long be if the scale factor that was used to make the model bus is 1 cm = 2 m?

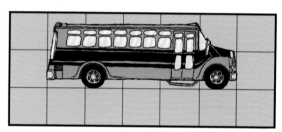

Figure 11.1 *How many centimeters long would a model of a 10-m school bus be if every centimeter represents 2 m?*

2. Set up your ratio as follows:

$$\frac{x}{10 \text{ m}} = \frac{1 \text{ cm}}{2 \text{ m}}$$

$$x \times 2 \text{ m} = 10 \text{ m} \times 1 \text{ cm}$$

$$x \times 2 \text{ m} = 10 \text{ m} \times \text{cm}$$

$$x = \frac{(10 \text{ m} \times \text{cm})}{2 \text{ m}}$$

$$x = 5 \text{ cm}$$

Divide the actual size of the bus by 2 m, and then multiply the answer by 1 cm. This will help you calculate the size of the model. That is, 10 m ÷ 2 m = 5 × 1 cm = 5 cm. The model bus would be 5 cm long.

3. Discuss with your teacher why the ratio "1 cm = 2 m" in Procedure Step 1 is considered a "scale factor." How would you define "scale factor?" Record your working definition of this term in your notebook.

4. Calculate the scaled diameter (SD) of Earth with a scale factor (sf) of 1 cm = 10,000 km (or, 1:10,000). Hint: Divide the actual diameter (AD) of Earth (12,756 km) by 10,000 km—the scale factor—and then multiply your answer by 1 cm. Here is what the formula might look like:

$$\text{Scaled Diameter (SD) : Actual Diameter (AD) =}$$
$$\text{1 cm : scale factor (sf)}$$

$$\frac{\text{Scaled Diameter (SD)}}{\text{Actual Diameter (AD)}} = \frac{\text{1 cm}}{\text{scale factor (sf)}}$$

$$\frac{\text{SD}}{\text{AD}} = \frac{\text{1 cm}}{\text{sf}}$$

$$\text{SD} \times \text{sf} = \text{AD} \times \text{1 cm}$$

$$\text{SD} \times \text{sf} = \text{AD} \times \text{cm}$$

$$\text{SD} = \frac{\text{AD} \times \text{cm}}{\text{sf}}$$

or

$$\text{SD} = (\text{AD} \div \text{sf}) \times \text{cm}$$

$$\text{SD} = \text{AD} \div \text{sf}$$

5. Review the actual diameters and distances of the planets listed in Table 1: Using a Scale Factor on Student Sheet 11.2. Calculate the approximate scaled distances and diameters for each planet by using a scale factor of 1 cm = 10,000 km. Record your calculations in the appropriate columns of Table 1 on Student Sheet 11.2. Show all your work.

REFLECTING ON WHAT YOU'VE DONE

1. Review your data on Student Sheet 11.2: Using a Scale Factor with the class.

2. Answer the following questions in your notebook, and then discuss them with your class:

A. How close was your model during Inquiry 11.1 to the scaled model calculated during Inquiry 11.2?

B. Does anything about your calculations on Student Sheet 11.2 surprise you? Explain.

Inquiry 11.3
Building a Scale Model of the Solar System

MATERIALS FOR INQUIRY 11.3

For you

1 copy of Student Sheet 11.3a: Calculating the Scale Factor

1 copy of Student Sheet 11.3b: Calculating Scaled Distance

1 copy of Student Sheet 10.1c: Planetary Chart

For your group

1 small plastic resealable bag labeled "11.3" and containing the following:

    2 small round beads, 0.2 cm

    2 peppercorns, 0.46 cm

    1 rubber ball, 5.5 cm

    1 fishing bobber, 4.6 cm

    2 acrylic beads, 1.7 cm

    1 straight pin with round head, 0.09 cm

1 metric ruler, 30 cm (12")

1 metric measuring tape

1 set of 9 Planet Data Cards

1 calculator

PROCEDURE

1. Collect one resealable bag of items labeled "11.3." These items *are* to scale with the actual diameter measurements of the planets.

2. Which object do you think represents each planet? Position the items so that they represent the size of the nine planets (do not consider distance at this point). Record the names of these objects in the third column of Table 1 on Student Sheet 11.3a: Calculating the Scale Factor.

3. Measure the diameter of each of your model planets by placing each object directly onto your ruler or measuring tape (or you can mathematically calculate its diameter from its circumference). Check your measurements against those in the Materials List. Record the diameter of each object in the fourth column of Table 1 on Student Sheet 11.3a.

4. Calculate the scale factor for each model planet. Remember to record your units. Use the example on Student Sheet 11.3a to guide you.

5. Calculate the average scale factor by adding all the scale factors together and dividing by 9. Remember to record your units. This average is the approximate scale factor for your entire model solar system.

6. Share your results with the class.

7. Using Student Sheet 11.3b and working with your group, calculate the scaled distance of each planet from the Sun. Refer to the actual distances of the planets from the Sun. Use the scale factor you calculated on Student Sheet 11.3a to determine how far from a model Sun to place each planet. This will help you to create an accurate scale solar system model for both size and distance. Use the example on Student Sheet 11.3b to help you. Note that each answer for scaled distance on Student Sheet 11.3b initially will be in centimeters. However, you will have to convert your answers to either meters or kilometers to make the measurements more meaningful.

8. If possible, go with the class to a long hall or gymnasium, or outdoors to an athletic field. Select one item in the area (for example, a wall or a goal post) to represent the Sun. Then, using your calculations, work with the class to measure the distances for each of the model planets as directed by your teacher. Label each planet with the appropriate planet data card. Don't be surprised that Pluto may be more than a mile away!

REFLECTING ON WHAT YOU'VE DONE

1. Answer the following questions in your notebook, and then discuss them as a class:

A. What observations and comparisons can you make about your model?

B. How does Earth compare with other planets in size and distance from the Sun?

C. How is your model different from the actual solar system?

D. How is your model similar to the actual solar system?

E. What is the relationship between the diameter of the planets and their positions from the Sun? What reasons do you have for your answer?

F. Analyze Table 1 on Student Sheet 11.3b. How do the distances between the first four planets compare with the distances between the other planets? What reasons do you have for your answer?

G. Think back to "Getting Started." How is your final solar system model different from your earlier statements about what a model of the solar system looks like?

2. Obtain one set of Planet Data Cards for your group. Examine the planetary distances and determine what units are used to describe this value. What do you think AU means?

3. Use your calculator to determine how the AU for each planet was calculated. AU is the scale factor most often used when describing planetary distances.

4. Read "The Orrery: A Model of the Solar System" and think about how your observations of the solar system model can be applied to a real model.

5. Read "Mission: Mercury." Add any information about Mercury to your working copy of Student Sheet 10.1c: Planetary Chart (and onto Student Sheet 10.1b: Planetary Brochure Outline if your Anchor Activity planet is Mercury).

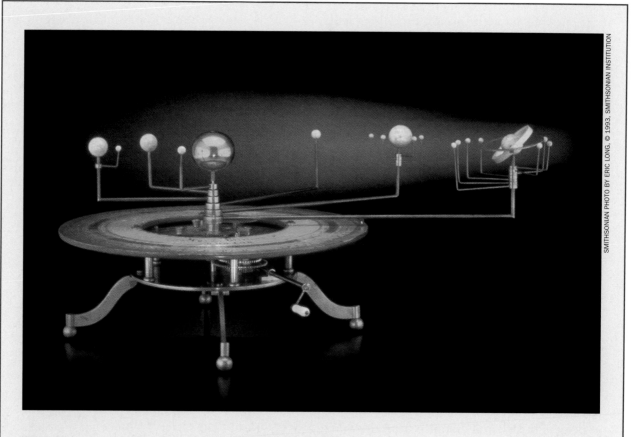

SMITHSONIAN PHOTO BY ERIC LONG. © 1993, SMITHSONIAN INSTITUTION

The Orrery: A Model of the Solar System

When you build a model of a ship, a rocket, or another object, you usually want it to look as much like the original as possible. When Englishman George Graham built the first mechanical model of the solar system in 1700, he had the same goal. He wanted his model to look like the actual solar system. He duplicated the positions of the Sun and the planets and moons that were known at that time. With Graham's model, people could see for the first time how Earth moved around the Sun. They could also follow the movements of Mercury, Venus, Mars, Jupiter, and Saturn.

Graham's model became known as an "orrery." It was named after Charles Boyce, the 4th Earl of Orrery, who commissioned such a model to be built. The orrery shown here was made in the 1780s. It belongs to the Smithsonian Institution in Washington, D.C. Is there an orrery at a science museum near you? ☐

The Astrarium: A Clock Without a Tock

This amazing clock was designed nearly 700 years ago by Giovanni de Dondi. The clock, or astrarium, works like this: One wheel turns once a day and moves another wheel, which makes one complete turn a year. The astrarium tracks the changing positions of the Earth, Moon, Sun, and the five other planets that were known at the time de Dondi designed the astrarium—Mercury, Venus, Mars, Jupiter, and Saturn. This complex astronomical tool even includes a calendar of all Roman Catholic feasts. De Dondi's invention eventually was dismantled so that its brass could be reused. Luckily, de Dondi left detailed notes about how to construct the astrarium, which were used to make this reproduction. ☐

SMITHSONIAN PHOTO BY ALFRED HARRELL, © 1992 SMITHSONIAN INSTITUTION

Mission: Mercury

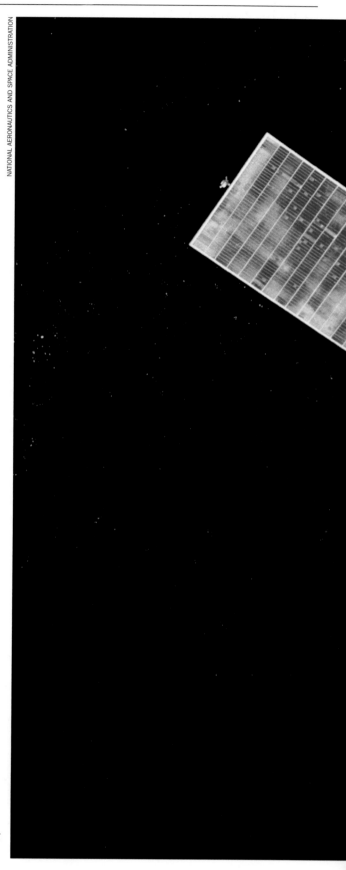

NATIONAL AERONAUTICS AND SPACE ADMINISTRATION

Five thousand years ago, astronomers in the ancient civilization of Sumeria (located in present-day Iraq) identified Mercury as a planet. Because it is so close to the Sun, Mercury can only be seen along the horizon just before sunrise or just after sunset. When Mercury is directly overhead, the Sun's light obscures any view of the planet.

The fact that Mercury is difficult to view didn't stop scientists from trying to learn about it. At the turn of the 20th century, the astronomer Eugenious Antoniadi used a telescope to observe Mercury. He created maps of the planet that were used for nearly 50 years.

Scientists once thought that Mercury's day was the same length as its year. But in 1965, scientists used Doppler radar observations to prove that Mercury rotates three times for every two times it orbits the Sun. Despite this new knowledge, scientists still had many questions about the innermost planet of our solar system. So, to learn more about Mercury, the *Mariner 10* mission was launched from Kennedy Space Center on November 3, 1973.

The *Mariner 10* Flight

Mariner 10 was a small spacecraft. Its body was only 1.39 meters by 0.457 meters—less than the width of most classroom desks! However, solar panels, antennae, and sunshades added to *Mariner 10*'s size. The spacecraft contained instruments to study the atmospheric, surface, and physical characteristics of Mercury. The solar panels and rocket engine helped *Mariner 10* reach the planet.

Mariner 10 *transmitted the first photographs of Mercury's surface.*

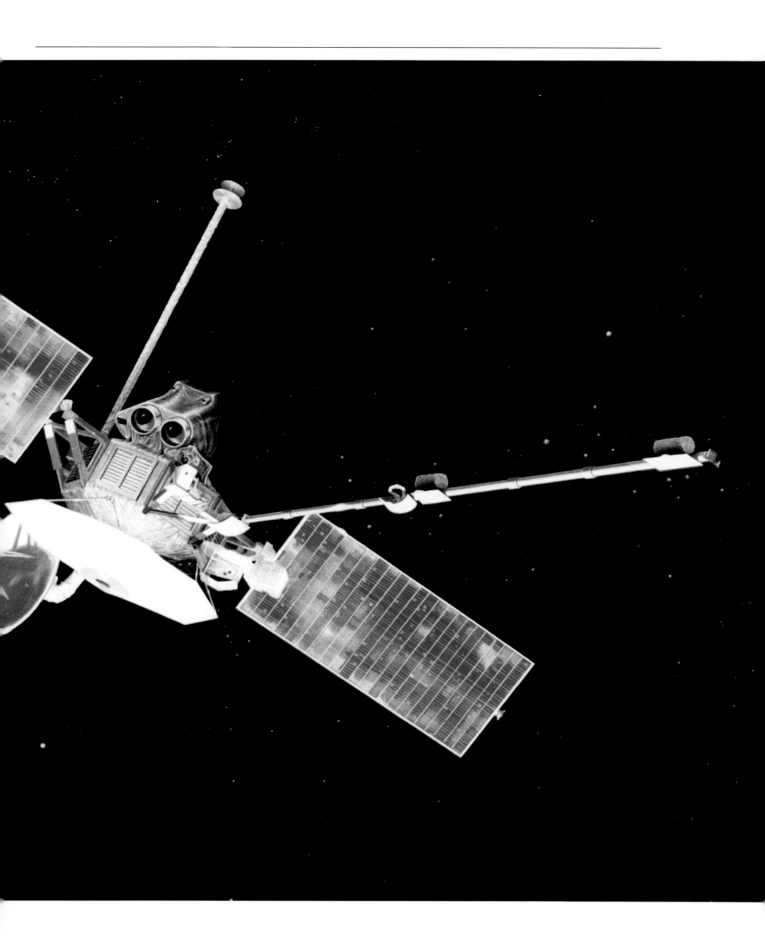

Mariner 10 did not fly directly to Mercury. After leaving Earth's atmosphere, it flew by Venus and used that planet's gravitational pull to bend its flight path toward Mercury. After almost five months in flight, *Mariner 10* made its first flyby of Mercury. The term "flyby" refers to a method astronomers use to observe a planet. Instead of having a spacecraft orbit or land on a planet, a flyby spacecraft does just that—it "flies by" a planet, taking pictures of it and gathering other scientific data. After *Mariner 10* completed its flyby of Mercury, it began orbiting the Sun. Using the last of its fuel, scientists were able to have *Mariner 10* fly over Mercury two more times in September 1974 and March 1975. Since then, *Mariner 10* has continued its orbit of the Sun, even though it is no longer operational.

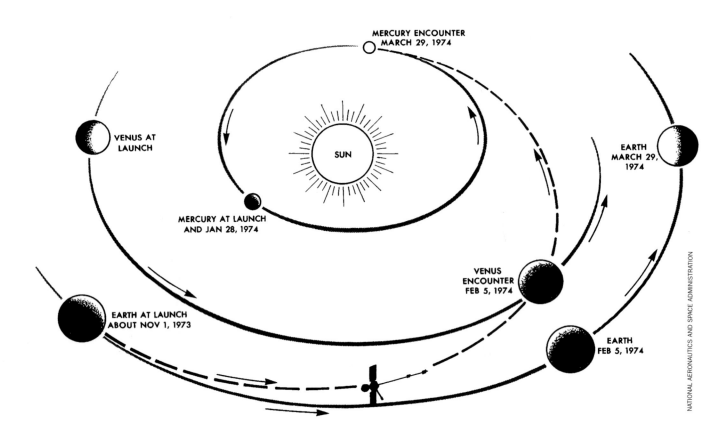

NASA diagram of the Mariner 10 *trajectory as outlined during mission planning in 1972. Follow the dashed line to trace the path of* Mariner 10 *from Earth to Mercury.*

Mariner's Look at Mercury

During each flyby, *Mariner 10* gathered images and data. Cameras on the spacecraft took more than 2500 images of Mercury. These images mapped almost half of Mercury's surface. Why only half? Because Mercury rotates so slowly that a single day on Mercury lasts longer than 58 Earth days! Because of the timing of the three flybys, the same side of the planet was always in the dark when *Mariner* was close enough to take photographs.

NATIONAL AERONAUTICS AND SPACE ADMINISTRATION. IMAGE PROCESSING BY UNITED STATES GEOLOGICAL SURVEY.

Half of Mercury's surface

Shock waves from the impact of a large meteorite formed these hills on Mercury.

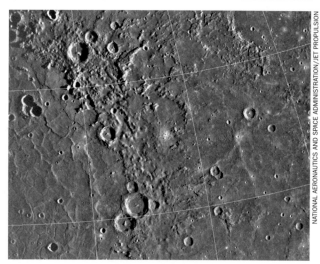

This image taken by Mariner 10 *shows one of the many faults on Mercury's surface.*

The photos taken by the *Mariner 10* revealed a heavily cratered surface much like that of the Moon. Craters with bright "rays" can be seen scattered among dark plains. These rays may be material ejected from the craters during impact. Scientists believe that some of Mercury's smooth plains were caused by lava flow. The cameras also took photos of a huge crater, Caloris Basin. This crater is 1300 kilometers across and may have been caused by an asteroid impact. Scientists believe this impact also caused the formation of hills on the other side of the planet. Other photographs taken by the *Mariner 10* showed faults on the surface. Evidence suggests that pieces of Mercury's crust have overlapped at these places.

The most surprising find of the *Mariner 10* mission was that Mercury has a magnetic field. Some scientists think the magnetic field indicates that the planet has an iron core that is partially molten. Others think that an ancient magnetic field may be frozen in the crust.

Future Missions

More missions to Mercury are planned, including sending an orbiter around Mercury. An orbiter is a spacecraft that studies a planet by orbiting it instead of just flying past the planet. By sending an orbiter around Mercury, scientists hope to make more detailed studies of this planet. They want to map the entire planet.

Another goal is to land equipment on the planet, such as a camera, a seismometer, and tools for studying Mercury's soil. A spacecraft that lands on the planet is called a "lander." In such a mission, scientists hope to gather data directly from the planet's surface to answer numerous questions: What is the composition and structure of Mercury's crust? Has it experienced volcanism? What is the nature of its polar caps? With future missions, perhaps we will have answers to these questions, and have a better understanding of this planet. □

PLANETARY FACTS: Mercury

Mercury: Quick Facts

Diameter	4878 km	**Average temperature**	179 °C
Average Distance from the Sun	57,900,000 km	**Length of sidereal day**	58 Earth days
Mass	33×10^{22} kg	**Length of year**	88 Earth days
Surface gravity (Earth = 1)	0.38	**Number of moons**	0

Relative size

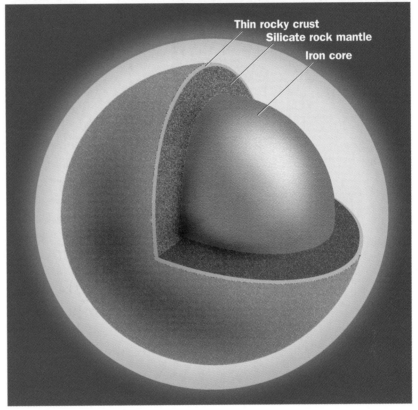

Thin rocky crust
Silicate rock mantle
Iron core

Did You Know?

- Mercury is barely larger than Earth's Moon. See the illustration "Relative Size" above, comparing Earth to Mercury.
- Mercury was named for the messenger of the gods because it moves so quickly across the sky. It races along in its orbit at a rate of 46.4 kilometers per second—faster than any other planet!

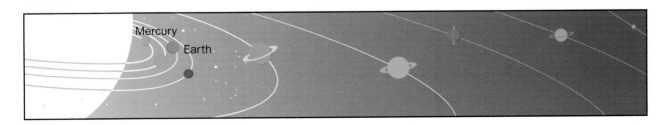

Mercury
Earth

12 Impact Craters

What would happen if a large asteroid collided with Earth?

INTRODUCTION

Impact! Suddenly, an enormous explosion occurs. The tremendous heat generated by the speed of the incoming asteroid causes the rock to vaporize upon impact. The impact creates a deep round hole.

Impact craters—bowl-shaped holes in the surface of a rocky planet, moon, or asteroid—are the most widespread landform in the solar system. Earth has not been spared from asteroid impacts, although the effects of water and wind erosion, volcanism, and other processes on Earth have erased much of the evidence. On our Moon, and on planets like Mercury where there is no atmosphere, craters remain intact and therefore may hold many secrets about the solar system's past.

What do craters look like and how do they form? In this lesson, you will examine photos of craters. You will model the formation of impact craters and design an investigation to test the factors that affect the size and shape of craters formed during an impact. You also will read about Venus.

OBJECTIVES FOR THIS LESSON

Classify photographs of planets, moons, and asteroids on the basis of their surface features.

Model the effects of impact cratering.

Design an experiment to investigate how the size, velocity, or shape of objects that strike a planet's surface affect the formation of craters.

Summarize and organize information about Venus, and compare Venus to other planets.

Getting Started

1. Review the photos shown in Figures 12.1–12.6. What observations can you make about them? How are the images alike? How are they different? Classify the photos. Record your classifications in your science notebook. Be prepared to justify your classifications to your class.

Figure 12.1 *Mercury*

Figure 12.2 *Earth's Barringer (Meteor) Crater in Arizona*

MATERIALS FOR LESSON 12

For you
- 1 pair of goggles
- 1 pair of red and blue 3-D stereo glasses
- 1 working copy of Student Sheet 10.1c: Planetary Chart

For your group
- 1 copy of the Planning Sheet
- 1 copy of Student Sheet 12.2: Recording Our Crater Data and Conclusions
- 1 plastic box filled with the following:
    - sand
    - flour
    - cocoa
- 1 large sifter cup filled with extra cocoa
- 1 large sifter cup with extra flour
- 1 large resealable plastic bag filled with the following:
    - 2 hand lenses
    - 1 plastic spreader
- 1 pack of 3 steel spheres
- 1 metric measuring tape
- 1 ring magnet
- 1 flashlight
- 2 D-cell batteries
- 1 metric ruler, 30 cm (12″)
- 1 protractor (optional)
- Newspaper
- Paper towels

NATIONAL AERONAUTICS AND SPACE ADMINISTRATION/JOHNSON SPACE CENTER

Figure 12.3 *The "never-seen-from-Earth" far side of the Moon*

NATIONAL AERONAUTICS AND SPACE ADMINISTRATION/JET PROPULSION LABORATORY

Figure 12.4 *Jupiter's moon Callisto*

NATIONAL AERONAUTICS AND SPACE ADMINISTRATION/JET PROPULSION LABORATORY

Figure 12.5 *The giant gaseous planets—Jupiter, Saturn, Uranus, and Neptune—are also known as the Jovian planets.*

NATIONAL AERONAUTICS AND SPACE ADMINISTRATION

Figure 12.6 *Asteroids Mathilde, Gaspra, and Ida*

2. Share your observations and classifications with the class.

3. Discuss these questions with your group or class, as instructed.

What do you notice when you look at the close-up view of the craters?

How old do you think the crater in Figure 12.2 is? Do you think Earth has a lot of craters like this? Why or why not?

How is Figure 12.5 similar to or different from the other images?

4. Brainstorm with the class on what you already know about craters and what you want to learn.

5. Record in your science notebook a description of what you think causes craters and where you think they are most likely to occur. Share your description with your partner.

6. Look at Figure 12.7. How does it compare to the craters shown in Figures 12.1–12.4 and 12.6? How do you think this feature was formed? Discuss these questions with your group and then share your ideas with the class.

Inquiry 12.1
Making General Observations About Impact Craters

PROCEDURE

1. Review the Safety Tips with your teacher.

SAFETY TIPS

Work in a well-ventilated area to minimize levels of dust in the air.

Wear indirectly vented goggles at all times during the inquiry.

Do not throw or project the metal spheres. Carefully release the metal spheres onto the powdered surface.

Do not stand on furniture to drop the metal spheres. Instead, place the box on the floor when testing drop heights greater than 60 cm.

2. Cover your workspace with newspaper. You may also want to protect your clothing. Obtain your group's plastic box, the large resealable bag of materials, and sifter cups of cocoa and flour.

3. Work with your group to investigate how craters form. Select one of the metal spheres. Drop it into the box. Use the magnet to carefully remove the metal sphere from the box without disturbing the surrounding powder. Observe the crater that it forms. Use your hand lens. Discuss what you see with your group.

J. P. LOCKWOOD, UNITED STATES GEOLOGICAL SURVEY

Figure 12.7 *Pu'u Ka Pele, Mauna Kea*

4. Repeat Step 3 several more times. Use a new part of the box each time. Observe the crater that forms each time.

5. Try dropping the sphere from a different height or rolling the sphere along your ruler at different angles. Or try using a different size sphere. Observe your results each time. If the surface becomes covered in craters, carefully smooth out the powder with the edge of your plastic spreader (see Figure 12.8). Use the sifter cup to shake a layer of extra flour over the surface. Then sprinkle a thin layer of cocoa on the flour (the cocoa needs to be added on top of the white layer).

Figure 12.8 *When you do not have any more room to create craters, (A) use your plastic spreader to smooth out the surface of your flour. (B) Cover the surface with a new layer of flour. (C) Cover the flour with a thin layer of cocoa.*

REFLECTING ON WHAT YOU'VE DONE

1. Share your general observations with the class.

2. Read "Craters in the Making" to find out more about crater formation. Discuss the parts of the crater with your class, referring to the illustration. What makes up the rays?

CRATERS IN THE MAKING

A crater is a large, bowl-shaped hole found in solid, rocky surfaces. Terrestrial planets, moons, and asteroids all contain craters. Some craters form when meteoroids, asteroids, or comets smash into the surface of a planet or moon. These craters—called "impact craters"—are usually circular. They range in size from tiny pits to huge basins hundreds of meters across. Impact craters are the most common geological feature in the solar system.

The Impact

The appearance of an impact crater depends on many things. For example, the size and speed of the object causing the crater affects its width or depth. With smaller or slower impacts, the surface material is simply thrown out, like sand that is thrown when a rock hits the surface of a beach. However, when the impacting object is large and traveling at higher speeds, it hits the surface with enormous force. The extreme temperatures and pressures from the collision cause the object to melt and mix with the surrounding rock.

Parts of a Crater

After impact, a crater forms with a high rim and central peak (see the illustration). Landslides may create terraces around the rim. The floor of the crater is often below the level of the surrounding terrain. Ejected materials, such as dust, sand, and—if the temperature is high enough—liquid rock, fall back around the crater to form an area of debris that looks like spokes on a wheel. These spokes, called rays, radiate outward in all directions. Some rays can go for hundreds of kilometers beyond the point of impact. Many smaller, secondary craters also form around the main crater.

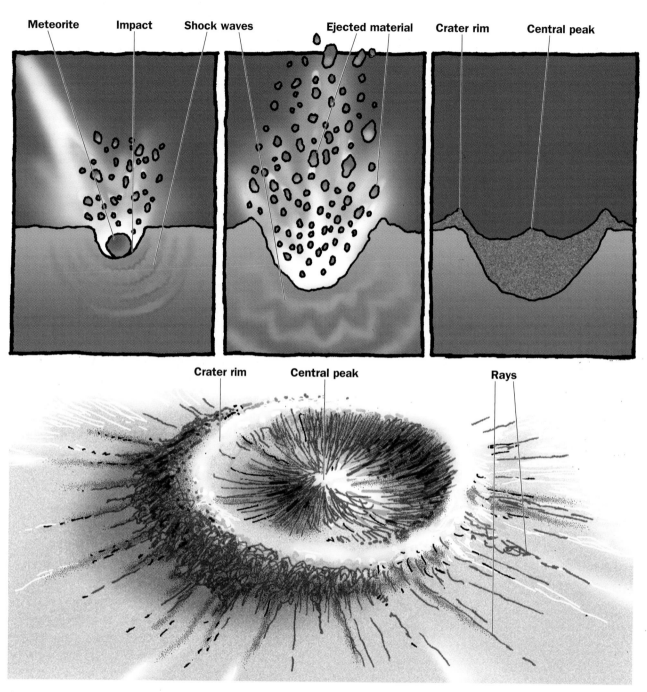

Meteorite   **Impact**   **Shock waves**   **Ejected material**   **Crater rim**   **Central peak**

Crater rim   **Central peak**   **Rays**

*Stages in the formation of impact craters include the impact,
the breakup and melting of the impacting object, the ejection
of broken and melted rock, and the formation of rays.*

Craters on moons and planets can be seen most easily when long shadows are cast on their surfaces. Craters along the border between the Moon's dark and light side are most visible from Earth when the Moon is in its quarter phase.

Craters: Links to the Past

Craters can tell us about a planet or moon's history. The more craters on a planet or moon's surface, the older that part of the planet's surface is. During the early formation of our solar system, many meteoroids bombarded the planets. The craters they caused can still be seen on the Moon and Mercury. This is because geological processes, such as wind and water erosion, stopped millions of years ago on these bodies (see Figures 12.1 and 12.3). The craters remain much as they were at the time of their creation.

Gaseous planets have little or no evidence of impact craters, even though meteoroids strike gaseous planets as often as they strike rocky planets. Craters leave only a temporary record in the gaseous atmosphere.

Craters on Earth

Earth also was heavily cratered during its formation, and it still receives impacts today. Many craters on Earth have been eroded by wind and water and destroyed by earthquakes and volcanism. About 120 impact craters have been identified on Earth. Some of Earth's craters are relatively young; for example, Barringer (Meteor) Crater in Arizona (see Figure 12.2) is only around 50,000 years old. Manicouagan Crater in Quebec, Canada, is much older; it was created about 214 million years ago. At 70 km in diameter, Manicouagan Crater is one of the largest impact craters on the surface of Earth.

Inquiry 12.2
Investigating Impact Craters

PROCEDURE

1. What question would you like to test to find out more about impact craters? Decide as a group what question you will investigate. Try to choose a topic that might not be represented by another group. (If you have trouble, your teacher will review some of the questions about impact craters that your group can answer using your materials from Inquiry 12.1.)

2. Use the planning sheet to design your group's crater investigation. Your teacher will approve your plan.

3. Decide how you will record your data.

4. Review the Safety Tips with your teacher.

SAFETY TIPS

Work in a well-ventilated area to minimize levels of dust in the air.

Wear indirectly vented goggles at all times during the investigation.

Do not throw or project the metal spheres. Carefully release them onto the powdered surface.

Do not stand on furniture to drop the metal spheres. Instead, place the plastic box on the floor when testing drop heights greater than 60 cm.

5. Cover your work surface with newspaper.

6. Conduct your investigation. Remember the following points as you work:

- Change only the independent variable—the variable you are testing (for example, the height from which you drop your steel sphere).

- If you vary the drop height (velocity of impact), use even increments such as 30, 60, or 90 cm. Start with the smallest measurement.

- Use the ring magnet to remove the metal sphere. Avoid disturbing the crater.

- Use your hand lens to observe the details of your crater.

- Use tools to measure your dependent variable (for example, crater depth, crater diameter, length of rays, or number of rays).

- If your surface becomes covered in craters, use the plastic spreader to smooth the surface. Use the sifter cups to create new layers of flour and cocoa.

- Record your data and conclusions in your notebook or use Student Sheet 12.2, as instructed. If you conduct multiple trials, calculate your average results.

7. When every group has completed its investigation, your teacher will turn off the classroom lights. Use your flashlight to examine your results (see Figure 12.9). Shine the light at the craters from all directions. From which direction are the crater features best seen? How does a flashlight change the appearance of the craters?

Figure 12.9 *Use your flashlight to examine the cratered surface.*

REFLECTING ON WHAT YOU'VE DONE

1. Share your data and conclusions with the class. Work with your group to determine what conclusions you can make about impact craters on the basis of your evidence. Consider crater depth, diameter, and length of rays.

2. Revisit the photographs in Figures 12.1–12.6. Answer the following questions in your notebook, and then discuss them as a class:

A. How are the craters in the photographs like the craters in your plastic box?

B. Can a crater's appearance help you understand how the crater formed? Explain.

C. Where is the impacting object in each photograph?

D. Think back to when you used your flashlight. When is the best time for scientists to observe craters?

3. Get one pair of red and blue glasses for yourself. The red lens goes over your left eye and the blue lens goes over your right eye. Use the glasses to observe the crater features shown in Figure 12.10. Give your eyes 30 seconds to adjust to the glasses. Can you observe any new features in the crater? If so, make a record of them in your science notebook.

4. Read "Mission: Venus." Add any new information about Venus to your working copy of Student Sheet 10.1c: Planetary Chart (and onto Student Sheet 10.1b: Planetary Brochure Outline if your Anchor Activity planet is Venus).

NATIONAL AERONAUTICS AND SPACE ADMINISTRATION

Figure 12.10 *This Apollo image shows the Moon's King Crater in 3-D.*

Mission: **Venus**

Sky gazers and astronomers have known about Venus for thousands of years. That's because it's the brightest object in our sky, except for the Sun and Moon. By looking through powerful telescopes over the last 100 years, we've learned much about our neighboring planet. Astronomers have discovered, for example, that thick clouds surround Venus.

Still, scientists wondered as they gazed at Earth's "sister planet." What is the weather like on Venus? Is there water? Wind? Life? In 1978, the United States launched two spacecraft to Venus in search of some answers. These two Pioneer Mission spacecraft were followed 11 years later with the launch of *Magellan*.

Pioneer 12—The Orbiter

The first of the two Pioneer missions, the *Pioneer 12 Venus Orbiter,* took off in May 1978. It was in orbit around Venus by December—and it stayed there for 14 years! At times, the orbiter was as close as 150 kilometers to Venus's surface.

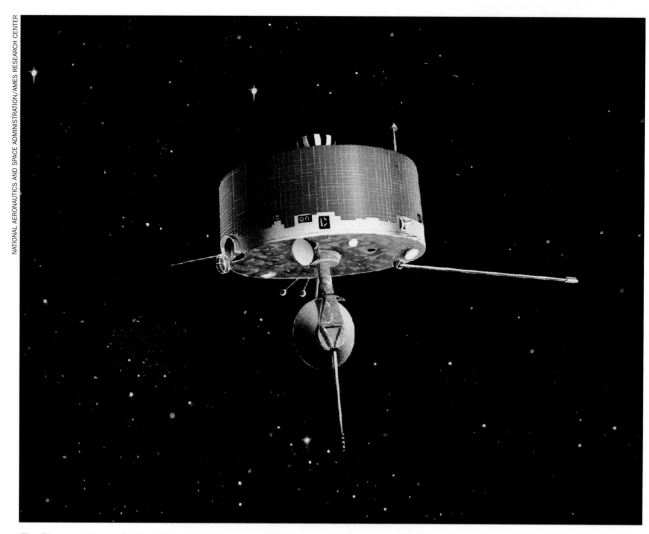

NATIONAL AERONAUTICS AND SPACE ADMINISTRATION/AMES RESEARCH CENTER

The Pioneer Venus Orbiter (Pioneer 12) *spacecraft is shown in its normal flight attitude (upside down).*

During its long stay in orbit, *Pioneer 12* measured, mapped, and photographed Venus's yellow cloud cover. Information from *Pioneer 12* showed that the upper layers of clouds contained droplets of sulfuric acid, a poisonous liquid that can destroy metals.

Pioneer 12 also proved what many scientists suspected—that a powerful "greenhouse effect" exists on Venus. This means that Venus's atmosphere, which is made up mostly of carbon dioxide, traps heat from the Sun. The heat can raise the surface temperature of Venus to about 475 °C —hot enough to melt lead! Venus may have constant lightning flashes and rain (although not rain water as we know it on Earth), but the intense heat means that the rain evaporates before it reaches the ground. If Venus's surface once had water, it has all boiled away and been lost to space. Today, the planet is very dry.

On October 8, 1992, *Pioneer 12* ran out of fuel. As it fell through the clouds of Venus, the orbiter burned up. It is gone forever, but the data and photos it radioed to Earth remain.

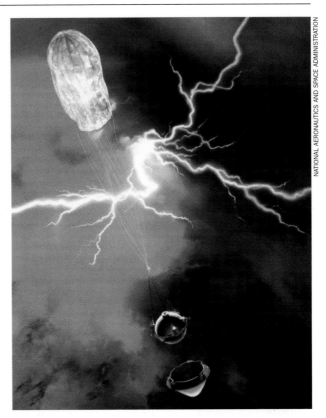

Artist's concept of a Pioneer Venus probe entering Venus' atmosphere

Pioneer 13—The Multiprobe

The second Pioneer spacecraft, *Pioneer 13 Venus Multiprobe,* was launched in August 1978. *Pioneer 13* was designed to enter Venus's atmosphere rather than to orbit the planet. It was equipped with one large probe and three small probes. The large probe was 1 meter long and weighed 315 kilograms. The small probes were 0.8 meters in diameter and weighed 75 kilograms each. Probes are packed with instruments to take observations and measurements such as atmospheric content, turbulence, temperature, particle size, and radiation. On December 9, 1978, each of the probes descended from the spacecraft for about 55 minutes before hitting the planet's surface.

Engineers who designed the probes knew they would not withstand the impact of landing on the planet's surface. It was the information the probes collected on the way down to the surface

that would be most important. However, one small probe did survive its impact with Venus's surface and continued to send data from the surface for 67 minutes before the heat and pressure ended its ability to transmit!

As they made their way through the atmosphere, all four probes captured a great deal of information. Data showed, for example, that winds in the upper layers of Venus's atmosphere move very fast. They circle the planet every four days! Winds near the surface, though, are strong enough only to move sand grains and dust particles.

Sensors on the probes also recorded atmospheric pressure on Venus. Venus's thick atmosphere pushes on things with 90 times the force of Earth's atmosphere. This kind of crushing pressure exists on Earth only about one kilometer down in the ocean.

NATIONAL AERONAUTICS AND SPACE ADMINISTRATION

Magellan

Named after the 16th-century Portuguese explorer, the *Magellan* spacecraft was launched on May 4, 1989. It arrived at Venus on August 10, 1990. For five years, *Magellan's* large main antenna bounced radar signals off the surface of Venus. A smaller antenna measured the heights of surface features. All radar data were transmitted back to Earth, where a computer used the data to create images of the planet's surface.

Magellan revealed that Venus is a planet of volcanoes. Thousands of them dot the planet—many small domes and some huge mountains. Smooth plains formed by flowing lava separate many of the volcanoes. Lava also carved channels—some as long as the width of the continental United States—on the surface of Venus.

Meteorites have left a few impact craters on Venus. *Magellan* also showed that in some places the surface of Venus has been pulled apart, possibly by the upwelling of magma from Venus's mantle. One such rift, or areas of weakened crust, tore a crater in two. Volcanoes often occur along these rift zones.

In 1995, *Magellan* burned up in the planet's atmosphere—but not before mapping nearly all of Venus's surface! This amazing spacecraft gave us our first global geological look at the planet in our solar system most like Earth. □

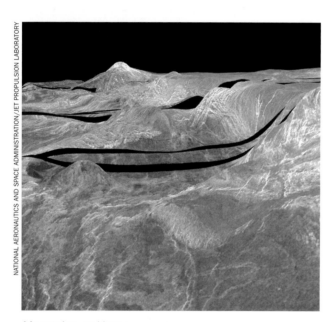

Mountains on Venus

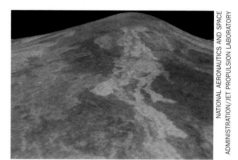

Volcanism on Venus

This image of Venus is made up of Magellan radar images

PLANETARY FACTS: Venus

Venus: Quick Facts

Diameter	12,102 km	**Average temperature**	464 °C
Distance from the Sun	108,200,000 km	**Length of day**	243 Earth days
Mass	487×10^{22} kg	**Length of year**	225 Earth days
Surface gravity (Earth = 1)	0.91	**Number of moons**	0

Relative size

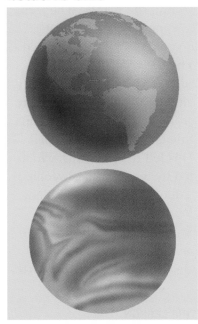

Venus atmosphere

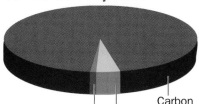

Sulfuric acid, helium, argon, and others (minor amounts)

Nitrogen (3.5%)

Carbon dioxide (96.5%)

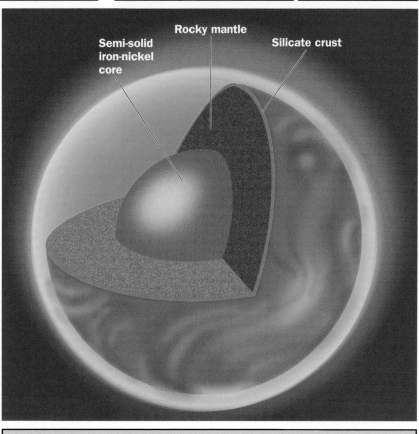

Semi-solid iron-nickel core

Rocky mantle

Silicate crust

Did You Know?

- Venus rotates from east to west—the opposite direction of Earth.
- Venus's gas clouds reflect the Sun's rays so well that Venus shines more brightly than any other planet.

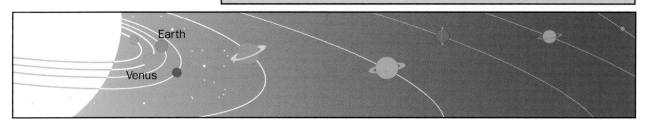

Earth

Venus

13
Surface Features

This image shows part of the Ophir Chasm in Valles Marineris, a huge 4000-kilometer-long canyon system on Mars. The Ophir Chasm is shaped by tectonics, wind, slumping, and perhaps by water and volcanism.

NATIONAL AERONAUTICS AND SPACE ADMINISTRATION. IMAGE PROCESSING BY UNITED STATES GEOLOGICAL SURVEY

INTRODUCTION

The most spectacular feature on Mars is the great canyon system called Valles Marineris. It extends for about 4000 kilometers. That's nearly a quarter the way around the planet! The term canyon, however, is somewhat misleading. Why? On Earth, canyons generally are formed by running water. The canyons of Valles Marineris are basically cracks produced by tensions in the crust, although water is believed to have played a later role in shaping the canyons. After the cracks formed, deep springs seeped through the cliffs. This led to landslides, which were probably eroded by windstorms sweeping down the canyons. All of these processes combined make Valles Marineris and its Ophir Chasm a spectacular planetary feature!

In this lesson, you will examine a set of photographs showing surface features on Earth.

OBJECTIVES FOR THIS LESSON

Review photographs showing planetary surface features on Earth; then consider whether the processes that formed these features exist on other planets and moons.

Brainstorm what you know and want to learn about planetary processes on Earth and other planets.

Investigate wind erosion, water erosion, tectonics, and volcanism and their effects.

Analyze photographs of planetary surface features and determine how each was formed.

Summarize and organize information about Mars, and compare Mars to other planets.

You will investigate whether these features exist on other planets as well. Various groups in your class will model one of the different planetary processes that create these features—wind erosion, water erosion, fractures caused by tectonics and other stresses, or volcanism. You then will match each group's model with photographs of different planets' surface features. The lesson ends as you read about three NASA missions to Mars.

MATERIALS FOR LESSON 13

For you

1 copy of Student Sheet 13.1a: Planetary Process Observations (or your notebook)
1 copy of Student Sheet 13.1b: Matching Planetary Processes (or your notebook)
1 pair of goggles
1 pair of red and blue 3-D stereo glasses
1 working copy of Student Sheet 10.1c: Planetary Chart

For your group

1 large resealable plastic bag (from Lesson 12) filled with the following:
  2 hand lenses
  1 plastic spreader
  1 pack of 3 steel spheres
  1 metric measuring tape
  1 ring magnet
  1 flashlight
  2 D-cell batteries
  1 metric ruler, 30 cm (12″)
Newspaper
Paper towels

1 set of four Planetary Process Photo Cards
1 set of process materials from the following:

Wind erosion
1 plastic box filled with sand, flour, and cocoa (from Lesson 12)
1 sifter cup of all-purpose sand
1 sifter cup of flour
4 flexible straws

Water erosion
1 plastic box with drain hole and Velcro® filled halfway with dry sand
1 rubber stopper
1 cup with hole and Velcro®
1 bottle of clear tap water
1 bucket
1 large absorbent pad
1 small absorbent pad

Tectonics
1 plastic box filled with sand, flour, and cocoa (from Lesson 12)
1 sifter cup of sand
1 sifter cup of flour

Volcanism
1 plastic box filled with sand, flour, and cocoa (from Lesson 12)
1 piece of wide acrylic tubing
1 large plastic syringe
1 cup of flour, with lid
1 bottle of red water
1 plastic cup
1 plastic spoon

Getting Started

1. Within your group, review the photos of surface features shown in Figures 13.1–13.5 and discuss the following questions:

What observations can you make about each surface feature?

How do you think the surface features shown in the photos were formed?

Do you think the processes that created these features exist on other planets? Explain your answer.

2. Share your observations with the class.

3. Discuss what you already know about planetary surface features and what you want to learn about them. You may be asked to record your ideas in your science notebook.

Figure 13.1 *Debris flow in San Jacinto Mountains, California*

R.L. SCHUSTER, UNITED STATES GEOLOGICAL SURVEY

Figure 13.2 *Rippled sand dunes in Tibet*

Figure 13.3 *Radar image of Galeras Volcano*

Figure 13.4 *The Colorado River cuts through limestone to create Marble Canyon, which is at the northeast end of the Grand Canyon in Arizona.*

Figure 13.5 *San Andreas Fault*

Inquiry 13.1
Investigating Planetary Processes

PROCEDURE

1. Look at the materials for this lesson. Which surface feature would your group like to model: wind erosion, water erosion, tectonics, or volcanism? Select one process, with your teacher's input.

2. Within your group, brainstorm ways that you might use the materials to model your selected process.

3. How will you record your observations? Discuss this with your teacher.

4. Review the Safety Tips with your teacher.

SAFETY TIPS

Work in a well-ventilated area to minimize the levels of dust in the air.

Wear indirectly vented goggles at all times during the investigation.

Do not throw or project the metal spheres.

Cover any work surface with newspaper to absorb excess water and to avoid slippery surfaces.

5. Read the appropriate background selection ("Wind Erosion," "Water Erosion," "Tectonics," or "Volcanism") to learn more about the planetary process you have selected. You will need your red and blue glasses to view some of the images. (Put the red lens over your left eye.) Use the information in the reading selection to help you plan how to model that process.

6. Gather the materials you will need. Each set is labeled with the name of the process. Cover your workspace with newspaper before beginning. If you are testing wind erosion, volcanism, or tectonics, use the boxes of sand, flour, and cocoa from Lesson 12. If you are testing water erosion, use a stream table (a plastic box that has a drain hole and is filled halfway with sand).

7. Conduct your investigation using the background reading selection as your guide.

8. When you are finished with your investigation, hold a flashlight parallel to the table to observe the surface features in your box. Record your observations on Student Sheet 13.1a or in your notebook, as instructed. Write what you did, what you observed, and why you think it happened. Record which photograph of Earth (Figures 13.1–13.5) most resembles your results.

REFLECTING ON WHAT YOU'VE DONE

1. Share your group's results with the class. With the classroom lights dimmed, again use your flashlight at "sunset" (parallel to the table) to show off the features of your new surface to other groups.

2. Once all groups have reported, get one set of Planetary Process Photo Cards. Review the four photo cards with your group. Discuss what you see. How do you think each surface feature was formed? Where do you think each photo was taken? Read the caption on the back of each photo.

3. With your teacher's guidance, go around the classroom to see other groups' results. Use your photo cards and Student Sheet 13.1b (or your notebook) to match each photo card to the results in each group's plastic box. How do you think these features were formed? Which feature on Earth (Figures 13.1–13.5) matches the feature shown in each photo card? Record your observations.

4. Discuss your findings with the class. Then clean up.

5. Did you know that the relative positions of surface features can help scientists decide the relative age of the surface feature? (For example, a crater on the surface of a lava flow shows that the crater is younger than the lava. However, if lava fills the crater, then the crater is older.) Look again at the photos in this lesson and Lesson 12. (You may even be able to use the computer program *Explore the Planets* to view additional images.) Can you tell whether each crater shown is younger or older than the land around it?

6. With your class, return to the Question F folder for Lesson 1 and its photo card. What processes created each landform? Do these landforms exist on other planets or moons? Review your self-stick responses from Lesson 1. As a class, work together to remove any notes that now seem incorrect. Add any new ideas you have to the folder.

7. Read "Wet Like Earth?" Answer the following question in your science notebook.

A. Does water exist on Mars? Explain.

8. Read "Mission: Mars." Add any new information about Mars to your working copy of Student Sheet 10.1c: Planetary Chart and to Student Sheet 10.1b: Planetary Brochure Outline if your Anchor Activity planet is Mars.

WIND EROSION

Planetary Winds

Wind is gas in motion. Wind can exist only on planets with atmospheres. Three of the terrestrial planets—Mars, Venus, and Earth—have atmospheres and therefore have winds. Mercury, the Moon, asteroids, and many of the moons of the gaseous planets do not have an atmosphere as we know it. This means they do not have winds.

The thinner (or less dense) the atmosphere, the faster the wind has to blow to make an impact on the planetary or lunar surface. It takes a powerful wind to move rock fragments on Mars, because its atmosphere is so thin. It takes very little wind to move rock fragments on Venus, which has a thick atmosphere. The density of Earth's atmosphere is somewhere between that of Mars and Venus. Streaks on a planet's surface caused by wind, like in the photo shown here, are evidence that wind moves smaller particles around. Wind erosion happens when gas molecules bounce against the rocks and other surfaces. A dense atmosphere has a lot of gas particles. This means that a dense atmosphere can erode a surface faster than a thin atmosphere in the same amount of time.

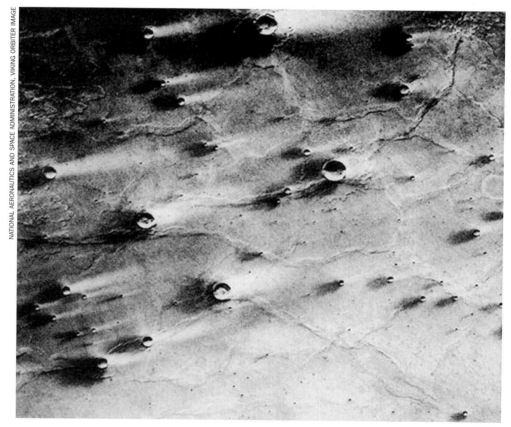

NATIONAL AERONAUTICS AND SPACE ADMINISTRATION, VIKING ORBITER IMAGE

Wind streaks on Mars

Martian Winds

The Martian surface has been eroded by winds that swept away fine particles and left behind boulders. Boulder fields that were found at the *Viking 1* landing site on Mars resemble deserts on Earth.

You've seen sand dunes on Earth. But do sand dunes exist on Mars? Get out your red and blue glasses and examine this dramatic photo of dunes on Mars. This field of wavy dunes is found in Nili Patera, a volcanic depression in central Syrtis Major, the most noticeable dark feature on Mars—the "red planet."

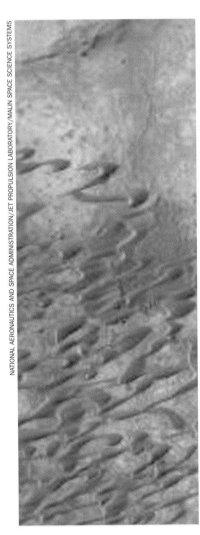

NATIONAL AERONAUTICS AND SPACE ADMINISTRATION/JET PROPULSION LABORATORY/MALIN SPACE SCIENCE SYSTEMS

3-D image of sand dunes on Mars. Two different images from the orbiting Mars Global Surveyor spacecraft were combined to make this stereo picture. Notice the ripples along the sand dunes.

Winds on Venus

The upper atmosphere of Venus is very windy. The winds there reach speeds of up to 350 kilometers per hour. In the lower atmosphere, the wind speed decreases until it is nearly zero at the surface. The wind blows in the direction of the planet's rotation. Since Venus rotates very slowly, the Sun shines for a long time on the surface. As the Sun heats the surface of Venus, the warm surface also heats the air above it. The rising warm air may be responsible for Venus's winds.

Modeling Wind

You can use a straw and a box of sand, flour, and cocoa to model the effect of wind on a planet's surface (see the illustration on the next page). Do the following:

1. With your plastic spreader, smooth the layers of sand, flour, and cocoa in your plastic box. Don't worry if they mix.
2. Sprinkle a layer of sand on top of your mixture.
3. Sprinkle a thin layer of flour on top of the sand.
4. Use your flexible straw and the illustration as your guide. Blow very gently onto the surface of your plastic box. (Do not share straws.) What happens when wind blows over a fine dust? In which direction does the dust move? How do large and small particles change the effects of wind? Can you create dunes and wind streaks like those shown in the photos?
5. Use your flashlight to examine the wind streaks and sand dunes you have created. Remember that the best time to view planetary surface features is when the Sun is setting (when your light is horizontal and parallel with the table), not when it is directly overhead.

(A) Use a flexible straw to model the wind's effects on a planet's surface. Don't share straws. (B) Use the flashlight to view your results. Keep the light parallel with the surface of your workspace.

WATER EROSION

A high mountain or plateau forms when forces within a planet lift up a relatively flat area. Flowing water cuts deep canyons into the highlands. Water typically flows from highlands to lowlands. The source of that water can include underwater springs, melting snow or ice caps, or rain. The flowing water erodes rock and creates canyons, valleys, and stream networks. Large boulders and small rock fragments may move with the water and help further erode the rock. Complex stream patterns often look like networks of nerves in the human body (see the illustration). These patterns are common signs of water erosion on a planet or moon. A stream pattern depends on the slope, topography, soil type, and amount of water that flows across the surface.

Water on Mars

Running water formed the Grand Canyon on Earth, but Valles Marineris—a huge canyon on Mars—was formed by a combination of forces, mostly tectonics, although water is believed to have played a later role in shaping the canyons. After the cracks formed from tension in Mars's crust, deep springs seeped through the cliffs. This led to landslides. Valles Marineris is about as wide as the United States—some 4000 kilometers. The entire Grand Canyon could fit inside a small section of Valles Marineris.

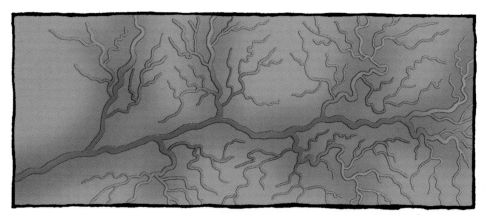

Stream patterns such as the one shown here are common signs of water erosion.

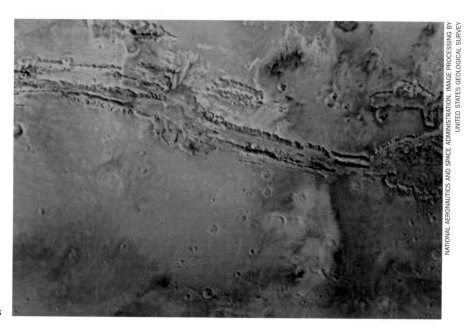

Valles Marineris

How does water erosion affect existing craters on a planet's surface? Get out your red and blue glasses and examine this dramatic view of water channels on Mars. The channels, which were carved by water, are probably 200–300 meters deep. Water from one set of channels broke through a 12–kilometer-wide impact crater (center left), and formed a large lake. The smooth floor may actually be lake sediment.

Modeling Water Erosion

You can use a stream table to model water erosion on planetary surfaces (see the illustration). Investigate water erosion by doing the following:

1. Place the large absorbent pad on your table with the plastic side face down over your newspaper. Place the small absorbent pad on the floor.

2. Position your "stream table" on the large pad so the drain hole hangs over the edge of your workspace.

3. Using the plastic spreader, push the sand away from the drain hole. Make the sand have a slope.

4. Remove the rubber stopper from the drain hole.

5. Hold the bucket directly under the drain hole, over the pad on the floor.

6. Attach the Velcro® on the cup to the Velcro on the stream table. Rock the cup back and forth until the cup is secured to the box.

7. Pour the water slowly into the cup. Try to keep the water at the top of the cup at all times. Do not touch the sand once you start to pour. Observe your results.

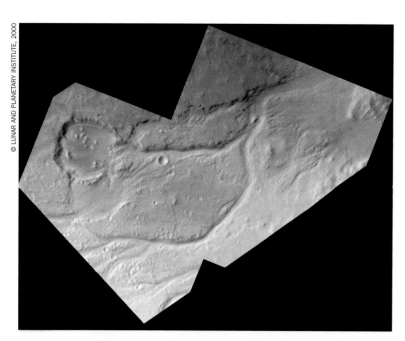

This Viking *3-D view shows Vedra Valles, a group of now-dry channels that once flowed eastward into the giant Chryse Basin on Mars. These channels were carved by running water when Mars had liquid water on its surface.*

You can use a stream table to model water erosion on a planet's surface.

TECTONICS

Tectonics is the study of how the outer layer of a planet can shift and break. Faulting occurs when parts of that outer layer move past one another. Folding (compression) occurs when parts of the outer layer collide and bend. Thinning occurs when the outer layer stretches. Jupiter's moon Ganymede (see the photo below) and Saturn's moon Enceladus both exhibit examples of faulting. Tremendous stress was created when large parts of the outer layer moved past each another. This buildup of stress eventually caused the rock to break along fault lines.

When the rocks on the outer layer of a planet collide, the rock folds. The compression stresses caused by those collisions can create wrinkle ridges in the surface of a planet or moon. Rock also can be stretched, which produces alternating large valleys and high standing blocks. These alternating blocks and valleys are evident on Mars and on Ganymede.

Earthquakes occur along faults on Earth. But what do faults look like on other planets? Get out your red and blue glasses and examine the dramatic view of faults on Mars. Acheron

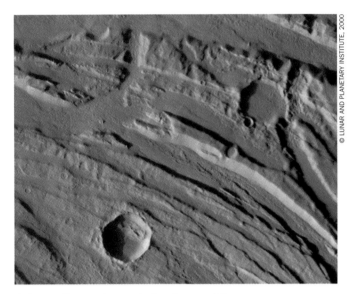

Acheron Fossae is a set of valleys on Mars

Fossae is a set of valleys on Mars formed when the crust stretched and fractured. When two parallel faults form, the block of crust between them may drop down, with a ridge forming between them.

If an asteroid or comet hits a planet or moon, it can fracture its surface. Strong seismic waves result from the energy of the impact and move through the planet's or moon's surface. Fracture lines might radiate outward from the crater. Extreme temperature changes from day to night also can cause fracturing. (Think of how an ice cube fractures when you place it in a cup of hot water.) Fracturing due to extreme temperature changes is especially common on planets or moons without an atmosphere. An atmosphere acts as a blanket that holds in heat at night and protects the surface from extreme high temperatures during the day.

The patterns of ridges and grooves indicate that pulling apart and horizontal sliding have both shaped the icy landscape of Jupiter's moon Ganymede.

Modeling Tectonics

You can model planetary tectonics by doing the following:

1. Use your large steel sphere and your plastic box of sand, flour, and cocoa from Lesson 12 to investigate the effects of impact cratering on a surface. Do fractures form around the crater?

2. Extreme changes in temperature, planetary shrinking, and other internal forces in a planet may cause it to twist or pull. Examine the effects of pulling and twisting forces on the surface of your box (see the illustration at right). Can you see cracks and wrinkle ridges forming in the surface as you twist and pull the sides of the box?

3. Now use your plastic spreader to push (compress) the layers of sand and flour (see the illustration below). Were you able to shift the layers? Do you see evidence of faulting?

You can use sand, flour, and cocoa in your model to test the effects of pushing, pulling, and twisting tectonic forces on a planet's surface.

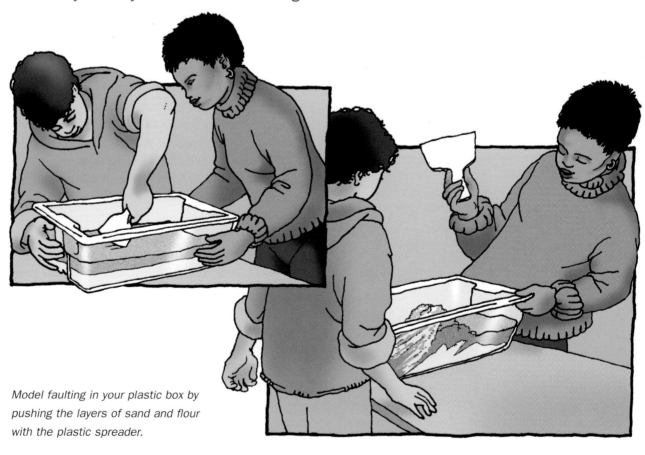

Model faulting in your plastic box by pushing the layers of sand and flour with the plastic spreader.

VOLCANISM

Magma is made up of melted rock, crystals, and dissolved gases. It is found deep in a planet's interior. When magma erupts onto the planet's surface, it forms lava. This eruption creates distinctive landforms, such as lava plains and volcanoes.

Volcanoes on Planets and Moons

Dark, flat lava plains cover about 17 percent of the Moon's total surface. These plains are called "maria," from the Latin word for "seas." You can see the maria on the surface of a full Moon on a clear night. The Moon's maria are made up of volcanic rock similar to the rock on Earth's ocean floor. The lava that formed the maria flowed long distances. Many maria were formed as lava flooded low-lying areas, such as the bottom of an impact crater. Older lava flows on the Moon have been covered by younger flows or have been pocked with impact craters.

Jupiter's moon Io has numerous low, flat volcanoes called "shield volcanoes." Most shield volcanoes have dark peaks with long lava flows streaming from them. The lava ran gently down the sides of the volcano. On Venus, the shield volcano Sif Mons resembles many of the shield volcanoes on Earth. The volcano Olympus Mons on Mars is the largest shield volcano in the solar system. It measures 600 kilometers across.

The volcanoes on Venus have unusual circular, flat-topped domes called pancake domes. Wearing the red and blue glasses, examine the view of pancake domes on Venus. The largest dome in this scene is 65 kilometers across and roughly 1 kilometer high. This group of pancake domes is called Carmenta Farra. A small crater near the center of each dome may be the source for that dome's lava flow.

Why are shield volcanoes on other planets so large? Scientists believe that the crust of other planets, unlike Earth's crust, is not made of moving plates. Without plate tectonics, the volcanic vents on other planets may remain undisturbed for a long time. As a result, other planets have huge shield volcanoes many times larger than those on Earth.

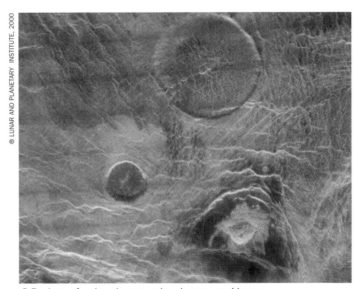

© LUNAR AND PLANETARY INSTITUTE, 2000

3-D view of volcanic pancake domes on Venus

Volcanism (continued)

Volcanism (continued)

Modeling Volcanism

You can model volcanism on other planets by doing the following:

1. Lava is often viscous (which means that it sometimes will flow slowly). Mix red water and a small amount of flour in a cup to create a viscous model "lava." Don't make it too thick, or it will not flow through your tube.
2. Bury one end of your 90-cm tubing beneath the sand. Turn the end so it faces up.
3. Attach the unburied end of the tubing to the syringe (see the illustration).
4. Pour lava into the syringe. Cap the syringe.
5. *Very slowly* compress your syringe to model lava eruption on your planetary surface. What do you observe? What happens when lava nears your craters?

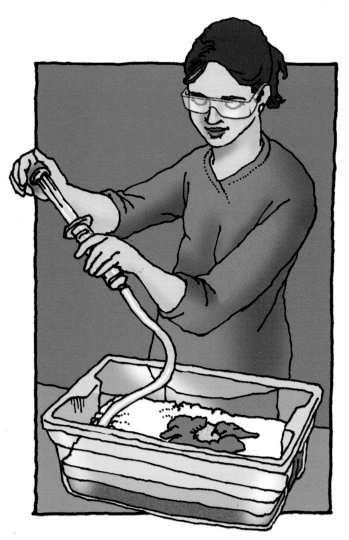

You can use a syringe and long tubing beneath the sand to model the eruption of lava onto a planet's surface. To create your lava, thicken your red water with flour. What would a lava flow do to the craters on the planet's surface?

Wet Like Earth?

Scientists have long known Mars has plenty of water in the form of ice. Its large polar ice caps have been visible to people looking through telescopes here on Earth for many years. Scientists also have observed channels and valleys on Mars that indicate that water might have flowed across its surface long ago.

But scientists did not believe that Mars had *liquid* water. How could it? Mars is colder than Antarctica and far dryer than any place on Earth.

However, in June 2000, scientists at the NASA announced an amazing discovery. New images transmitted from the Mars *Global Surveyor* spacecraft showed what looked like gullies on the surface of that planet. Gullies are ravine-like features on a planet's surface that have been carved out by flash floods. If NASA scientists were correct, then there is evidence Mars has had flowing, liquid water in its very recent past.

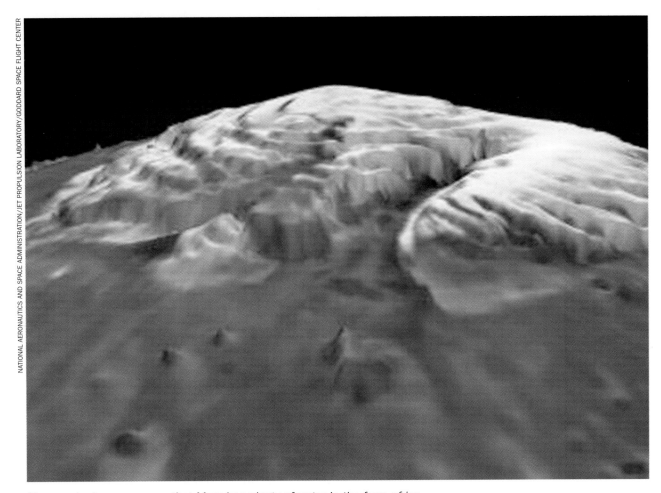

NATIONAL AERONAUTICS AND SPACE ADMINISTRATION/JET PROPULSION LABORATORY/GODDARD SPACE FLIGHT CENTER

These polar ice caps prove that Mars has plenty of water in the form of ice.

Strong Evidence

The gullies in the NASA images are found on the sides of large craters or valley walls. Large pools of water, either from the surface of the planet or from beneath the surface, have flowed from them. Areas of accumulated rocks and other debris at the lower ends of the gullies are evidence that the water flow probably had great force.

These gullies are important evidence that liquid water existed in the recent past on Mars. The gullies have not been disturbed by wind erosion, asteroid impact, or volcanic activity. Scientists conclude that this means the gullies are extremely young.

During the first two decades of this century, NASA will send at least six missions to Mars to explore the planet's surface. The spacecraft will include orbiters with powerful telescopes and other sensors, a roving robot laboratory, and even a vehicle that will scoop up Martian soil and return it to Earth. These Mars missions will be looking for liquid water.

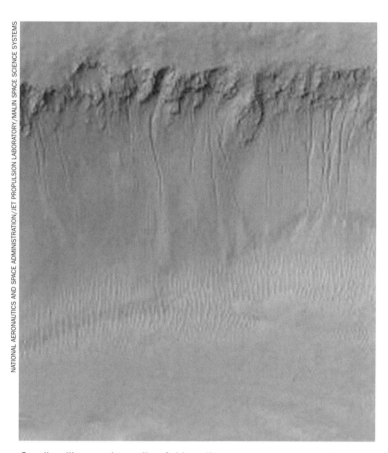

NATIONAL AERONAUTICS AND SPACE ADMINISTRATION/JET PROPULSION LABORATORY/MALIN SPACE SCIENCE SYSTEMS

Small gullies on the walls of this valley system were created when a liquid—probably water—trickled through the walls until it reached the cliff, where it ran downhill to form the channels and fan-shaped aprons at the bottom of the slope.

The Martian Riddle

A long time ago, conditions on Mars may have been similar to those on Earth today. The channels tell us that mighty Martian rivers may have once flowed into oceans. The atmosphere then may have been more dense and full of oxygen. Temperatures may have been much warmer. If so, life may have existed there—and may exist there still. ☐

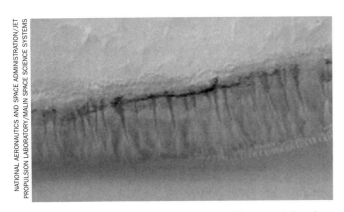

Evidence of liquid water in a crater on Mars, as taken by the Mars Global Surveyor Orbiter

Colonizing Mars

If scientists detect liquid water on Mars, will humans try to live on the planet? Even though the Martian atmosphere is too thin to breathe, humans can make oxygen from water. They also could generate hydrogen for rocket fuel from water. Water also means that humans could grow their own food.

When humans do reach Mars, they will begin to try to answer an important question—what happened to Mars? We need to know what caused the dramatic change in the Martian climate, which used to be so like our own. If we can find out, we might be better able to protect Earth. Martian water will help us learn such lessons.

Mission: **Mars**

Mars's reddish color can be seen from Earth. So can its white polar caps. Some astronomers in the late 1800s saw dark lines running across the surface of the planet. Percival Lowell and other U.S. scientists believed these lines were canals, built by Martians to transport water!

Not until 1965 would people know for sure what those lines were. In that year, *Mariner 4* flew by Mars and found a moonlike landscape, but no signs of life. Four years later, two other Mariner flyby missions confirmed these findings. Still, scientists believed that more time was needed to understand the red planet. That meant going into orbit.

Mariner 9 was the first spacecraft to orbit another planet. It arrived at Mars in November 1971, and orbited the planet for nearly a year. During that time, it witnessed a month-long dust storm. It also found canyons, floodplains, and other signs of ancient water. Before the century was over, other spacecraft—including *Viking 1* and *2*, the Mars *Pathfinder*, and the Mars *Global Surveyor*—would visit Mars.

Viking 1 and *2*

Both *Viking 1* and *2* arrived at Mars in 1976. Each spacecraft was made up of an orbiter and a lander. The orbiter was designed to find a landing site for the lander, and to relay information from the lander to scientists on Earth. *Viking 1* and *2* were designed to study Mars for several months—instead, they provided scientists with data for several years.

Images from the orbiters showed volcanoes, lava plains, canyons, and craters. They also showed dry valleys and channels. As expected,

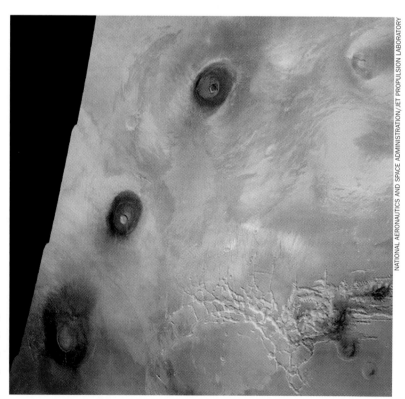

A color mosaic of images taken by the Viking 1 orbiter shows the eastern Tharsis region on Mars. Notice the three volcanoes on the left and the canyon in the lower right-hand corner.

NATIONAL AERONAUTICS AND SPACE ADMINISTRATION/JET PROPULSION LABORATORY

NATIONAL AERONAUTICS AND SPACE ADMINISTRATION/JET PROPULSION LABORATORY

Viking *lander*

much of the landscape looked as if it had been carved by running water. The images also showed that Mars is divided into two main regions: northern low plains and southern cratered highlands.

With the orbiters flying overhead, the *Viking* landers descended through the thin Martian atmosphere. Their instruments revealed that carbon dioxide is the major gas surrounding Mars. They landed safely on opposite sides of the planet in iron-rich soil—it is this iron that gives Mars its reddish color.

The landers' cameras searched the landscape for large forms of life, but they didn't find any. Instruments on the landers conducted experiments to determine if the Martian soil at those sites contained microscopic life. They didn't find any.

The *Viking* landers did find a crusty surface that resembles Earth's crust. Tests also showed that Mars is extremely stable. There were no tremors, quakes, or volcanic eruptions.

As of this writing, the *Viking* landers and orbiters were the longest-lived laboratories on another world, and they have provided the most complete view of Mars.

Mars *Pathfinder*

On July 4, 1997, the Mars *Pathfinder,* surrounded by huge air bags, bounced to a stop on the Martian surface. It had landed in an ancient plain where scientists believe a catastrophic flood left behind loads of rocks. Inside the *Pathfinder* spacecraft was a rover named *Sojourner.* It would become the first rover to operate on another planet. *Sojourner's* job was to analyze rocks and soils.

Data also showed that Mars is drier and dustier than any desert on Earth. The dust often spins in gusts, called "dust devils." Clouds that cover parts of Mars consist of water ice condensed on the reddish dust.

Pathfinder's lander operated nearly three times longer than its expected lifetime of 30 days. *Sojourner* operated 12 times its expected lifetime of seven days. Together, they sent back 2.3 billion bits of information, including more than 16,500 images.

NATIONAL AERONAUTICS AND SPACE ADMINISTRATION/JET PROPULSION LABORATORY

Sojourner *is taking a measurement. Notice the two-toned surface of the large rock. Windblown dust may have collected on the surface (the rock is leaning into the wind). Or this rock may have broken off from a larger boulder as it was deposited in the ancient flood that scoured this area.*

Name This Roving Robot!

Imagine what it would be like to name the rover for the Mars Pathfinder mission. Valerie Ambrose, a 12-year-old student from Bridgeport, Connecticut, didn't have to imagine. In 1995, she won a contest held by the Planetary Society, a nonprofit organization dedicated to the exploration of the solar system.

Kids between the ages of 5 and 18 could enter the contest. The Society said that the rover had to be named for a heroine from mythology, fiction, or history (no longer living). Entrants had to submit a fully researched, 300-word essay explaining their choice of a name for the rover.

Entries came from around the world. Valerie suggested that the rover be named after Sojourner Truth, the African-American activist who wanted slavery abolished and who promoted women's rights. Sojourner Truth lived in the Civil War era, and she traveled around the United States speaking for the rights of all people to be free and for women to fully participate in society.

Finally, the day to name the winner arrived. Valerie won! NASA chose the name *Sojourner* for its Mars *Pathfinder* rover. The name honors Sojourner Truth. It is also appropriate because "sojourner" means traveler.

Another student's entry was also a winner. Second-place winner Deepti Rohatgi suggested Marie Curie, after the Polish-born chemist who won the Nobel Prize in 1911 for her discovery of the elements radium and polonium. NASA used Marie Curie as the name for its second Mars rover.

It's exciting to think that students just like you named these famous rovers. Who knows, maybe one day you may name a rover, a comet, an asteroid, or even the next planet in space!

This image shows the Global Surveyor *above Mars. Olympus Mons is in the background.*

NATIONAL AERONAUTICS AND SPACE ADMINISTRATION/JET PROPULSION LABORATORY/MALIN SPACE SCIENCE SYSTEMS

Twelve orbits a day provide wide-angle cameras a global "snapshot" of weather patterns across Mars. Here, bluish-white water ice clouds hang above the Tharsis volcanoes.

Global Surveyor

The Mars *Global Surveyor,* launched in November 1996, was equipped to fly at a low altitude in a nearly pole-to-pole orbit. This speedy spacecraft orbited Mars 12 times a day.

Surveyor has returned images of clouds hanging over gigantic volcanoes, dust storms that blow around the entire planet, and polar caps that enlarge in the winter and shrink in the summer.

Surveyor confirmed that these polar caps consist of layers of dust and frozen carbon dioxide. Scientists believe that such layers hold secrets to seasonal changes on Mars. They also may be one of the best places to search for evidence of past life on the planet.

Surveyor made another discovery that increases the chances of finding traces of past life. Mars, it turns out, once had a magnetic field, much as Earth does today. This is significant because magnetic fields shield planets from harmful radiation.

Only Earth and Mars have just the right temperature—neither too hot nor too cold—to support life as we know it. Scientists don't yet know if Mars ever developed life. But this rocky world is the only other planet in our solar system where it is possible for humans to walk around and explore. It may even one day be a place to live. □

PLANETARY FACTS: Mars

Mars: Quick Facts

Diameter	6792 km	**Average temperature**	–55 °C
Average distance from the Sun	228,000,000 km	**Length of sidereal day**	24.62 hours
Mass	64×10^{22} kg	**Length of year**	687 Earth days
Surface gravity (Earth = 1)	0.38	**Number of observed moons**	2

Relative size

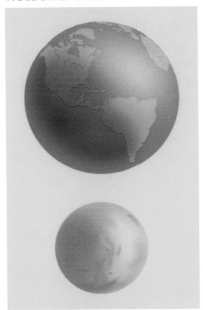

Mars atmosphere

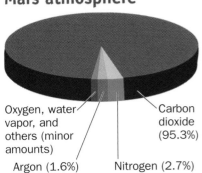

Oxygen, water vapor, and others (minor amounts)

Argon (1.6%)

Nitrogen (2.7%)

Carbon dioxide (95.3%)

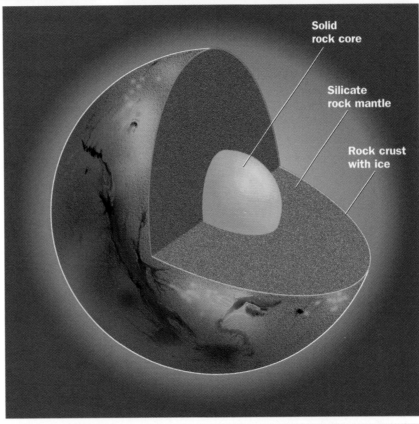

Solid rock core

Silicate rock mantle

Rock crust with ice

Did You Know?

- Mars was named after the Roman god of war because the red color of Mars looks like spilled blood.
- Olympus Mons, a volcano on Mars, is 24 kilometers high—more than twice as high as the tallest volcano on Earth, and three times as high as Mount Everest.

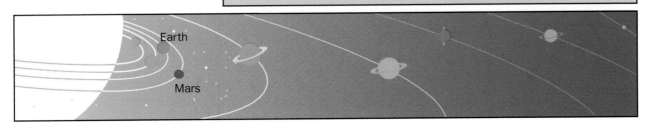

Earth

Mars

14
Surface Gravity

NATIONAL AERONAUTICS AND SPACE ADMINISTRATION/JOHNSON SPACE CENTER

On the Moon, this astronaut weighs one-sixth of his weight on Earth. This is because the Moon's surface gravity is not as strong as Earth's.

INTRODUCTION

How much do you weigh? How massive are you? Suppose you could travel to other planets. What would happen to your weight and mass? In this lesson you will explore these questions. You will simulate what it is like to pick up objects on different planets. Then, using a spring scale, you will relate what you observe about the weights of objects to the force called gravity. The lesson ends as you continue the series of Mission readers to learn more about the Galileo mission to Jupiter.

OBJECTIVES FOR THIS LESSON

Use a model to compare the weight of a can of soda on different planets.

Analyze the relationship between an object's weight on each planet and the planet's mass and diameter.

Measure the weight of objects that have different masses.

Describe how mass and weight (force of gravity) are related.

Summarize and organize information about Jupiter and compare Jupiter to other planets.

Getting Started

1. What do you know about gravity as a characteristic of a planet's surface? Record your ideas in your science notebook.

2. Share what you have written with the class and discuss your ideas about the following questions:

What is gravity?

How are gravity and weight related?

How can you measure gravity?

MATERIALS

For you

1 copy of Student Sheet 14.1: How Much Would a Can of Soda Weigh?

1 working copy of Student Sheet 10.1c: Planetary Chart

For your group to share

9 prepared cans

1 set of Planet Data Cards

For your group

1 spring scale

1 plastic cylinder

25 large steel washers

Inquiry 14.1
Analyzing Weight on Each Planet

PROCEDURE

1. Examine the prepared cans at your assigned station. Every can represents the same full can of soda but on different planets. Pick up each can and observe how heavy that can is on each planet (see Figure 14.1). On which planet does the can weigh the least? On which planet does the can weigh the most? Why do you think this is? Discuss your ideas with your group.

2. Rank the weight of each can on Student Sheet 14.1 by recording a "1" next to the name of the planet with the lightest can. Increase the numbers until you get to the heaviest can. If any cans seem to weigh the same, use the same number to rank them.

3. Turn over the following three Planet Data Cards: the planet you ranked "1" (the lightest can); the planet you ranked with the highest number (the heaviest can); and the planet with a number somewhere in between. Examine the data printed on the back of these three cards. What characteristics about each planet could explain why the weight of the can is different on each planet? Discuss your ideas with your group. Record your ideas below Table 1 on Student Sheet 14.1.

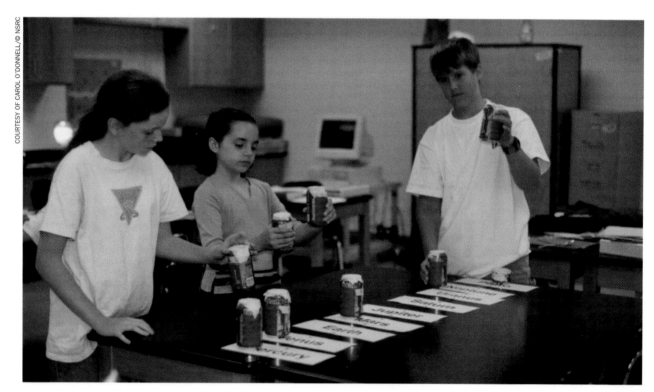

Figure 14.1 *Observe how heavy the can is on each planet. On which planet does the can weigh the most? On which planet does it weigh the least?*

REFLECTING ON WHAT YOU'VE DONE

1. Share your rankings from Student Sheet 14.1 with the class.

2. How do the characteristics of a planet affect its ability to pull on an object—giving the object its weight? Share your ideas with the class, using your explanation on Student Sheet 14.1 as your guide.

3. Record in your notebook what you know about the relationship between mass and weight. Then share your ideas with the class.

4. Read "Mass and Weight: What's the Difference?" Then record a working definition of these two terms in your notebook.

Inquiry 14.2
Investigating Mass and Weight

PROCEDURE

1. Why does mass affect weight? Discuss this question with your group or class. Record your group's ideas in your student notebook.

2. How do you think the spring scale works? Discuss your ideas with your group. Then watch as your teacher demonstrates how to use it. Discuss what a newton is. Try calibrating the spring scale by holding it vertically with nothing attached to the hook. Make sure the scale registers zero. If necessary, use the metal tab at the top of the spring scale to adjust the setting to zero (see Figure 14.2).

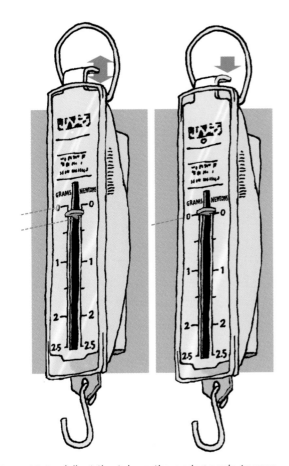

Figure 14.2 *Adjust the tab on the spring scale to zero before each trial.*

3. Lay the spring scale flat (horizontally) on the table. Place two to three washers on the spring scale's hook. What do you observe? Discuss your ideas with your group.

4. Hold the spring scale up vertically. Place two to three washers on the spring scale's hook. What do you observe? Are your results different from Step 3? Why or why not? Discuss your ideas with your group.

5. Pick up the clear plastic cylinder. Describe its weight to your group.

6. Increase the mass of the plastic cylinder by adding five washers to it and hold the cylinder in your hands. Did the mass of the cylinder change? Did the weight of the cylinder change? Discuss your ideas with your group.

7. Increase the mass of the cylinder to 25 washers and hold the cylinder in your hand. Did the mass of the cylinder change? Did the weight of the cylinder change? Discuss your ideas with your group.

8. Hang the cylinder with 25 washers from the spring scale hook, as shown in Figure 14.3. What is the weight of the cylinder with 25 washers? Record this number in your notebook. Discuss your observations with your group.

9. Design an investigation with your group to prove that mass and weight are related. Record your design plan in your science notebook. Consider what you will change (independent variable), what you will measure (dependent variable), and what you will keep the same (controlled variable).

10. Create a data table in your notebook. For each trial, record the mass of the cylinder (number of washers) and the weight of the cylinder in newtons (a measure of the

Figure 14.3 *Use the spring scale to measure the weight of the cylinder and 25 washers.*

force of gravity). If you conduct more than one trial, average your results.

11. Before you begin each trial, remember to calibrate the spring scale by adjusting the setting to zero each time. Then complete your investigation.

REFLECTING ON WHAT YOU'VE DONE

1. Share your results from Inquiry 14.2 with the class.

2. Answer the following questions in your science notebook, and then discuss them as a class:

A. What is the weight of five washers?

B. When you increased the mass of the cylinder, what happened to its weight?

C. How are mass and weight related?

D. From your reading, you know that a force is a push or pull on or by an object. What is the name of the force that makes the cylinder have weight?

E. In what direction does this force pull on the cylinder?

F. Think back to Inquiry 14.1. If weight is the measure of the force of gravity pulling on an object, which planet has a greater force of gravity pulling on objects at its surface—Pluto or Jupiter? Explain your answer.

G. What force holds us to Earth's surface?

H. What two factors affect the gravity at a planet's surface?

I. If Mars has more mass than Mercury, why is the force of gravity on the surface of Mars nearly the same as the force of gravity on the surface of Mercury?

3. With your class, return to the Question G folder for Lesson 1 and its photo card. As a class, review the self-stick notes about where gravity exists and remove any that seem incorrect. Add your new ideas to the folder.

4. Read the "Mission: Jupiter" reading selection. Add any information about Jupiter to your working copy of Student Sheet 10.1c: Planetary Chart (and onto Student Sheet 10.1b: Planetary Brochure Outline if your Anchor Activity planet assigned during Lesson 10 was Jupiter).

Mass & Weight:

What's the Difference?

Many people think that there is no difference between the terms "weight" and "mass." But there is! Mass is related to the amount of matter (or "stuff") in an object, regardless of how much space the object takes up. As long as you do not add or take away any matter from an object, its mass stays the same, even at different locations. If you take an object to the Moon or Mars, it will have the same mass that it had on Earth.

But what about its weight? Would an object weigh the same on the Moon or Mars as it does on Earth? As you found out in your investigation, the answer is "no." The weight of an object changes from planet to planet. Weight even changes from one place on a planet (such as a mountaintop, where you might weigh less) to another (such as the bottom of a deep valley, where you might weigh more).

Measuring Mass and Weight

Weight is a measure of the force of gravity on an object. (A force is a push or pull on or by an object.) We use a spring scale to measure the strength of the gravitational pull on the mass of an object. Objects with the same mass have the same weight. An object with more mass has a stronger gravitational force pulling on it than an object with less mass. The spring scale is pulled down farther, showing that the object weighs more. In the metric system, weight is measured in newtons.

Mass is measured in kilograms and grams in the metric system. To find the mass of an object, we use a balance. When equal amounts of matter are placed on opposite sides of a beam balance, for example, the pull of gravity is the same on both sides, and the beam balances. If the mass of an object were measured with a balance on

Weight is measured using a spring scale.
Mass is measured using a balance.

Earth, and then with the same balance on the Moon, the results would be identical. The amount of "stuff" in the object hasn't changed.

Mass and Weight on the Nine Planets

An object with mass attracts any other object with mass. The strength of that attraction depends on the mass of each object and their distance from each other. This gravitational pull is very small between objects of ordinary size and therefore is hard to measure. The pull between an object with a large amount of mass, such as Earth, and another object, such as a person on the planet's surface, can easily be measured.

Weight on a planet's surface is a measure of the pull of gravity between an object and the planet on which it is located. This force of gravity on an object on a planet's surface depends on the object's mass and the mass of the planet. If the

(continued)

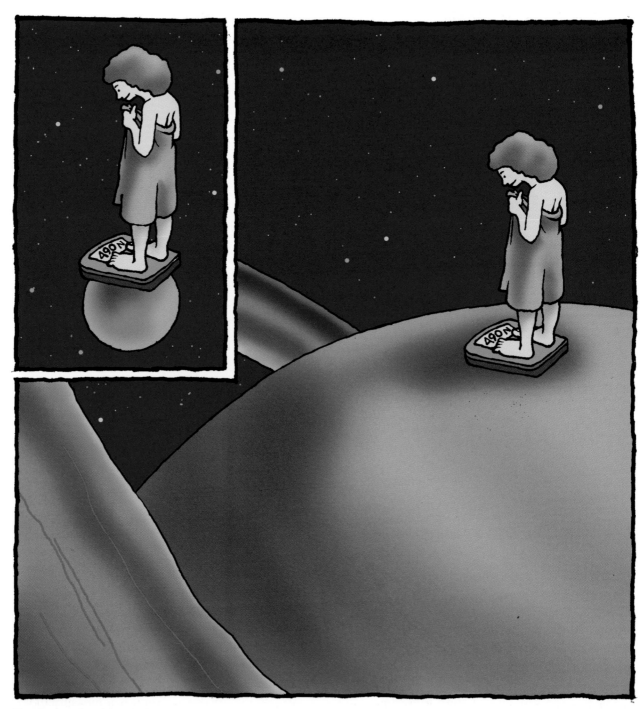

The farther the object is from the center of the planet, the weaker the pull between the planet and the object. This means that your weight on Saturn would be about the same as your weight on Venus, even though Saturn is more massive than Venus.

What Would You Weigh on Jupiter?

Jupiter has 318 times more mass than Earth, so you might assume that you would weigh 318 times more on Jupiter than you weigh on Earth. This would be true if Jupiter were the same size as Earth, but the diameter of Jupiter is more than 10 times the diameter of Earth. This means that if you stood on Jupiter, you would actually be farther from the planet's center than you would be if you stood on Earth. This reduces Jupiter's gravitational pull on you to only about 2.36 times (and not 318 times) your weight on Earth.

The number 2.36 is referred to as Jupiter's "gravity factor." The gravity factor is the ratio of each planet's gravity to that on Earth. Earth's gravity factor is 1 and Jupiter's gravity factor is 2.36. By multiplying your Earth weight by a planet's gravity factor, you can determine your weight on that planet. Use the table to find out how much you would weigh on each of the nine planets.

Table 1 Mass, Radius, and Surface Gravity of Each Planet

Planet	Mass (10^{22} kg)	Radius (km)	Surface Gravity Factor (Earth = 1)
Mercury	33	2439	0.38
Venus	487	6051	0.91
Earth	597	6378	1.00
Mars	64	3396	0.38
Jupiter	189,900	71,492	2.36
Saturn	56,850	60,268	0.92
Uranus	8683	25,559	0.89
Neptune	10,240	24,764	1.12
Pluto	1	1170	0.06

mass of that object is doubled, gravity pulls on it twice as hard. If the mass of the planet is doubled, gravity pulls on the object twice as hard.

The force of gravity also depends on the distance of an object from the center of the planet to its surface. This distance is called the radius of the planet. The farther an object is from the planet's center, the weaker the pull between the planet and the object. This force gets weaker quite rapidly, but there is a pattern to it. If you double the radius of the planet, the weight of the object will be one-fourth as much. If you triple the radius of the planet, the weight will be only one-ninth as much. The force of gravity drops off with the square of the distance between the center of the planet and the object.

Each planet in our solar system has a different mass and a different size. This means that the weight of the same object on the surface of each planet will be different. For example, you would weigh less on the Moon than you do on Earth because although the Moon is smaller than Earth, it also has less mass than Earth— and Earth's mass wins out. This means that the Moon exerts less gravitational force at its surface than Earth. Any given object will have the same *mass* on Earth and on the Moon, but that object's *weight* on the Moon will be only about 16 percent (one-sixth) of the weight as measured on Earth. □

Mission: **Jupiter**

In the early 1600s, astronomer Galileo Galilei looked at cloud-covered Jupiter through one of the world's first telescopes. What he saw amazed everyone—four moons!

Telescopes improved over the years and other moons of Jupiter were found. More than 300 years after Galileo's discovery, spacecraft flew close enough to Jupiter to take detailed pictures. *Pioneer 10* flew by Jupiter first, in 1973. *Pioneer 11* followed a year later. *Voyager 1* and *2,* en route to the outer planets, sped past Jupiter in 1979.

These flyby missions added to our knowledge, but they also left us with many questions. What are Jupiter's rings made of? How fast do the winds on Jupiter blow? And what *is* beneath those clouds?

Many scientists believed that only an orbiter could answer such questions, because an orbiter can observe a planet for a long time. The *Viking* orbiter had revealed much about Mars. And the *Pioneer* orbiter answered many questions about Venus. But how could an orbiter "see" beneath Jupiter's clouds? A probe would have to do that!

Plans got underway to send a spacecraft with an orbiter *and* a probe to Jupiter. The mission would be named after the Italian scientist who first spotted Jupiter's four large moons—Galileo.

The *Galileo* spacecraft was launched in 1989. Six years later, as it approached Jupiter, the probe and orbiter separated. In December 1995, the probe finally plunged into Jupiter's clouds.

NATIONAL AERONAUTICS AND SPACE ADMINISTRATION/JET PROPULSION LABORATORY/UNIVERSITY OF ARIZONA

Jupiter

The orbiter, meanwhile, was starting on its path around the largest planet in the solar system.

Galileo Probe Findings

Descending through Jupiter's atmosphere, frictional forces on the surface of the probe's heat shield raised the heat shield's surface temperatures to levels twice as hot as those of the Sun's surface! Still, it sent data for nearly 58 minutes before the heat and pressure destroyed it.

What can a space probe discover in less than an hour? As it turns out—lots! To the surprise of scientists, the probe showed there were no clouds in the lower part of Jupiter's atmosphere. The air below the clouds also was much drier than scientists expected. Scientists think the probe may have descended into a part of Jupiter's atmosphere that was unusually dry. Yet the wind speed—540 kilometers an hour—was the same both in the clouds and below them.

These winds puzzled scientists. On Earth, the Sun's heat helps make winds. But Jupiter receives only about ⅒ as much sunlight as Earth. So what's the source of Jupiter's winds? Some scientists believe they are powered by heat escaping from deep inside the planet.

The probe journeyed 600 kilometers into Jupiter's atmosphere. As expected, it hit no solid object or surface along the way. Jupiter is, after all, a *gaseous* giant. Its solid surface lies below tens of thousands of kilometers of atmosphere.

NATIONAL AERONAUTICS AND SPACE ADMINISTRATION/JET PROPULSION LABORATORY

The Galileo *probe's descent through Jupiter's atmosphere*

The ring system of Jupiter was imaged by the Galileo spacecraft on November 9, 1996.

Galileo Orbiter Findings

In the late 1970s, the *Voyager* spacecraft discovered two, possibly three, rings around Jupiter. In 1995, the *Galileo* orbiter confirmed the presence of a third thin ring but also found a fourth ring inside it! According to the data transmitted by *Galileo,* all the rings consist of small grains of dust. It seems that meteoroid impacts blasted the grains off the surface of the four innermost moons.

Galileo also revealed that Jupiter is home to many more huge storms than once thought. The largest is the Great Red Spot. This raging storm is three times the size of Earth!

While Jupiter has more storms than expected, it has less lightning than scientists predicted. Lightning occurs on Jupiter only about one-tenth as often as on Earth. On our planet, there is an average of about 100 lightning flashes every second.

While orbiting Jupiter, *Galileo* flew near several of Jupiter's moons. Scientists knew that Io, the innermost of Jupiter's four major moons, has active volcanoes. The *Voyager* spacecraft discovered several of them in 1979. But the *Galileo* orbiter showed that hundreds of volcanoes cover Io. Many spew lava from deep below the moon's surface.

The Great Red Spot on Jupiter

NATIONAL AERONAUTICS AND SPACE ADMINISTRATION/JET PROPULSION LABORATORY

Jupiter's moon Europa seems to have an ocean beneath its cracked icy surface. In this ocean, gigantic blocks of ice the size of cities appear to have broken off and drifted apart. Callisto, the outermost of Jupiter's four major moons, also may have an ocean below its cratered surface.

Ganymede is the largest moon in the entire solar system. The data transmitted by the *Galileo* orbiter show that it is the only moon known to have a magnetic field.

The orbiter is scheduled to end its mission with a dive into Jupiter's deadly atmosphere—a dramatic ending for one mind-expanding trip! ☐

Jupiter's four largest moons: Io, Europa, Ganymede, and Callisto (top to bottom). Jupiter's Great Red Spot is shown in the background.

PLANETARY FACTS: Jupiter

Jupiter: Quick Facts

Diameter	142,980 km	**Average temperature**	−108 °C
Average distance from the Sun	778,400,000 km	**Length of sidereal day**	9.92 hours
Mass	$189,900 \times 10^{22}$ kg	**Length of year**	11.86 Earth years
Surface gravity (Earth = 1)	2.36	**Number of observed moons**	39*

Relative size

Jupiter atmosphere

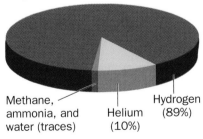

Methane, ammonia, and water (traces)

Helium (10%)

Hydrogen (89%)

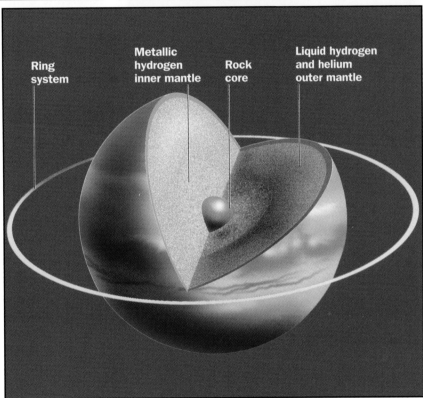

Ring system

Metallic hydrogen inner mantle

Rock core

Liquid hydrogen and helium outer mantle

Did You Know?

- Jupiter (like the other gaseous planets) has a ring system. Although Jupiter's ring system is essentially transparent, the ring particles are visible when there is light behind them.
- Jupiter's swirling cloud patterns are caused by its rapid rotation.

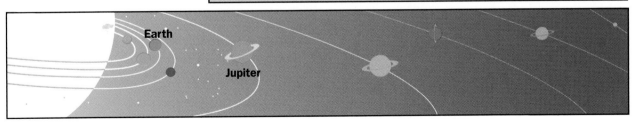

Earth

Jupiter

*As of 2002

Gravity and Orbital Motion

What keeps a satellite orbiting in space? Gravity! Gravity also helps planets like Earth orbit the Sun.

NATIONAL AERONAUTICS AND SPACE ADMINISTRATION/JET PROPULSION LABORATORY

INTRODUCTION

How does a manmade satellite get into orbit? A satellite is launched by a rocket to a height (or altitude) at which Earth's gravitational force keeps the satellite in orbit around Earth. A satellite, like the Moon, must travel at just the right speed to stay in Earth's orbit. If the satellite moves too slowly, gravity might pull it back down to Earth. If the satellite moves too fast, it might escape Earth's gravitational pull and zoom out into space.

In Lesson 14, you investigated the effects of surface gravity on weight. In this lesson, you will conduct four inquiries that focus on gravity and its effects on the orbits of moons and planets. What part does gravity play in keeping the planets in orbit around the Sun? How do the moons stay in orbit around each planet? In this lesson, you will investigate these and other questions. You will also read to learn more about missions to Saturn, Uranus, and Neptune.

OBJECTIVES FOR THIS LESSON

Analyze patterns in planetary motion.

Observe the motion of a marble when acted upon by different forces.

Investigate the effect of a pulling force on the orbital period of a sphere.

Relate the observed behavior of a marble and sphere to the motion of moons and planets.

Summarize, organize, and compare information about Saturn, Uranus, and Neptune.

Getting Started

MATERIALS FOR LESSON 15

For you
1 working copy of Student Sheet 10.1c: Planetary Chart

1. Review the Introduction section of the software *Explore the Planets* with your class.

2. Use what you learned from *Explore the Planets* to make general observations about the planets' motion around the Sun. Record your ideas in your notebooks if instructed to do so by your teacher. Discuss your ideas with the class.

3. To get a better sense of how the planets' orbits differ from each other, use the software *Starry Night Enthusiast.* Observe the orbits of the inner planets. Then observe the orbits of the outer planets. Record or discuss your observations as instructed.

4. Review the objectives of this lesson with your teacher. Discuss the Procedures and Safety Tips listed in each inquiry. A summary of each procedure will be posted at each station.

5. Divide your notebook page into quadrants. Label the quadrants 15.1, 15.2, 15.3, and 15.4.

6. Complete all four inquiries in the order given to you by your teacher. Remember to return all of your equipment and its inquiry master to the plastic box or bag before moving on to the next station.

MATERIALS FOR INQUIRY 15.1

For you

1 pair of goggles

For your group

1 copy of Inquiry Master 15.1: Gravity's Effect on Objects in Motion
1 plastic box from Lesson 12 (filled with sand, flour, and cocoa)
1 large resealable bag containing the following:
   1 metric ruler, 30 cm (12″)
   1 marble
   1 metric measuring tape

Inquiry 15.1
Gravity's Effect on Objects in Motion

PROCEDURE

1. Hold the marble 40 cm above the plastic box. With the marble in your hand, decide what two forces are acting on the marble. Are the forces balanced (both pulling equally) or unbalanced (one is pulling more than the other)? Discuss your ideas with your group.

2. What will happen if you release the marble from your hand into the box? Discuss your predictions with your group.

SAFETY TIPS

Wear safety goggles at all times.

Work in a well-ventilated area to minimize the level of dust in the air.

3. Let go of the marble. Discuss your observations of the marble's motion with your group. (Do not be concerned about the crater that the marble makes. The sand and flour keep the marble from moving once it lands in the box.) Compare your observations to your predictions.

4. Repeat Procedure Steps 1–3. Does the marble move the same way each time? Discuss your observations and record them in quadrant 15.1 in your notebook.

5. Use the ruler as a ramp to gently roll the marble into the plastic box, as shown in Figure 15.1. Keep the ruler nearly flat. Discuss your observations. How did the marble move once it left the ruler?

Figure 15.1 *Roll the marble down the ruler into the plastic box.*

6. Experiment by rolling the marble down the ruler at different speeds. Keep the ruler nearly flat. How does the marble move each time it leaves the ruler? If possible, measure the distance that your marble travels each time. Record your observations in your notebook.

7. Answer these questions in your notebook:

A. What pulling force acts on the marble at all times?

B. When you rolled the marble slowly, how did it move once it left the ruler?

C. How does the forward speed of the marble affect the motion of the marble once it leaves the ruler?

D. All planets that orbit the Sun are traveling forward due to inertia and falling toward the Sun due to gravity. Describe the path of something that has forward motion (like your marble) but is also being pulled down by gravity.

8. Clean up. Return all materials to their original condition.

MATERIALS FOR INQUIRY 15.2

For you
1 pair of goggles

For your group
1 copy of Inquiry Master 15.2: Testing Balanced and Unbalanced Forces
1 plastic box (empty)
1 metal canning jar ring
1 marble
1 sheet of white paper

Inquiry 15.2
Testing Balanced and Unbalanced Forces

PROCEDURE

1. Place the white paper in the bottom of the plastic box. Put the metal ring on top of the paper with the lip up, as if you were putting the metal ring on a jar.

2. Trace an outline of the ring onto the paper. Remove the metal ring from the paper. Mark four points at equal distances around the circle. Number the marks 1 to 4 going clockwise, as shown in Figure 15.2.

Figure 15.2 *Mark the outline of the circle with 1, 2, 3, and 4 at quarter intervals.*

> **SAFETY TIP**
> Wear safety goggles at all times.

3. Place the metal ring on the circle, again with the lip up. Place the marble inside the metal ring. Without moving the metal ring, describe the motion of the marble. Record your observations in quadrant 15.2 in your notebook.

4. Use the ring to move the marble in circles. Keep the ring on the paper at all times. Record your observations. Discuss with your group how the ring creates a force (called an "unbalanced force") that influences the marble's motion.

5. Make a prediction about what will happen if you lift the ring (remove the unbalanced force).

6. Move the marble in circles again, then lift the ring. What happens? In quadrant 15.2 in your notebook, describe the motion of the marble without the unbalanced force of the ring. Try this several times. Record your observations in both words and pictures. Use your numbered markings to pinpoint the motion of the marble each time.

7. Answer these questions in your notebook:

A. Describe the motion of the marble when an unbalanced force (the metal ring) influences it.

B. Describe the motion of the marble when the unbalanced force is removed.

C. Suppose you lifted the ring when the clockwise orbiting marble was at the "1." Draw the path the marble would take.

D. Suppose you lifted the ring when the clockwise orbiting marble was at the "4." Draw the path the marble would take.

E. Like the marble, the planets move forward due to inertia and inward due to an unbalanced force. Together, these forces cause the planets' paths to curve. What is the unbalanced force that keeps the planets in orbit? What would happen to the planets without this unbalanced force?

8. Clean up. Return all materials to their original condition.

MATERIALS FOR INQUIRY 15.3

For you

1 pair of goggles

For your group

1 copy of Inquiry Master 15.3: Observing Planetary Motion
1 Planetary Motion Model™
4 plastic boxes or boxes of the same height
1 large resealable plastic bag containing the following:
    1 yellow balloon, filled with water
    1 metric ruler, 30 cm (12″)
    1 marble

Inquiry 15.3
Observing Planetary Motion

PROCEDURE

1. Check the setup of the Planetary Motion Model™. The lip of the hoop should be facing up to prevent the marble from falling off the latex sheet, as shown in Figure 15.3. Allow any extra sheeting to hang down under the hoop. Make sure the hoop rests on the edges of the boxes so they do not interfere with the marble once it is on the sheet.

2. You will use your ruler as a ramp to roll the marble onto the latex sheet. Before you do, make a prediction about the path the marble will take on the sheet. Discuss your predictions with your group.

3. Hold the ruler as shown in Figure 15.3 so that it faces the edge of the hoop. Roll the marble onto the flat sheet. Observe the marble. Repeat this several times. Discuss your observations with your group. Record your results in quadrant 15.3 in your notebook.

4. Place the balloon in the center of the sheet. Let go of the balloon. Discuss what the balloon does to the sheet. Then roll the marble onto the sheet toward the edge of the hoop. Watch the balloon and marble carefully. What do you observe about the motion of the marble? What do you observe about the behavior of the balloon? Discuss and record your observations with your group.

Figure 15.3 *The Planetary Motion Model™ should be set up as shown.
(A) Face the lip of the hoop up. (B) Hang the extra sheeting under the
hoop. (C) Place the hoop on the edge of each box.*

5. Now push down on the balloon as shown in Figure 15.4. Keep a constant pressure on the balloon.

Figure 15.4 *Press down continuously on the water-filled balloon.*

6. Predict how the marble will move now that the center of the sheet has more mass. Have one of your partners roll the marble onto the sheet as you keep pressure on the balloon. Discuss your observations. Record your observations in words and pictures in your notebook.

7. Test the motion of the marble several times and observe its motion carefully. Let everyone take a turn. How does the motion of the marble change as it nears the balloon?

8. Now wobble the balloon very slightly as the marble orbits it. What happens? Try to use a gentle wobble on the balloon to keep the marble in motion. Discuss your observations. Then let go of the balloon. Does the balloon wobble on its own as the marble orbits it?

9. Answer these questions in your notebook:

A. Describe how the marble moved when the mass in the center (the balloon) was not present.

B. Describe how the marble moved when the mass in the center was present.

C. As the distance between the balloon and marble decreased, what happened to the marble's speed?

D. Based on your observations, which planet do you think would have the fastest orbital speed? What evidence do you have to support your answer?

E. What force keeps the planets in their orbital paths around the Sun?

F. Read "Stars Wobble." Why does a star's "wobble" indicate that a planet is nearby?

10. Clean up. Return all materials to their original condition.

STARS WOBBLE

There are many stars like our Sun. Some of these other stars also may have planets that orbit them. Even though Earth-based astronomers may not have yet seen a planet orbiting another star, they know such orbiting planets exist. How do they know? Because when a planet orbits a star, it makes the star wobble. Astronomers can examine a star's wobble and figure out how big, how massive, and how far away from its star the planet is. At the start of the new millennium, nearly 60 planets had been discovered by using the "wobble" method.

It all begins with gravity. Because of gravity, the Sun pulls on the planets, but it also means that the planets pull on the Sun. (And moons and planets tug at each other.) An orbiting planet exerts a gravitational force that makes the star wobble in a tiny circular or oval path. The star's wobbly path mirrors in miniature the planet's orbit. It's like two twirling dancers tugging each other in circles.

Scientists use powerful space-based telescopes that orbit Earth to look for wobbling stars. Since they are outside of Earth's atmosphere, these telescopes can see the stars more clearly than telescopes on Earth's surface. Who knows? Someday scientists may use the wobble method to discover another solar system just like ours.

MATERIALS FOR INQUIRY 15.4

For you
  1 pair of goggles

For your group
  1 copy of Inquiry Master 15.4: Investigating the Effect of Planetary Mass on a Moon's Orbit
  1 plastic box or large resealable plastic bag containing the following:
    1 pre-assembled Moon Orbiter™
  25 large steel washers
    1 student timer

Inquiry 15.4
Investigating the Effect of Planetary Mass on a Moon's Orbit

PROCEDURE

1. Examine the Moon Orbiter™. Discuss with your group how you think the Moon Orbiter might work.

2. Move to an area in the classroom where no other groups are working. Check to see that all nylon knots are secured to the large white sphere.

SAFETY TIPS
Wear safety goggles at all times.

Do not swing the Moon Orbiter at other students. Make sure that other students are not nearby when you swing the white sphere.

Always swing the Moon Orbiter above your head.

3. Hold the narrow plastic tubing of the Moon Orbiter in your hand like a handle. Practice holding the Moon Orbiter over your head and moving your hand in circles to get the white sphere to orbit your hand. Use a steady and regular motion. When the sphere is in full orbit, the bottom of the tube should nearly touch the cylinder.

4. Increase the mass of the Moon Orbiter by adding five washers to the cylinder. Move your hand in circles over your head to get the white sphere to orbit your hand, as shown in Figure 15.5. Describe how fast the sphere has to move to stay in orbit around your hand with a mass of five washers pulling on it. (If possible, calculate its orbital period—the time it takes the sphere to orbit your hand. For

example, count the number of seconds it takes the sphere to orbit your hand 10 times. To get the orbital period, divide the number of seconds by 10.) Record your observations and data in quadrant 15.4 in your notebook.

5. Let everyone in your group try to swing the Moon Orbiter. Remember, when the sphere is in full orbit, the tube should nearly touch the cylinder.

6. Predict what will happen if you increase the mass of the Moon Orbiter's cylinder to 25 washers.

7. Fill the cylinder of the Moon Orbiter with 25 washers. Repeat Procedure Step 4 and discuss your observations. Let everyone in your group have a turn. Describe how fast the sphere has to move to stay in orbit around your hand with 25 washers pulling on it. (Try calculating the sphere's orbital period.) Record your observations.

8. Answer these questions in your notebook:

A. How does the mass of the cylinder affect how fast or slow the sphere orbits your hand?

B. Examine Table 15.1. Compare the mass of Jupiter with the mass of Earth. Which planet has more mass?

C. Examine Table 15.1. Compare Jupiter's moon Io with Earth's Moon. How are they alike? How are they different?

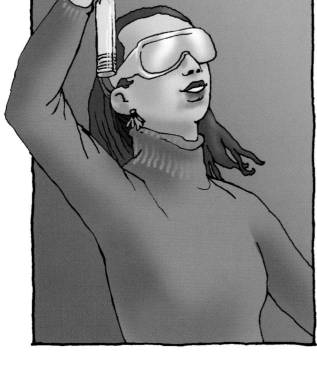

Figure 15.5 *Swing the white sphere in a circle above your head.*

Table 15.1 Planetary Mass Versus Moon's Orbital Period

Solar System Body	Approximate Mass (kg)	Diameter (km)	Distance From Planet (km)	Orbital Speed (km/sec)	Orbital Period (days)
Jupiter	$189,900 \times 10^{22}$	142,984			
Earth	597×10^{22}	12,756			
Io	9×10^{22}	3643	421,600	17	~ 2 days
Moon	7×10^{22}	3475	384,400	1	~ 27 days

D. Compare Io and the Moon. Which planetary satellite travels faster (has a greater orbital speed)? Given your results from the inquiry, why do you think this is?

E. Orbital period is the time it takes a revolving object to orbit a central object. Which planetary satellite has a shorter orbital period? What is the relationship between orbital speed and orbital period?

F. In Lesson 14, you learned the approximate mass of each planet. How do you think scientists determine the mass of the planets?

9. Clean up. Return all materials to their original condition.

REFLECTING ON WHAT YOU'VE DONE

1. Share your answers to the inquiry questions with the class.

2. Read "Heavy Thoughts." In your notebook, answer the questions at the end of the reading selection.

3. With your class, return to the Question H folder for Lesson 1. Is there anything you would now change or add? Discuss your ideas with the class.

4. Return to your list of ideas about gravity from Lesson 14. What new information about gravity do you want to add to your list?

5. Read the "Mission" reading selections on Saturn, Uranus, and Neptune. Add any information about these planets to your working copy of Student Sheet 10.1c: Planetary Chart (and onto Student Sheet 10.1b: Planetary Brochure Outline if your Anchor Activity planet assigned during Lesson 10 was Saturn, Uranus, or Neptune).

HEAVY THOUGHTS

Do you ever wonder why when you jump up, you always come back down? Or do you ever wonder why the Moon keeps circling around Earth rather than drifting off into space? Throughout history, people have wondered about these things. Now we know that a property of the universe called "gravity" is responsible.

If you jump up, Earth's gravity will pull you back down. Your gravity also pulls Earth toward you. The same thing happens between the Sun and the planets, and between all the planets and their moons. Gravity guides the movements of everything on Earth, and all the objects in the sky.

Newton's Apple

According to a well-known story, a 23-year-old English scientist named Isaac Newton was sitting under an apple tree one afternoon in 1666, when an apple hit him on the head. Newton began thinking about the force that pulled the apple from the tree.

Newton concluded that the force we know as gravity must be an invisible force, like the one you can feel when you place a magnet near a metal object (although gravity is

A famous story says that Isaac Newton began thinking about gravity on our planet and in our universe after an apple fell from a tree and hit him on the head.

not as strong as electromagnetic forces). He also determined that gravity affects apples falling from trees and holds planets and moons in their orbits.

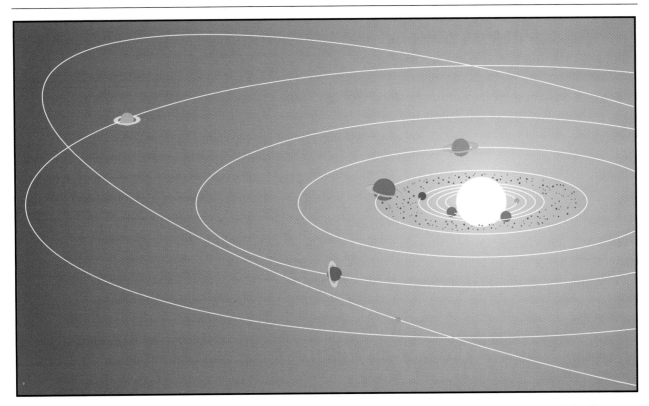

Gravity keeps the nine planets and their moons, and thousands of asteroids and comets, in orbit around the Sun.

Newton's Law of Inertia

Newton wrote two famous laws about gravity: the Law of Inertia and the Law of Universal Gravitation. The Law of Inertia says that a body in motion tends to travel in a straight line unless it is disturbed by an unbalanced force. The Law of Inertia explains why you don't keep rising when you jump up in the air. The unbalanced force of gravity disturbs your motion and pulls you back down.

The Law of Inertia governs the motion of the planets and moons. If they weren't affected by gravity, they would travel in straight lines and leave the solar system. The Sun's gravity holds all the planets in orbit around it, and each planet's gravity captures and holds its moon(s) in orbit.

What is an unbalanced force?

If two individual forces are of equal magnitude (size) and opposite direction, then the forces are balanced. Think of the marble you held in your hand during Inquiry 15.1. One force—the Earth's gravitational pull—exerts a downward force on the marble. The other force—your hand—pulls upward on the marble. The forces acting on the marble are balanced; as a result, the marble's motion does not slow down or speed up. But if the two forces are not balanced, the marble will change its speed or direction. If you let go of the marble, the unbalanced force of gravity disturbs the marble's motion and the marble falls into the box. Unbalanced forces cause objects to accelerate (change their speed or direction).

Newton's Law of Universal Gravitation

From his experimental results, Newton formulated the Law of Universal Gravitation, which states that any two objects in the universe have gravity and will attract each other. Just how much those objects attract each other depends on two things—the mass of each object, and the distance between the objects.

The more mass a star—like our Sun—has, and the closer a planet is to that star, the greater the star's ability to hold the planet in its orbit (Mercury is a perfect example). Planets with a lot of mass can probably hold more moons in their orbit (Jupiter is a good example).

Mutual Attraction

An object with a large amount of mass can exert a huge gravitational pull even on objects that are quite distant and massive. The Sun's gravitational pull is so enormous that it easily hangs onto Jupiter, which weighs two-and-a-half times as much as all the other planets combined. The Sun also exerts a gravitational hold over Pluto. But more amazingly, tiny Pluto exerts a gravitational pull on the Sun, even though they are more than 4.5 billion kilometers apart!

Like the end of a lasso that circles around the head of a cowboy, an orbiting planet is "tied" to the Sun by gravity. However, the farther a planet is from the Sun, the more slowly it travels in its orbit. The closer a planet is to the Sun, the faster it travels in its orbit. Mercury, the planet closest to the Sun, travels at about 48 km/s (kilometers per second). But Pluto is quite a different story. Look at Table 15.2: Orbital Velocity of Planets and compare the orbital velocity of the planets. Do you notice patterns in the data? If so, what are they?

The attraction between two objects decreases as the distance between them increases. The Sun's pull on distant Pluto is much less than its pull on nearby Mercury. As a result, Pluto orbits the Sun at a much slower speed.

Table 15.2 Orbital Velocity of Planets

Planet	Orbital Velocity (km/s)	Approximate Distance from Sun (km)
Mercury	48	57,900,000
Venus	35	108,200,000
Earth	29	149,600,000
Mars	24	228,000,000
Jupiter	13	778,400,000
Saturn	9	1,426,700,000
Uranus	6	2,866,900,000
Neptune	5	4,486,100,000
Pluto	4	5,890,000,000

Newton and other scientists made important discoveries that describe how gravity works. These discoveries demonstrate that objects on Earth operate under the same principles as objects in space. Newton's work will influence planetary science for centuries. ☐

QUESTIONS

1. What force keeps the planets in their orbits around the Sun?
2. What would happen to the planets if there were no gravitational influences from the Sun?
3. Based on your classroom observations and the data in Table 15.2, how does an orbiting object's velocity depend on its distance from the Sun?
4. Given what you have learned in your investigations and in your reading, which planet should be able to hold the greatest number of moons in its planetary orbit?

The great mass of Jupiter helps it hold its many moons in orbit around the giant planet.

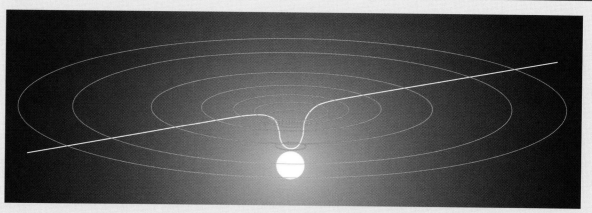

Space curves around matter, just like the surface of a rubber sheet curves when a heavy balloon rests on it.

How Matter Affects Space

Is gravity a force, or is it something else? About 250 years after Newton, another genius started thinking about gravity. His name was Albert Einstein. Einstein's theories changed the way we think about the universe.

Einstein came to believe that gravity isn't really a force, but simply the way that matter affects space. According to Einstein, wherever there's a chunk of matter—an apple, a person, a planet, or a star—space must curve around it. The bigger the matter, the more that space must curve. And when space curves, anything traveling through that space must follow those curves.

According to Einstein, the planets are caught in the curved space around the Sun. Our Moon is caught in the curved space around Earth. If you were far enough away from the gravitational force of Earth or the Sun, small objects would become caught in the curved space around you!

Modeling Curved Space

Einstein believed that the more massive the object, the more space curved around it. Think back to your lab in which you placed a water-filled balloon in the center of a rubber sheet. The rubber sheet curved around the balloon. A marble placed on the sheet rolled toward the balloon, but not in a straight line. Instead, the marble followed the curves of the sheet and "orbited" the water-filled balloon in the center. The closer the marble got to the balloon in the center, the faster the marble rolled. Something similar happens with stars such as our Sun. Space curves around the star's mass and keeps other objects, such as planets, "rolling" around them.

Mission: **Saturn, Uranus, and Neptune**

What a mission! The twin spacecraft, *Voyagers 1* and *2*, left Earth in the summer of 1977. Three years later, after its visit to Jupiter, *Voyager 1* flew past Saturn and sped north toward the outer edge of the solar system, as planned. *Voyager 2* was supposed to take the same course. But the spacecraft was performing so well, scientists and engineers on Earth found it not only possible, but irresistible, to send it on to Uranus and Neptune for a closer look. An alignment of the outer planets like this would not occur again until the year 2157.

Voyager 2 would be the first spacecraft to offer close-up views of the outer solar system. Saturn's huge gravitational field would hurl *Voyager 2* toward Uranus. A similar boost from Uranus would send *Voyager 2* to Neptune. This maneuver, called gravity assist, took decades off *Voyager's* flying time. (Unfortunately, the grand tour of the solar system conducted by *Voyager* couldn't include Pluto because Pluto's orbit took it far from the spacecraft's path.)

The remarkable journey of *Voyager 2* yielded many riches.

(continued)

NATIONAL AERONAUTICS AND SPACE ADMINISTRATION/JET PROPULSION LABORATORY

Voyager *spacecraft*

Saturn

Voyager 2 gave us new insights into Saturn's rings. The rings are like a necklace with 10,000 strands, and they proved to be more beautiful and strange than once thought.

Evidence indicates that Saturn's rings formed from large moons that were shattered by impacts from comets and meteoroids. The resulting ice and rock fragments—some as small as a speck of sand and others as large as houses—gathered in a broad plane around the planet. The rings themselves are very thin, but together they are 171,000 kilometers in width!

(continued)

Mosaic of Saturn's rings created from pictures taken on August 28, 1981, by Voyager 2.

NATIONAL AERONAUTICS AND SPACE ADMINISTRATION/JET PROPULSION LABORATORY

The irregular shapes of Saturn's eight smallest moons indicate that they, too, are fragments of larger bodies. Two of these small moons—Prometheus and Pandora—are located in one of Saturn's many rings.

Voyager 2 showed a kind of war going on at Saturn—a gravitational tug of war between the planet, its many moons and moonlets, and the ring fragments. This struggle has caused variations in the thickness of the rings. Some particles are even rising above the ring band as if they are trying to escape.

(continued)

NASA's Voyager 1 *took this photograph of Saturn on November 3, 1980, when the spacecraft was 13 million kilometers from the planet. Two bright cloud patterns are visible in the mid-northern hemisphere and several dark spoke-like features can be seen in the rings left of the planet. The moons Tethys and Dione appear as dots to the south and southeast of Saturn.*

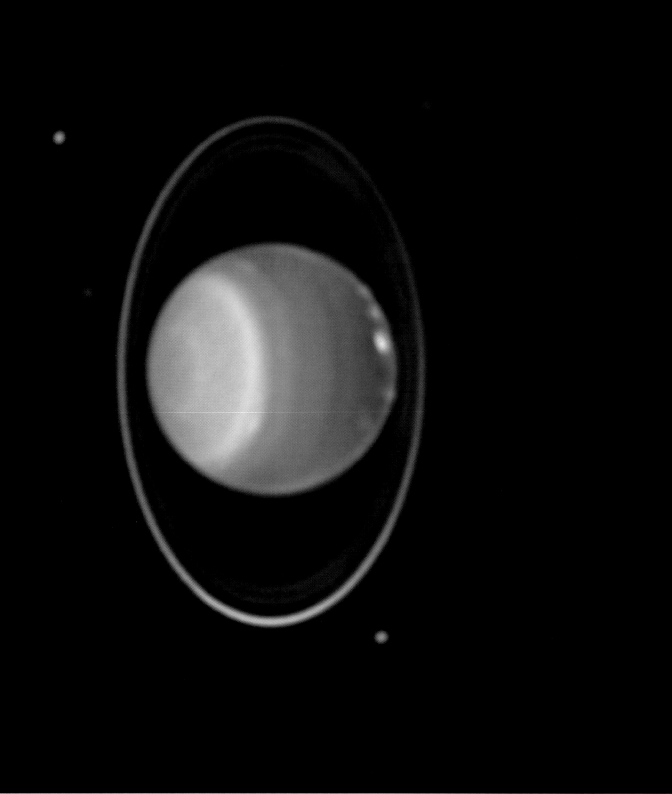

The rings of Uranus. Notice that Uranus is tilted 98 degrees on its axis.

SPACE TELESCOPE SCIENCE INSTITUTE, KENNETH SEIDELMANN, U.S. NAVAL OBSERVATORY, AND NATIONAL AERONAUTICS AND SPACE ADMINISTRATION

This view of Uranus was acquired by Voyager 2 in January 1986. The greenish color of its atmosphere is due to methane and smog. Methane absorbs red light and reflects blue/green light.

Uranus

After its tug from Saturn's gravitational field, *Voyager 2* arrived at Uranus in 1986 where it discovered 10 new moons. With the moons already discovered by astronomers on Earth, the total number of moons was brought to 20. Scientists believed that there may be several more tiny satellites within the rings, and they were right!

The *Voyager* cameras detected a few additional rings around Uranus. They also showed that belts of fine dust surround the planet's nine major rings.

According to data, Uranian rings probably formed after Uranus. Particles that make up the rings may be remnants of a moon that was broken apart by a collision.

Voyager 2 made another major discovery at Uranus. It turns out that the planet has a magnetic field as strong as Earth's. The cause of this field isn't clear, but it's shaped like a long corkscrew. And, according to *Voyager's* measurements, it reaches 10 million kilometers behind the planet!

(continued)

Neptune is true blue.

Neptune

Until the *Voyager* encounter with Neptune in August 1989, scientists believed that the planet had arcs, or partial rings. But *Voyager* showed that Neptune has complete rings with bright clumps. *Voyager* also discovered six new moons, bringing Neptune's total to eight.

Voyager flew within 5000 kilometers of Neptune's long, bright clouds, which resemble

(continued)

Voyager 2 observed bright cirrus-like cloud cover in the region around the Great Dark Spot. The rapid changes in the clouds over 18 hours prove that Neptune's weather is perhaps as dynamic as Earth's. Neptune's dark spot is no longer visible. Could this "storm" finally have ended?

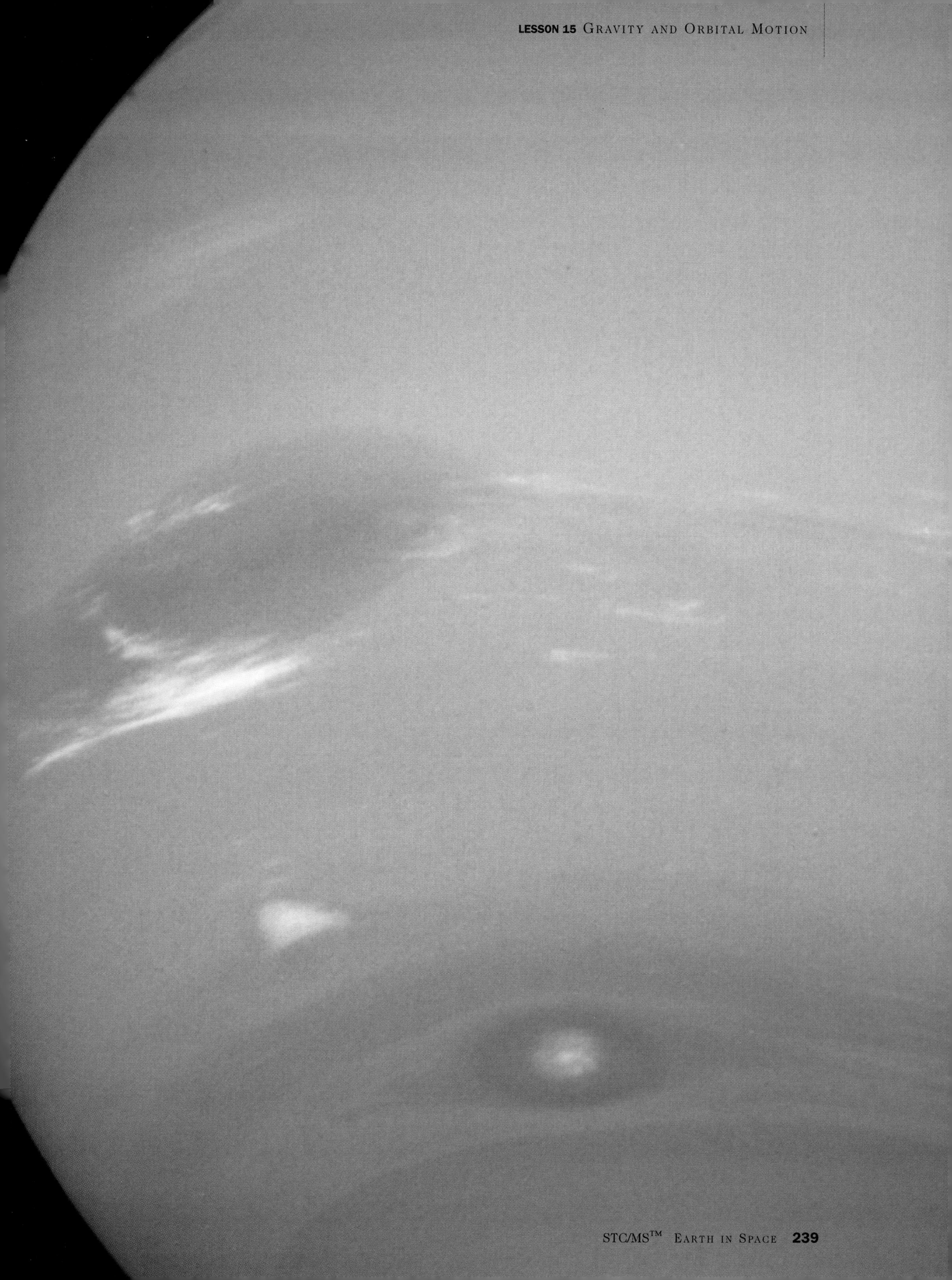

A partial view of Triton, Neptune's largest moon.

cirrus clouds on Earth. Instruments aboard *Voyager* measured winds up to 2000 kilometers an hour—the strongest winds on any planet.

Triton, Neptune's largest moon, is one of the most fascinating satellites in the solar system. Images from *Voyager 2* revealed volcanoes spewing invisible nitrogen gas and dust particles several kilometers into the atmosphere!

In 1989, *Voyager 2* left Neptune and headed south onto a course that will take it, like *Voyager 1,* to the edge of our solar system and beyond. The tireless spacecraft—fueled by the radioactive decay of plutonium—is expected to continue operating for another 25 years. □

PLANETARY FACTS: Saturn

Saturn: Quick Facts

Diameter	120,536 km	**Average temperature**	−185 °C
Average distance from the Sun	1.4 billion km	**Length of sidereal day**	10.66 hours
Mass	$56,850 \times 10^{22}$ kg	**Length of year**	29.46 Earth years
Surface gravity (Earth = 1)	0.92	**Number of observed moons**	30*

Relative size

Saturn atmosphere

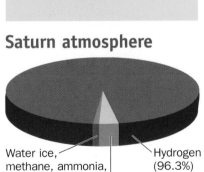

Water ice, methane, ammonia, and other compounds (traces)

Helium (3.3%)

Hydrogen (96.3%)

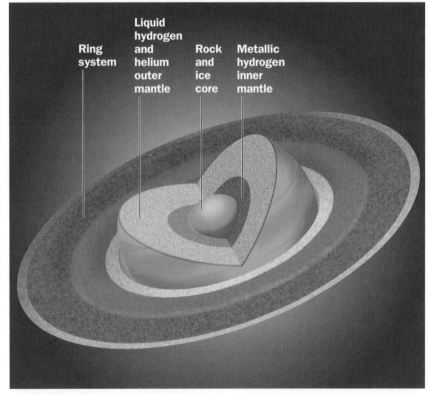

Ring system

Liquid hydrogen and helium outer mantle

Rock and ice core

Metallic hydrogen inner mantle

Did You Know?

- If there were an ocean big enough to plop Saturn into, the planet would float—just like an iceberg does on planet Earth! That's because of Saturn's low density. Saturn is the only planet that is lighter than the same volume of water.
- Saturn's winds reach 1800 km/hour. (The strongest tornadoes on Earth have wind speeds of only 350 km /hour.)

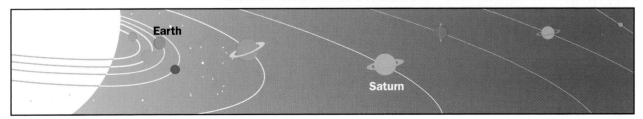

Earth

Saturn

*As of 2002

PLANETARY FACTS: Uranus

Uranus: Quick Facts

Diameter	51,118 km	**Average temperature**	−200 °C
Average distance from the Sun	2.9 billion km	**Length of sidereal day**	17.24 hours
Mass	8683×10^{22} kg	**Length of year**	84.01 Earth years
Surface gravity (Earth = 1)	0.89	**Number of observed moons**	20*

Relative size

Uranus atmosphere

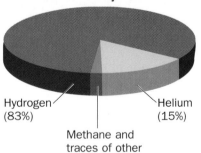

Hydrogen (83%)

Helium (15%)

Methane and traces of other compounds (2%)

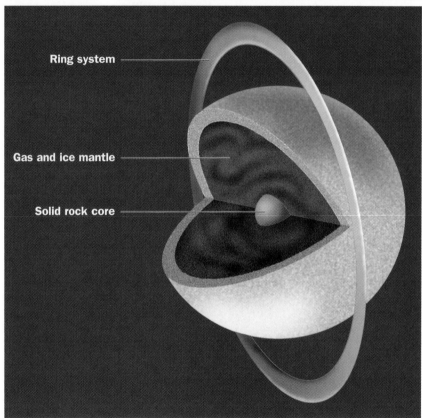

Ring system

Gas and ice mantle

Solid rock core

Did You Know?

- The *poles* of Uranus are in the same position as the *equators* on other planets. That's because Uranus rotates on its side.
- It takes nearly 2½ hours for light from the Sun to reach Uranus. (It only takes about eight minutes for the Sun's light to reach Earth!)

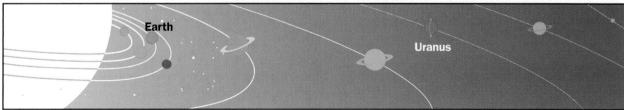

Earth

Uranus

*As of 2002

PLANETARY FACTS: Neptune

Neptune: Quick Facts

Diameter	49,528 km	**Average temperature**	–225 °C
Average distance from the Sun	4.5 billion km	**Length of sidereal day**	16.11 hours
Mass	$10,240 \times 10^{22}$ kg	**Length of year**	164 Earth years
Surface gravity (Earth = 1)	1.12	**Number of observed moons**	8*

Relative size

Neptune atmosphere

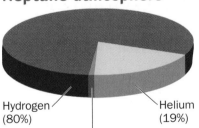

Hydrogen (80%)

Helium (19%)

Methane and traces of other compounds (0.5%)

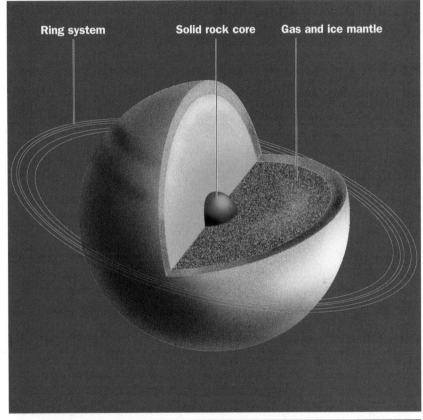

Ring system   Solid rock core   Gas and ice mantle

Did You Know?

- Neptune was named after the god of the sea, probably because of its blue color.
- Neptune gives off more heat than it receives from the Sun. This means it probably has its own heat source.

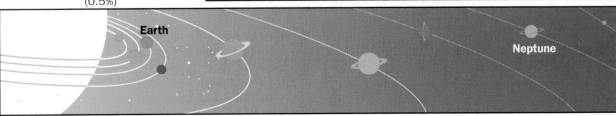

Earth

Neptune

*As of 2002

16
Gravity and Tides

DAN AND MARCI RIVERA, © 2000

Ocean tides along the shore rise and fall throughout the day under the influence of the Moon and Sun's gravitational pull on Earth. The height of an ocean tide depends on its location on Earth. Can you see evidence of the Sun's and Moon's tidal effects on Earth's ocean in this photograph?

INTRODUCTION

Have you ever built a sandcastle on an ocean beach only to find it washed away a few hours later? Every 6 to 12 hours or so in most places along the shore, the water rises and falls in a regular cycle called "tides." What causes this phenomenon? In Lessons 14 and 15, you investigated the effects of gravity on weight and orbital motion. In this lesson, which concludes Part 2 of the module, you will apply what you know about gravity to the Sun-Earth-Moon system and to the occurrence of tides on Earth. To begin, you will read about the effect of tides on organisms along the shore. You will brainstorm what you know about ocean tides. Consider how the relative position of the Sun, Earth, and Moon causes ocean tides on Earth. How do the times of high and low tide along the Atlantic Ocean change each day and throughout the month? Is there any relationship between moonrise and

OBJECTIVES FOR THIS LESSON

Graph and analyze patterns in the times and heights of tides, moonrise and moonset times, and phases of the Moon along Virginia Beach.

Draw conclusions about the cause and occurrence of tides.

Consider whether tidal processes exist on other planets and moons.

Summarize and organize information about Pluto and compare Pluto to other planets.

moonset times and tides? Does the phase of the Moon affect tides? In this lesson, you will discover answers to these questions.

Getting Started

1. Read "Marching to the Beat of Tides." Discuss with your class the following question and give one example of an organism that is affected by tidal rhythms. Why does the story say that tides are like clocks?

2. Record in your science notebook what you already know about ocean tides.

3. Share your ideas within your group or with the class.

4. Examine the water-filled balloon that your teacher is holding. Observe its shape. A volunteer will trace the shadow of the balloon onto the board.

5. Watch as your teacher removes the hand that supported the balloon, and holds the balloon by its neck. Again, a volunteer will trace the shape of the balloon on the board. How did the balloon's shape change under the influence of the "pull" of your teacher's hand and Earth's gravity? How does the Moon "pull" on Earth to create tides? Discuss your observations.

MATERIALS FOR LESSON 16

For you
- 1 copy of Student Sheet 16: Bode's Law
- 1 sheet of graph paper
- 1 working copy of Student Sheet 10.1c: Planetary Chart

For your group
- 1 copy of Inquiry Master 16.1a: Earth's Tidal Bulge (copied onto blue cardstock)
- 1 Sun-Earth-Moon Board™
- 1 set of 8 rods, labeled #1–#8
- 1 rod labeled E
- 1 globe of Earth
- 1 Mini Maglite®
- 2 AA batteries
- 1 white sphere, 3.5 cm
- 1 pair of scissors

Inquiry 16.1
Analyzing Tidal Data

PROCEDURE

1. Examine the data in Table 16.1: Tides for Virginia Beach: April 3–30, 2001. With your teacher, discuss how to read the table by answering questions such as the following:

At what time did the high tides occur on April 5, 2001?

How high were the high tides on April 5?

At what time did the Moon rise on April 9, 2001?

At what time did the second high tide occur on April 9, 2001?

How much of the Moon was visible on April 8, 2001? Given this percentage, what phase was the Moon in on April 8?

How much of the Moon was visible on April 16, 2001? Given this percentage, what phase was the Moon in on April 16?

Where did the tides in Table 16.1 occur?

Table 16.1 Tides for Virginia Beach: April 3–30, 2001

Day	High/Low	Tide Time	Height Feet	Moon	Time	% MoonVisible
Tu 3	High	4:11 AM	3.7	Set	4:07 AM	67
3	Low	10:39 AM	0.3	Rise	2:29 PM	
3	High	4:42 PM	3.3			
3	Low	10:49 PM	0.0			
W 4	High	5:18 AM	3.9	Set	4:52 AM	77
4	Low	11:38 AM	0.0	Rise	3:40 PM	
4	High	5:45 PM	3.6			
4	Low	11:54 PM	-0.3			
Th 5	High	6:17 AM	4.0	Set	5:32 AM	86
5	Low	12:31 PM	-0.1	Rise	4:51 PM	
5	High	6:42 PM	3.9			
F 6	Low	12:53 AM	-0.4	Set	6:08 AM	93
6	High	7:11 AM	4.0	Rise	6:01 PM	
6	Low	1:20 PM	-0.4			
6	High	7:34 PM	4.1			

Table 16.1 Tides for Virginia Beach: April 3–30, 2001 (continued)

Day	High/Low	Tide Time	Height Feet	Moon	Time	% MoonVisible
Sa 7	Low	1:47 AM	-0.5	Set	6:42 AM	98
7	High	8:01 AM	4.0	Rise	7:11 PM	
7	Low	2:07 PM	-0.4			
7	High	8:23 PM	4.3			
Su 8	Low	2:38 AM	-0.7	Set	7:15 AM	99
8	High	8:49 AM	4.0	Rise	8:19 PM	
8	Low	2:51 PM	-0.5			
8	High	9:09 PM	4.4			
M 9	Low	3:27 AM	-0.5	Set	7:48 AM	99
9	High	9:34 AM	3.9	Rise	9:26 PM	
9	Low	3:34 PM	-0.4			
9	High	9:55 PM	4.3			
Tu 10	Low	4:14 AM	-0.4	Set	8:23 AM	95
10	High	10:18 AM	3.7	Rise	10:31 PM	
10	Low	4:17 PM	-0.3			
10	High	10:39 PM	4.1			
W 11	Low	5:01 AM	-0.1	Set	9:01 AM	90
11	High	11:02 AM	3.5	Rise	11:34 PM	
11	Low	5:00 PM	0.0			
11	High	11:24 PM	4.0			
Th 12	Low	5:48 AM	0.1	Set	9:42 AM	83
12	High	11:47 AM	3.3			
12	Low	5:44 PM	0.1			

Table 16.1 Tides for Virginia Beach: April 3–30, 2001 (continued)

Day	High/Low	Tide Time	Height Feet	Moon	Time	% MoonVisible
F 13	High	12:10 AM	3.7	Rise	12:33 AM	74
13	Low	6:37 AM	0.4	Set	10:27 AM	
13	High	12:34 PM	3.0			
13	Low	6:32 PM	0.4			
Sa 14	High	1:00 AM	3.5	Rise	1:27 AM	65
14	Low	7:29 AM	0.5	Set	11:16 AM	
14	High	1:25 PM	2.9			
14	Low	7:25 PM	0.5			
Su 15	High	1:55 AM	3.3	Rise	2:15 AM	56
15	Low	8:24 AM	0.8	Set	12:09 PM	
15	High	2:22 PM	2.9			
15	Low	8:24 PM	0.7			
M 16	High	2:54 AM	3.2	Rise	2:58 AM	46
16	Low	9:21 AM	0.8	Set	1:04 PM	
16	High	3:22 PM	2.9			
16	Low	9:26 PM	0.8			
Tu 17	High	3:54 AM	3.2	Rise	3:37 AM	37
17	Low	10:16 AM	0.8	Set	2:00 PM	
17	High	4:20 PM	3.0			
17	Low	10:26 PM	0.7			
W 18	High	4:49 AM	3.2	Rise	4:11 AM	28
18	Low	11:06 AM	0.7	Set	2:57 PM	
18	High	5:13 PM	3.2			
18	Low	11:21 PM	0.7			

Table 16.1 Tides for Virginia Beach: April 3–30, 2001 (continued)

Day	High/Low	Tide Time	Height Feet	Moon	Time	% MoonVisible
Th 19	High	5:38 AM	3.3	Rise	4:43 AM	20
19	Low	11:50 AM	0.5	Set	3:55 PM	
19	High	6:00 PM	3.5			
F 20	Low	12:10 AM	0.4	Rise	5:12 AM	13
20	High	6:23 AM	3.5	Set	4:53 PM	
20	Low	12:30 PM	0.4			
20	High	6:43 PM	3.6			
Sa 21	Low	12:56 AM	0.3	Rise	5:40 AM	7
21	High	7:05 AM	3.6	Set	5:52 PM	
21	Low	1:09 PM	0.3			
21	High	7:23 PM	3.9			
Su 22	Low	1:39 AM	0.1	Rise	6:08 AM	2
22	High	7:45 AM	3.6	Set	6:53 PM	
22	Low	1:46 PM	0.3			
22	High	8:01 PM	4.0			
M 23	Low	2:20 AM	0.1	Rise	6:38 AM	0
23	High	8:24 AM	3.7	Set	7:55 PM	
23	Low	2:22 PM	0.1			
23	High	8:40 PM	4.1			
Tu 24	Low	3:01 AM	0.0	Rise	7:09 AM	0
24	High	9:04 AM	3.7	Set	8:59 PM	
24	Low	3:00 PM	0.1			
24	High	9:19 PM	4.3			

Table 16.1 Tides for Virginia Beach: April 3–30, 2001 (continued)

Day	High/Low	Tide Time	Height Feet	Moon	Time	% MoonVisible
W 25	Low	3:44 AM	0.0	Rise	7:45 AM	2
25	High	9:45 AM	3.6	Set	10:05 PM	
25	Low	3:40 PM	0.1			
25	High	10:01 PM	4.3			
Th 26	Low	4:28 AM	0.0	Rise	8:26 AM	6
26	High	10:29 AM	3.5	Set	11:10 PM	
26	Low	4:23 PM	0.1			
26	High	10:47 PM	4.1			
F 27	Low	5:16 AM	0.1	Rise	9:14 AM	12
27	High	11:16 AM	3.5			
27	Low	5:11 PM	0.1			
27	High	11:37 PM	4.1			
Sa 28	Low	6:09 AM	0.3	Set	12:14 AM	20
28	High	12:09 PM	3.3	Rise	10:10 AM	
28	Low	6:06 PM	0.3			
Su 29	High	12:34 AM	3.9	Set	1:13 AM	30
29	Low	7:07 AM	0.3	Rise	11:11 AM	
29	High	1:09 PM	3.2			
29	Low	7:09 PM	0.3			
M 30	High	1:37 AM	3.7	Set	2:05 AM	41
30	Low	8:10 AM	0.3	Rise	12:18 PM	
30	High	2:15 PM	3.2			
30	Low	8:19 PM	0.3			

Source: www.saltwatertides.com

NOTE Some of the information in this table is incomplete.

2. Use Table 16.1 and work with your group to analyze the patterns that exist in the rise and fall of tides, then answer the following questions in your notebook:

A. Examine the height of tides each day. How does the height change over 24 hours?

B. A high tide occurs when the tide reaches its maximum height on each rise. How many high tides normally occur along Virginia Beach in 24 hours?

C. A low tide occurs when the tide reaches its minimum height on each fall. How many low tides normally occur along Virginia Beach in 24 hours?

D. Why do you think this pattern in high and low tides exists?

E. Compare the times that high and low tides occur each day over a two-week period. What do you observe? Explain why you think this happens.

F. Examine the data showing moonrise and moonset times. Compare these times to the times of high and low tides. What patterns do you observe? What explanation can you give for these patterns?

G. Examine the data showing phases. Compare the phases of the Moon to the times of high and low tides. During what phase(s) do the lowest high tides occur? During what phases do highest high tides occur? What explanation can you give for these patterns?

3. Use your graph paper to show the relationship between two sets of data examined during this inquiry. Work with your teacher to decide what to graph. Graphs might include one or more of the following:

• times and heights of tides for each day over 4 days
• times and heights of tides and times of moonrise and moonset for each day over 4 days
• times and heights of tides and phases of the Moon over 1 month

4. When you have completed your graph, cut out the cardboard pattern of the tidal bulge from Inquiry Master 16.1a. Place the tidal bulge pattern around the 12-cm Earth globe on your Sun-Earth-Moon (SEM) Board to model how Earth's high and low tides occur throughout the day and month (see Figure 16.1 for one setup). For example, put the Moon on rod #1. Face the

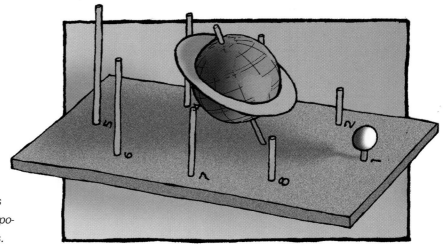

Figure 16.1 *One method for modeling the patterns in Earth's ocean tides. Notice how the locations of high tides Earth fall along the line that connects Earth and the Moon. This means that a high tide faces the Moon (and is opposite the Moon) as Earth rotates on its axis.*

"high tide" bulge in the cardboard toward rod #1. Slowly rotate Earth one complete turn on its axis, but keep the "high tide" bulge facing the Moon. This represents one day on Earth. Watch how in 24 hours, each body of water experiences a high tide as Earth rotates on its axis. Now move the Moon to rod #2. Face the "high tide" bulge to rod #2 and repeat this process.

REFLECTING ON WHAT YOU'VE DONE

1. Share your findings with the class. Use your graphs as needed.

2. Read "Can Water Fall Up?" In your science notebook, answer the questions that follow the reading selection. Be prepared to share your notebook entries with the class.

3. What new information about tides do you want to add to your brainstorming list from "Getting Started" Step 2? Discuss that information with the class.

4. With your class, return to the Question I folder for Lesson 1. Is there anything you would now change or add? Discuss your ideas with the class.

5. Read the "Mission" reading selection on Pluto. Add any information about Pluto to your working copy of Student Sheet 10.1c: Planetary Chart (and onto Student Sheet 10.1b: Planetary Brochure Outline if your Anchor Activity planet assigned during Lesson 10 was Pluto).

Marching to the Beat of Tides

We live on a round, rotating planet. Every day, as Earth turns on its axis, we experience the natural cycle of day and night. By day, most humans are busy. During the dark hours of night, we rest. Have you ever wondered why we follow this pattern? Why do we wake up in the morning, even without an alarm clock ringing in our ears?

All living things have internal systems that function like clocks. These timekeepers are called "biological clocks." In humans, these biological clocks keep us in sync with our environment. They wake us up in the morning and let us know when it is time to sleep. We follow a daily rhythm. But some marine animals follow a different rhythm. Their activities correspond to the rise and fall of ocean tides.

Tidal Rhythms

A fiddler crab dashes about on the beach, finding food and fighting other crabs. It is low tide, and the crab has a limited amount of time to do its business. Once the water starts to rise, the crab returns to its burrow. A fiddler crab's activities do not coincide with day and night, but are linked to the tides. At low tide, the crab is active. When high tide comes about six hours later, the crab rests. This pattern repeats throughout both day and night.

In an ocean environment, tides are like clocks. They provide a steady beat that some animals use to regulate their behavior. Animals that live near the beach in the intertidal zone—the area between the high- and low-water marks—often follow a tidal rhythm.

COURTESY OF CAROLINA BIOLOGICAL SUPPLY COMPANY

A male fiddler crab

The fiddler crab is not the only animal you might see at low tide. Shorebirds, such as sandpipers and plovers, scurry along the beach feeding at low tide. You might also see a plough snail using its large foot to move up and down the beach. It is searching for stranded jellyfish and other prey. As the tide comes in, the snail burrows into the sand.

Some animals are active during high tide. Oysters and scallops, for example, open their shells to feed during high tide. They close their shells during low tide. Rock barnacles are creatures that permanently attach to rocks and other objects along the coast. During high tide, their feathery feet emerge from their shells to screen the water for plankton and other food. Barnacles close their shells at low tide. Razor clams live between the tide lines in a vertical position, with part of their shells sticking out of the sand. During high tide, these clams open their shells to gather food. At low tide, their shells close.

Rock barnacles

The Beat Goes On

What happens when fiddler crabs are taken from their natural home and put in a scientist's lab, where there are no tides to regulate their activities?

Surprisingly, even when the crabs are away from the sea, they still become active at the same times as low tides. This behavior occurs in other animals, too. For example, some kinds of snails will remain inactive until it's time for low tide, even when they are in a tank or aquarium. Then they start moving about. Oysters, too, continue to open and close their shells with the tides, even when they are in a closed tank that has no tidal activity. For these marine animals, their biological clocks are still keeping time to the rhythm of the sea. ☐

A fresh water mussel opens its shell to feed as the tide comes in.

Can Water Fall Up?

On a hot summer day, you might pick a spot on the beach only to find that hours later you have to find a new spot farther from the water. The tide has come in. What does this mean? The Moon's gravity pulls on Earth in a way that we can easily see—the tides.

Tides

The gravitational pull of the Moon causes tides, or the periodic rise and fall of the ocean sea level and other waters on Earth. Every 12 hours or so, the ocean water swells to its highest point, called "high tide." When the water

(continued)

IMAGES OF NEW BRUNSWICK, IMAGES DU NOUVEAU-BRUNSWICK
PHOTOGRAPHER: ROBERT D. H. WARREN

High tide at the Hopewell Rocks in New Brunswick, Canada

IMAGES OF NEW BRUNSWICK, IMAGES DU NOUVEAU-BRUNSWICK
PHOTOGRAPHER: ROBERT D. H. WARREN

Low tide at the Hopewell Rocks in New Brunswick, Canada

sinks to its lowest level, it is called "low tide."

The Sun, the Moon, and all of the planets in the solar system tug on the waters and land of Earth, but only the Moon and Sun have significant effects. Because the Moon is so close to Earth, it exerts twice the tidal effect on Earth that the Sun does, even though the Sun is much larger.

Tides on Opposite Sides of Earth

The water on the side of Earth that faces the Moon is more strongly attracted by the gravitational force of the Moon than the water on the opposite side of Earth. However, both sides of Earth experience high tide at the same time.

Why? Look at the illustration showing Earth and the Moon. Imagine a line that connects their two centers. High tides will occur along this line. Low tides occur away from (and perpendicular to) this line. This means that water tends to get deeper on the side of Earth nearest the Moon. On the opposite side of Earth, away from the Moon, the solid Earth is pulled away from the water. This gives Earth a football-like shape. This pulling of the solid Earth causes the water to be left behind, and a high tide occurs on the opposite side, too. Low tides occur on the sides of Earth that are not in line with the Moon.

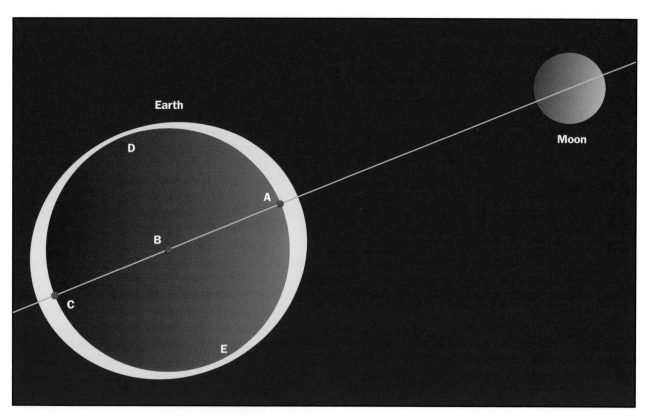

The ocean water rises along the line joining the center of the elongated Earth and the center of the Moon. High tides occur at points (A) and (C). Low tides occur at points (D) and (E).

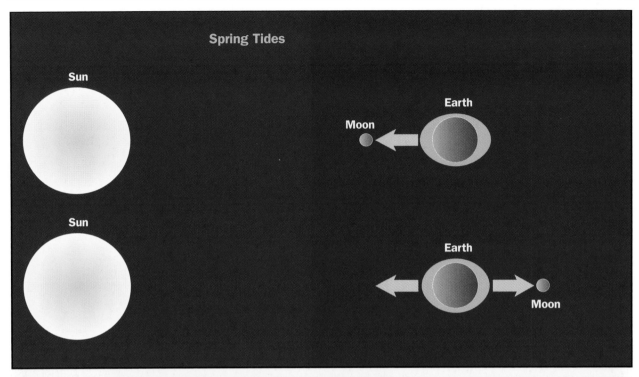

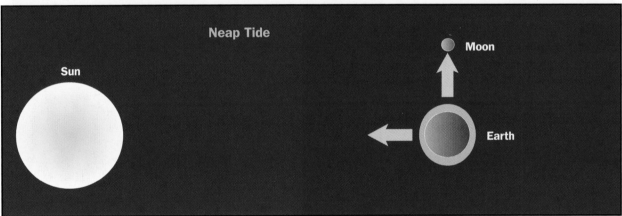

The relative position of the Sun, Moon, and Earth affect the formation of spring and neap tides.

Spring and Neap Tides

When the Moon is overhead, a high tide can occur. But tides are particularly high when the Sun, Moon, and Earth are in line. From your study of lunar phases, you know that this alignment occurs when the Moon is in its full moon and new moon phases. These high tides are called "spring tides," even though they happen year-round and have nothing to do with the seasons.

When the Moon is in its first and last quarters, the Sun and the Moon are at right angles to one another. During this time, the gravitational force of the Sun partially offsets the gravitational force of the Moon. This causes lower-than-normal high tides, called neap tides. There are two spring tides and two neap tides for each revolution of the Moon around Earth.

(continued)

Tides on the Moon

While the Moon produces tides on Earth, Earth produces tidal effects on the Moon. Although the Moon doesn't have oceans, there are signs of Earth's tidal effects on the Moon. For example, the Moon rotates on its axis one time in 27.3 days. It also takes 27.3 days for the Moon to orbit Earth. Earth's tidal forces probably slowed the Moon down until it reached its current state. With a synchronous (same) rotation and revolution, the same side of the Moon—the "near side"—always faces Earth; while the side that faces away from Earth—the "far side"—is always turned away from our view (see the photos). Other signs that tidal forces are at work on the Moon are in the Moon's shape (it is elongated, like the balloon) and in how the Moon leans toward Earth.

Another tidal effect on the Moon occurs when the Moon lines up with the Sun and Earth. During this alignment, the Moon is wracked with "moonquakes" as the bigger bodies literally fracture the Moon and pull it out of shape.

The Moon's near side

Jupiter's Moon, Io

One of the most dramatic examples of tidal forces is the effect that Jupiter has on Io, one of its moons. Io has many active volcanoes. It has more volcanoes than any of the larger planets. This is because of Jupiter's gravitational effect on Io. Io is about the same distance from Jupiter as our Moon is from Earth, but Jupiter is 300 times more massive than Earth. Io's tremendous tides are a result of Jupiter's powerful gravitational pull on that moon.

Jupiter's gravitational force squeezes Io. The friction caused by this "squeezing and releasing" causes the moon to heat up. This heat melts the rocks under Io's surface and gives rise to that moon's continuous volcanic activity.

The Moon's far side

QUESTIONS

1. Why does the Moon exert twice the amount of tidal effect on Earth than the larger Sun?
2. During which two Moon phases do spring tides (higher than normal high tides) occur?
3. During which two Moon phases do neap tides (lower than normal high tides) occur?
4. What are two effects of Earth's gravitational pull on the Moon?
5. How does Jupiter's gravitational pull cause volcanic activity on its moon Io? ☐

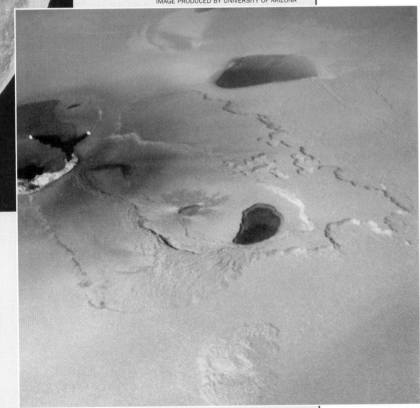

Volcanoes on Jupiter's moon, Io

Mission: **Pluto**

Pluto is the smallest planet in our solar system—approximately two-thirds the size of Earth's Moon. Pluto is also the planet farthest from the Sun. No spacecraft has ever visited this tiny planet, discovered in 1930 by a young astronomer named Clyde Tombaugh.

Pluto's distance from Earth and its small size do not mean that we don't know a great deal about it. For that, we can thank the Hubble Space Telescope (HST), an instrument that has made some of the most incredible discoveries in the history of astronomy.

Hubble's History

Launched by the space shuttle *Discovery* on April 24, 1990, the Hubble Space Telescope is a joint project of the European Space Agency and NASA. Hubble is more than a telescope. It is a space-based observatory that is expected to remain in operation until 2010. It makes a complete orbit around the Earth every 96 to 97 minutes.

Hubble travels in a low orbit of approximately 600 kilometers above Earth's surface, well above Earth's atmosphere. As a result, the images Hubble transmits to Earth are not distorted like images taken from Earth's surface. Hubble's lenses are 10 times sharper than those of the largest ground-based telescope. What's more, Hubble operates across the entire spectrum of light—from infrared through the visible to ultraviolet light. This means it can register wavelengths that are normally filtered out by the atmosphere. Not bad for an instrument that is barely 16 meters long and slightly more than 4 meters in diameter!

(continued)

Hubble Space Telescope

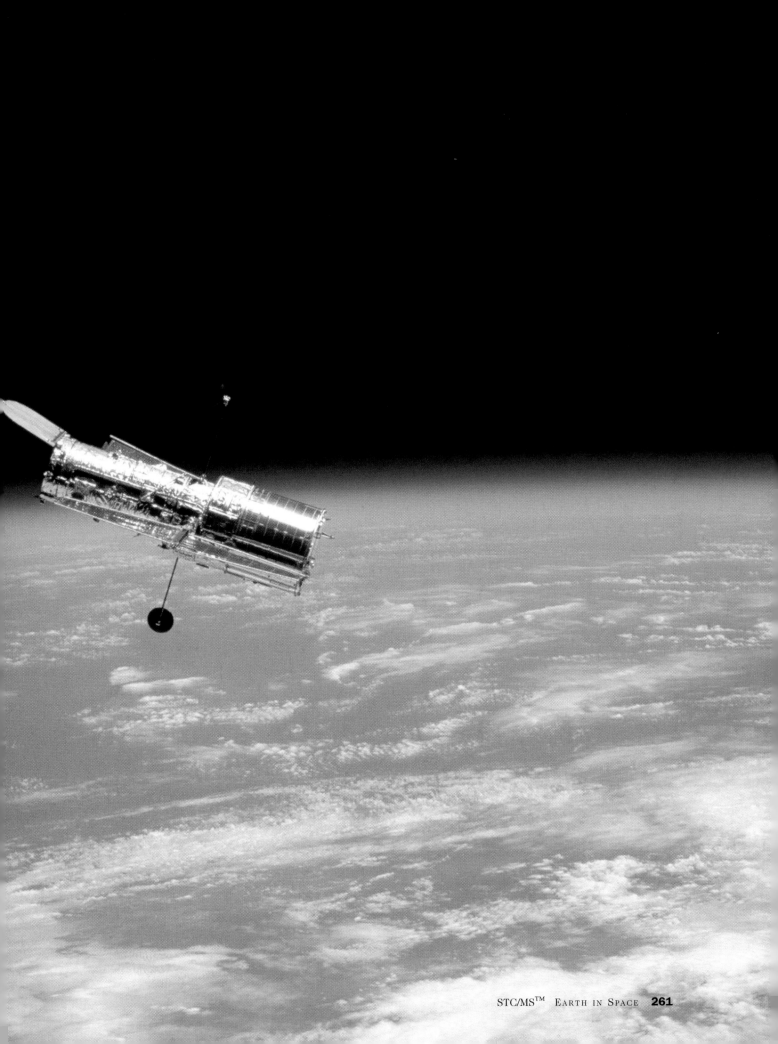

The Hubble Space Telescope being refurbished by astronauts Story Musgrave and Jeffrey Hoffman. Australia's West Coast can be seen in the background.

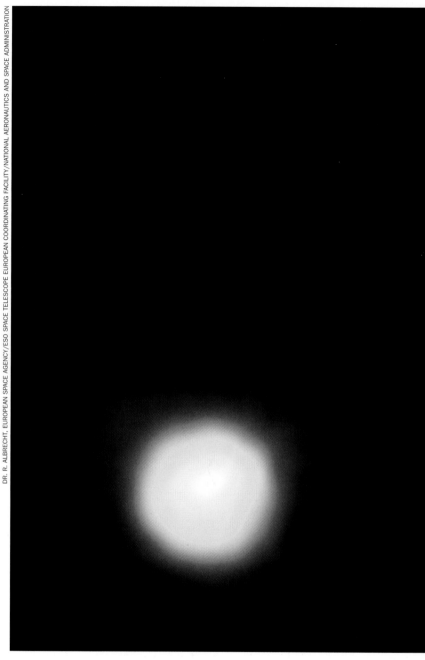

Pluto and Charon are like a double planet.

Another important feature of Hubble is that it is modular. If something goes wrong, it can most likely be repaired. When the Hubble Space Telescope had been in orbit only two months, scientists discovered that its main mirror was not perfectly shaped and it had to be fixed. Likewise, if a system becomes obsolete, it can be replaced. For example, the cameras on board have been replaced twice—in 1993 and 1997.

When it is in sunlight, Hubble is powered by solar energy. When Hubble moves into the Sun's shadow, it relies on nickel-hydrogen batteries that have also been charged by the Sun.

A Fuzzy Planet Comes Into Focus

In pre-Hubble days, few details were known about Pluto. From even the most powerful land telescopes, Pluto looked like a fuzzy yellow ball.

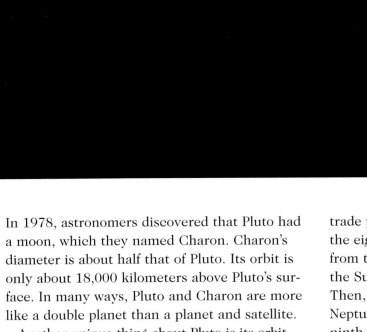

In 1978, astronomers discovered that Pluto had a moon, which they named Charon. Charon's diameter is about half that of Pluto. Its orbit is only about 18,000 kilometers above Pluto's surface. In many ways, Pluto and Charon are more like a double planet than a planet and satellite.

Another unique thing about Pluto is its orbit. At times, Pluto is closer to the Sun than Neptune is. Every 248 years, the two planets trade places. For about 20 years, Pluto becomes the eighth planet and Neptune the ninth planet from the Sun. For example, Pluto was closer to the Sun than Neptune from 1979 until 1999. Then, in 1999, Pluto switched places with Neptune, and Pluto once again became the ninth planet from the Sun.

(continued)

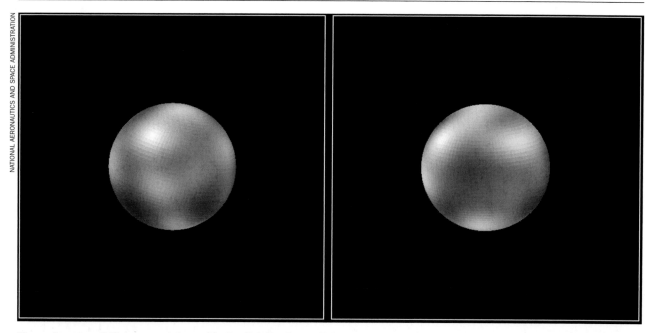

NATIONAL AERONAUTICS AND SPACE ADMINISTRATION

These images of Pluto were taken with the Hubble Space Telescope during one solar day on Pluto. Notice the polar ice caps and bright features near the equator. Some of the dark areas may be valleys or fresh impact craters.

The Hubble Space Telescope sent back its first images of Pluto in 1994, when it mapped about 85 percent of the planet's surface. These images show a planet of enormous contrasts. Parts of the planet's surface are bright white, while other parts look black. Pluto also has a cap on its north pole. Dr. Marc Buie, a member of the Hubble team, said, "It's fantastic. Hubble has brought Pluto from a fuzzy, distant dot of light to a world that we can begin to map and watch for surface changes. The results ... are much better than I ever hoped for."

Pluto the Planet?

We still know less about Pluto than about any other planet. Its size, its odd orbit, and its relationship with Charon are unique. What's more, Pluto's composition—a mixture of rock and ice—makes it stand out. All the other rocky

planets are in the inner solar system. In the outer part of the solar system, the huge, gaseous planets reign—with the exception of rocky Pluto.

Some astronomers believe that Pluto was once a satellite of Neptune that got knocked out of its orbit. Others think that both Pluto and Charon are part of the Kuiper belt. The Kuiper belt is a ring of comets—rocky, icy objects—that orbit the Sun just beyond Neptune. It was formed at the time of origin of the solar system. It's possible that Pluto is an exceptional "KBO"— Kuiper Belt Object— that broke away from the crowd!

Future explorations will let scientists learn more about Pluto—its surface properties and its interior makeup. In the meantime, photos from Hubble help us prepare for future missions by telling us more about this distant little planet. ☐

PLANETARY FACTS: Pluto

Pluto: Quick Facts

Diameter	2340 km	Average temperature	−230 °C
Average distance from the Sun	5.9 billion km	Length of sidereal day	6.39 Earth days
Mass	1×10^{22} kg	Length of year	248 Earth years
Surface gravity (Earth = 1)	0.06	Number of observed moons	1

Relative size

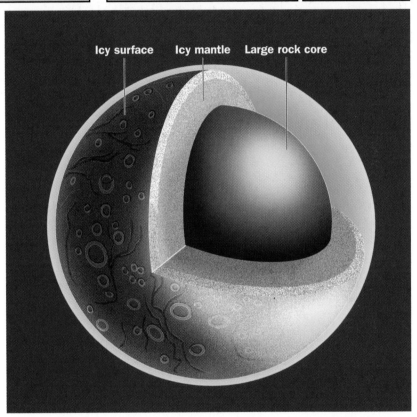

Icy surface   Icy mantle   Large rock core

Did You Know?

- Pluto's orbit is the least like a circle of all the plants. Its distance from the Sun varies from less than 4½ billion km to over 7 billion km.
- Pluto's orbit around the Sun is tilted 17 degrees, more than any other planet in the solar system.

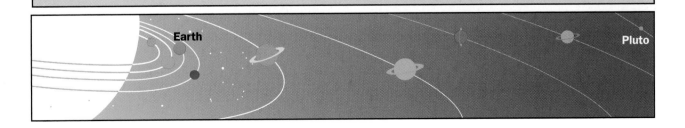

Earth   Pluto

PART 3 Earth's History as a Planet

17

Asteroids, Comets, and Meteoroids

Comet Hale-Bopp. The white dust tail is composed of large particles of dust and ice. The gas tail is blue.

© WILLIAM JAMES WARREN/CORBIS

INTRODUCTION

On the night of July 23, 1995, astronomers Alan Hale and Tom Bopp discovered Comet Hale-Bopp from different locations. Hale and Bopp were the first people in more than 3000 years to view what is now officially known as Comet Hale-Bopp (Comet H-B for short). This may have been the biggest comet ever visible from Earth.

During this lesson, you will examine the orbits of asteroids and comets within the solar system and the possible effects of asteroid and comet impact on the planets. What do you already know and want to know about asteroids, comets, and meteoroids? How are they alike or different? What are some of the possible effects of their impact on Earth and other planets? In this lesson, you will explore these and other questions.

OBJECTIVES FOR THIS LESSON

Analyze the position of the asteroid belt using mathematical patterns.

Brainstorm what you know and want to know about asteroids, comets, and meteoroids; make comparisons among them.

Analyze the ability of scientists to forecast asteroid and comet impact, and explore the challenges of making such forecasts.

Read to learn more about Earth-observing missions.

Getting Started

1. With your class, review your homework from Lesson 16, Student Sheet 16: Bode's Law.

2. Read "Asteroids, Comets, and Meteoroids." Carefully examine the photos in the reading selection. How are asteroids similar to or different from comets and meteoroids? Record a summary of your ideas in your science notebooks. Then discuss them as a class or within your group, as instructed by your teacher.

MATERIALS FOR
LESSON 17

For you
1 completed copy of Student Sheet 16: Bode's Law
1 working copy of Student Sheet 10.1c: Planetary Chart

Inquiry 17.1
Examining Asteroids

PROCEDURE

1. In the program *Explore the Planets,* review the Asteroids segment in the "Tour the Planets" section. Discuss the concepts with your class.

2. Make general observations about the asteroids shown on the program. Look back at Lesson 12. How do you think Barringer (Meteor) Crater and the craters on the surface of asteroids Gaspra and Ida were formed? Discuss or record your ideas, as instructed by your teacher.

REFLECTING ON WHAT YOU'VE DONE

Answer the following questions in your science notebook, and be prepared to discuss your ideas with the class:

A. How and when do scientists think asteroids may have formed?

B. Why do you think the belt of asteroids exists between Jupiter and Mars?

C. How are the orbits of asteroids similar to, or different from, planetary orbits?

Inquiry 17.2
Studying Asteroid Impact

PROCEDURE

1. Read "A Fiery Necklace." How did Dr. Eugene Shoemaker contribute to the understanding of asteroid and comet impacts? Record your ideas in your notebook.

REFLECTING ON WHAT YOU'VE DONE

1. In your notebook, record your ideas to the following, and be prepared to discuss them with your class:

A. How has Earth's history been influenced by occasional natural catastrophes, such as asteroid impacts?

B. An asteroid impact is considered a natural hazard on Earth, but it is not considered a natural hazard on any other planet or moon. Given this information, how would you define "natural hazard?"

C. What is the scientist's role in forecasting asteroid and comet impacts?

D. What challenges do scientists face when they forecast asteroid or comet impacts?

E. What is the scientist's role in reducing the risks of such an event?

2. Return to your list of ideas about asteroids, comets, and meteoroids. What new things do you want to add to your list? Make your changes and additions now.

3. With your class, return to the Question J folder for Lesson 1. Is there anything that you would now change or add? Discuss your ideas with the class.

4. Read "Mission: Earth." Add any new information about Earth to your working copy of Student Sheet 10.1c: Planetary Chart. Complete your planetary brochure. You will present your planetary brochure and your team's mission design to the class in Lesson 19.

Asteroids, Comets, and Meteoroids

Among the planets in the solar system are countless numbers of asteroids, comets, and meteoroids. Let's take a look at how these solar system objects are different from planets.

Asteroids

Asteroids are metallic, rocky objects in space. They have no atmospheres and move in independent orbits around the Sun. Tens of thousands of asteroids are found in an area called the asteroid belt—a vast, doughnut-shaped ring located between the orbits of Mars and Jupiter (see the illustration below). Gaspra and Ida, pictured on the next page, are two asteroids found in the main belt. Some scientists theorize that asteroids may be pieces of a planet that never formed because Jupiter's great mass exerted too much gravitational force to allow the pieces to combine into one planet.

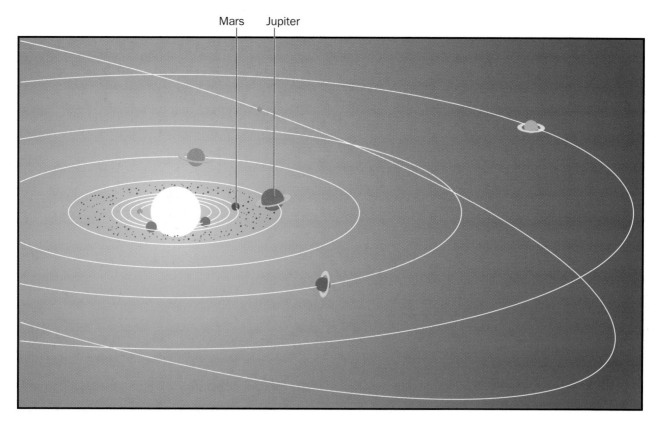

Mars   Jupiter

The asteroid belt is located between Jupiter and Mars.

Because asteroids are too small to be classified as planets, they are often called "minor planets." Some asteroids are the size of a small building. Ceres was the first asteroid scientists observed. Discovered in 1801, it is about 1000 kilometers across and one of the largest known asteroids. Another asteroid, discovered in 2001, is about half the size of Pluto (or 1150 kilometers). Most asteroids are actually less than a kilometer wide. If we could combine all of these asteroids, they would be smaller than half the size of the Moon.

(continued)

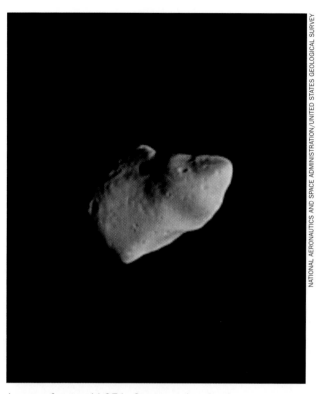

Image of asteroid 951, Gaspra, taken by the Galileo *spacecraft*

Image of the asteroid 243, Ida, and its small satellite, Dactyl. Dactyl is the small object to the right of Ida.

Comets

A comet is a mass of frozen gas, cosmic dust, and ice crystals. Comets are often described as "dirty icebergs." They circle the Sun in long, narrow orbits, mainly located in the cold outer reaches of our solar system. They orbit the Sun in the Kuiper Belt, which begins just past Neptune. A trillion more comets may live even farther out in a cold area called the "Oort Cloud."

Some comets leave their orbits in the Kuiper Belt or the Oort Cloud and journey toward the Sun. When a comet flies near the Sun, its ice begins to "boil" away. As it vaporizes, a tail of glowing gases and dust forms behind it, always pointing away from the Sun. If Earth happens to pass through comet

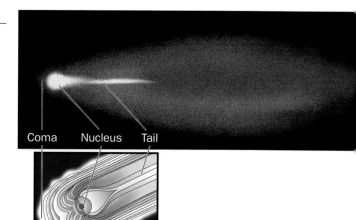

Coma   Nucleus   Tail

The parts of a comet

dust, burning particles can be seen streaking through the sky in a spectacular display called a "meteor shower."

This photo shows two tails shed by Comet Hale-Bopp. The blue tail points directly away from the Sun. The white tail is created by bits of grit that have come off the comet's nucleus. They are being pushed away by the solar winds from the Sun.

A meteorite stone discovered on Earth weighing 452.6 grams.
A 1-cm square cube is shown for scale.

Meteoroids, Meteors, and Meteorites

Meteoroids are pieces of rock and metal dislodged from comets, planets, asteroids, or moons. Most meteoroids are made up of dust-sized particles. When a meteoroid enters a planet's atmosphere, it burns up due to friction. As it burns, a meteoroid creates a bright streak of light in the sky that we call a "meteor." Sometimes large meteoroids do not burn up completely—one may make it all the way through a planet, moon, or asteroid's atmosphere and land on its surface, after which it is called a "meteorite." □

Meteors streak through the night sky.

A FIERY NECKLACE

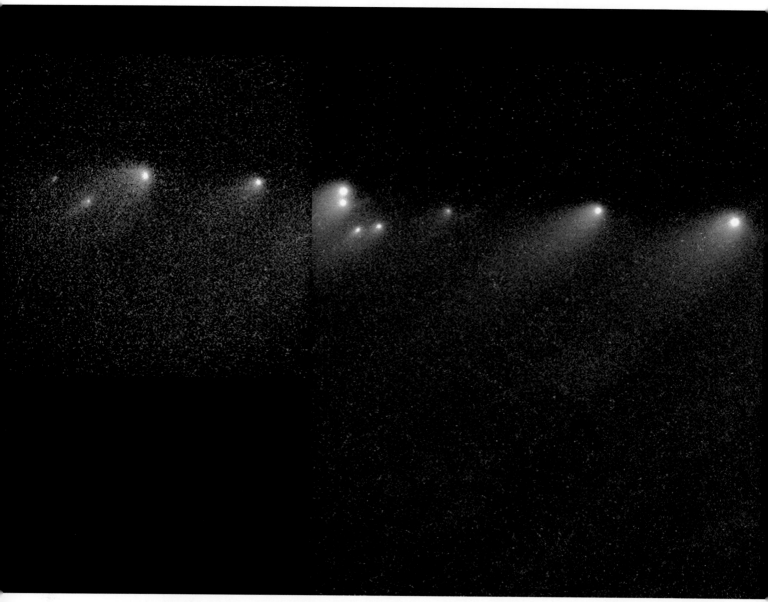

A NASA Hubble Space Telescope image of comet Shoemaker-Levy 9, taken on May 17, 1994. When the comet was observed, its train of 21 icy fragments stretched across 1.1 million km of space, or three times the distance between Earth and the Moon.

It's not often that you get to see a comet strike a planet. Until July 1994, only one comet strike had ever been observed. That was in 1178, when five English monks reported seeing "a flaming torch" on the Moon "spewing out fire, hot coals, and sparks." Modern astronomers have confirmed that those monks had seen a comet or a small asteroid hit the Moon, forming the crater that is now named Giordano Bruno.

Those 12th century monks weren't equipped with cameras. But in 1994, astronomers all over the world got a chance to see and photograph a similar event when Comet Shoemaker-Levy 9 collided with Jupiter.

NATIONAL AERONAUTICS AND SPACE ADMINISTRATION

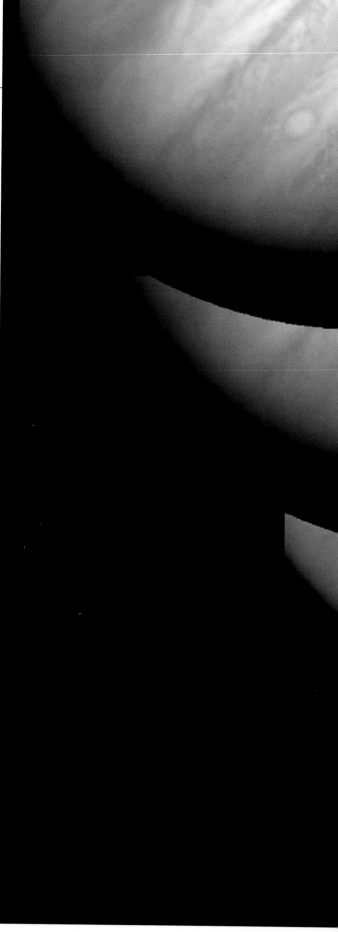

Big News

In 1993, astronomers Eugene and Carolyn Shoemaker, a husband-and-wife team, and David Levy discovered the comet Shoemaker-Levy 9. The three astronomers were working at the Mt. Palomar Observatory in California.

New comets are discovered all the time, but this one made headlines. Shoemaker-Levy 9 was a comet that had been ripped to pieces. Instead of being a single ball, the comet was made up of 21 fragments, each one trailing a large cloud of ice and dust. It looked like a fiery necklace blazing across the night sky. The astronomers calculated that about 9 months before they spotted it, Shoemaker-Levy 9 had passed within about 21,000 kilometers of Jupiter. Jupiter's gravitational force (which is 2.36 times that of Earth's) had pulled the comet apart.

Next came even bigger news: The pieces of Shoemaker-Levy 9 were on a collision course with Jupiter. Astronomers predicted that Jupiter's gravitational force was about to grab those fragments, once and for all. That set the stage for one of the most photographed events in astronomical history.

Ringing the Bell

Between July 16 and July 22, 1994, Shoemaker-Levy 9's fragments hit Jupiter's upper atmosphere one by one. Virtually every large telescope on Earth recorded the collisions. The Hubble Space Telescope recorded the event as it orbited Earth, and so did the *Galileo* spacecraft, which was on its way to Jupiter.

The 21 fragments hit Jupiter at speeds of more than 60 kilometers per second. The impacts created plumes of hot gas that rose thousands of kilometers high. They left marks on the planet's surface that lasted for nearly a year. The pieces plowed into the planet's atmosphere with enormous energy. One astronomer described the impacts as "ringing Jupiter like a bell." □

The impact of a fragment of Comet Shoemaker-Levy 9 with Jupiter

Tribute to Eugene Shoemaker

In July 1997, three years after Shoemaker-Levy 9 collided with Jupiter, Eugene Shoemaker met his own end. He was killed in a car crash in Australia, where he was studying an ancient impact crater.

The following year, Shoemaker's ashes were carried aboard the *Lunar Prospector* spacecraft in a small capsule. In a fitting tribute, the spacecraft was deliberately crashed onto the Moon's surface on July 31, 1999.

"I don't think Gene ever dreamed his ashes would go to the Moon," said his wife, Carolyn. "He would be thrilled."

UNITED STATES GEOLOGICAL SURVEY

Eugene Shoemaker and wife, Carolyn

Mission: **Earth**

We have learned much about Earth's neighboring planets in the solar system. We've sent flyby spacecraft to photograph them, put orbiters around them for longer study, deposited landers on their surfaces, and flown probes through their atmospheres. But what have we learned about Earth as a planet using space technology?

Earth's seven continents and vast oceans set it apart from the other planets. Liquid water surrounds its continents, which are covered by contrasting lush vegetation and desert landscapes. From space we can see frozen white polar caps—like those on Mars—that cover Earth's poles. Swirling clouds, flashes of lightning, and volcanic gases are evidence of an active atmosphere.

The presence of life on planet Earth is one of its unique features. Macro- and microscopic organisms are teeming on land and in water. One hint that life exists on Earth can be detected from space—the electromagnetic noise caused by radios and TV broadcasts. But the presence of life is only one aspect of our world when considered as a whole.

(continued)

NATIONAL AERONAUTICS AND SPACE ADMINISTRATION/GODDARD SPACE FLIGHT CENTER/
IMAGE CREATED BY RETO STOCKLI, NAZMI EL SALEOUS, AND MARIT JENTOFT-NILSEN

This image came from a single remote-sensing device flying more than 700 kilometers above the Earth on the Terra *Earth-observing satellite.*

Earth System Enterprise

The key to a better understanding of Earth is to explore how its systems of atmosphere (air), geosphere (land), hydrosphere (water), and biosphere (life) interact with each other. And the best way to study all of these systems together is from space. Mission to Planet Earth—now called Earth System Enterprise (ESE)—was established in 1991 and is the foundation of NASA's Earth-observing program.

This program has three main components: a series of Earth Observing System (EOS) satellites, a system to collect data, and teams of scientists around the world who study the data. ESE uses satellites, such as *Terra*, and other tools to study Earth. Through ESE, NASA hopes to explain how natural processes affect life on Earth—and how life on Earth is affecting Earth's natural processes. Data from these studies may help improve weather forecasts, help manage agriculture and forests, provide information to fishermen and local planners, and, eventually, help predict how the climate may change in the future.

Let's look at a few examples of how the ESE mission helps scientists and engineers observe Earth as a planet.

The Cooling and Warming Power of Clouds

Clouds act to regulate Earth's climate. Cirrus clouds—high, wispy clouds—warm Earth by trapping radiation from Earth's surface. Stratocumulus clouds—soft, gray clouds in globular patches or rolls—cool Earth's surface by reflecting incoming solar radiation back into space. Scientists who work with Earth-observing satellites are studying how clouds affect Earth's climate. By using global cloud observations from EOS satellites, scientists can determine to what extent warming or cooling caused by clouds has an impact on the global climate.

(continued)

Terra, *an Earth-observing satellite*

Global Ice and Sea Level Changes

Earth's glacial ice contains more than 77 percent of Earth's fresh water. Over the last century, many of the world's mountain glaciers and ice caps have been retreating (getting smaller). Melting glaciers cause sea levels to rise. One of the jobs of the EOS scientists is to figure out whether Greenland and Antarctic ice sheets are growing or shrinking by studying changes in sea level. Scientists examine changes in sea level by looking at satellite, laser, and radar data.

Greenhouse Effect

Scientists use the EOS satellites to measure levels of greenhouse gases such as carbon dioxide, methane, and chlorofluorocarbons (CFCs) in our atmosphere. Carbon dioxide is released into the atmosphere when solid waste, fossil fuels (oil, natural gas, and coal), and wood and wood products are burned. CFCs are found in aerosol sprays, in blowing agents for foams and packing materials, as solvents, and as refrigerants. CFCs do not occur naturally; therefore, their increase in the

This photo of the San Quintín Glacier in southern Chile was taken by the crew of mission STS-068 in October 1994.

This photo of the San Quintín Glacier was taken nearly 6 years later in May 2000. Like many glaciers worldwide, San Quintin appears to be retreating.

atmosphere is entirely the result of human activity. The levels of these gases have been increasing steadily. These gases trap heat within Earth's atmosphere preventing it from escaping into space.

Ocean Processes

Oceans cover more than 70 percent of Earth's surface. These bodies of water transport heat and weather conditions around the globe. Satellites can measure sea surface temperatures. These temperatures are each assigned a color on the satellite image. A global view of Earth can show the locations of the warmest and coolest ocean temperatures. Scientists can also use satellite imagery to study El Niño—an occurrence of unusually warm surface water in the Pacific Ocean. EOS can help scientists investigate the role Earth's oceans play in regulating the amount of greenhouse gases in the atmosphere.

The EOS satellite called *Terra* collects detailed measurements of the ocean's surface temperatures every day all over the globe. This sensor acts like a sophisticated thermometer in space. It helps scientists understand how Earth's oceans and atmosphere interact and drive weather patterns. These patterns define our climate.

(continued)

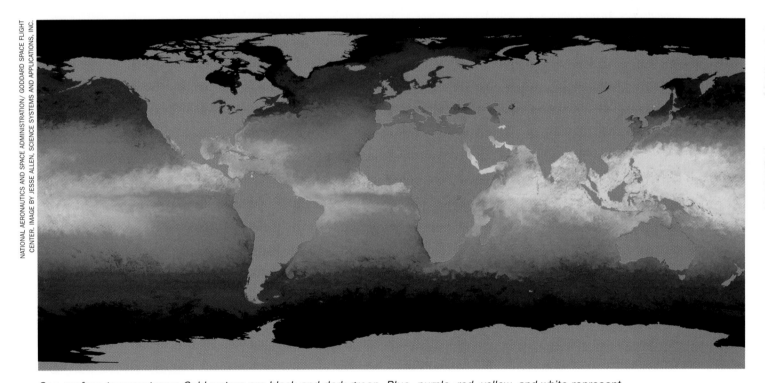

NATIONAL AERONAUTICS AND SPACE ADMINISTRATION/ GODDARD SPACE FLIGHT CENTER. IMAGE BY JESSE ALLEN, SCIENCE SYSTEMS AND APPLICATIONS, INC.

Sea surface temperatures: Cold waters are black and dark green. Blue, purple, red, yellow, and white represent progressively warmer water.

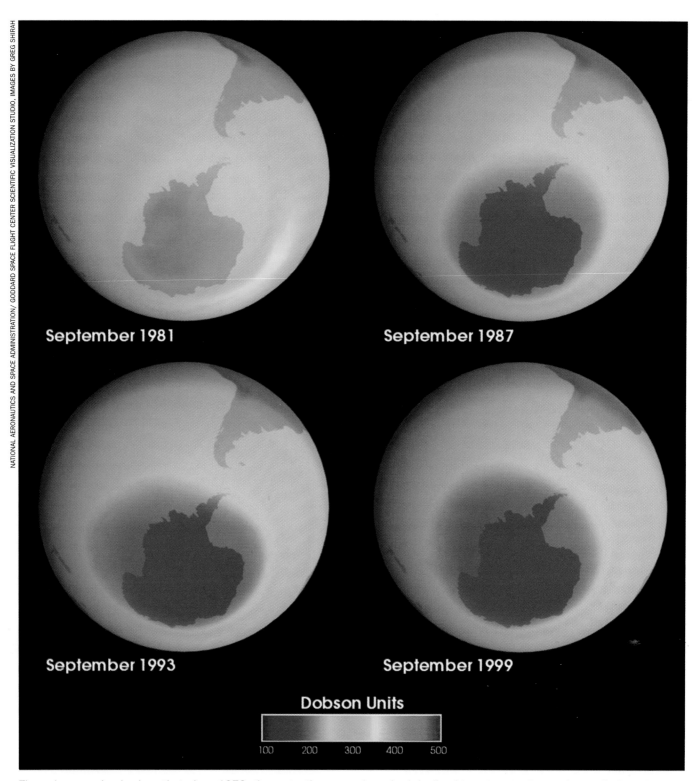

September 1981

September 1987

September 1993

September 1999

Dobson Units

100   200   300   400   500

These images clearly show that since 1979, the protective ozone layer had declined in concentration and area. In fact, the ozone hole had grown so much over the years that in 1999, it was about the size of the entire Antarctic continent.

Madagascar was once covered in lush green vegetation. Today, an estimated 80 percent of its forests have been destroyed. The reddish-brown exposed terrain can be seen in this true-color image of northern Madagascar taken in May 2000.

Ozone, Vegetation, and Snow

Both satellite and ground-based measurement tools have detected a hole in the ozone over the Antarctic. The ozone is a layer of O_3 in the stratosphere, the second layer of the atmosphere above Earth's surface. Decreased ozone levels allow more ultraviolet radiation from the Sun to reach Earth's surface. Ultraviolet radiation can harm organisms, including humans. In New Zealand, for example, school children are required to wear hats while outside, since exposure to the Sun's rays due to ozone depletion is particularly dangerous in that region. EOS analyzes the natural and human activities on Earth that cause the decrease in the ozone.

Scientists at NASA also can evaluate processes that directly affect Earth's energy and water cycles. For example, satellite imagery continuously monitors the rate of deforestation (the process of taking down trees) in the Brazilian rainforest. Satellite images of Africa can show characteristics of vegetation. Instruments can measure how much sunlight the leaves absorb.

Satellites can monitor snow cover as well. A decrease in the amount of snow cover may indicate increased global temperatures.

The Future of Earth as a Planet

In its natural state, Earth is in perfect balance. Water exists in all three states (liquid, gas, and solid). Its atmosphere is oxygen rich, and life is abundant. To maintain this balance, humans must have an understanding of how Earth functions as a system. The technology of the Earth System Enterprise mission promotes the study of Earth as an integrated system. ◻

PLANETARY FACTS: Earth

Earth: Quick Facts

Diameter	12,756 km	**Average temperature**	–55 °C to 70 °C
Average distance from the Sun	149,600,000 km	**Length of sidereal day**	23.93 hours
Mass	597×10^{22} kg	**Length of year**	365.25 days
Surface gravity	1*	**Number of observed moons**	1

Relative size

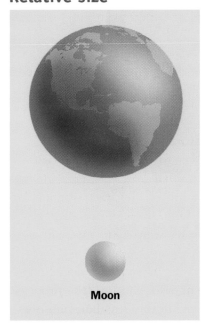

Moon

Earth atmosphere

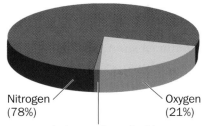

Nitrogen (78%)

Oxygen (21%)

Argon, carbon dioxide, and water vapor (trace amounts) (1%)

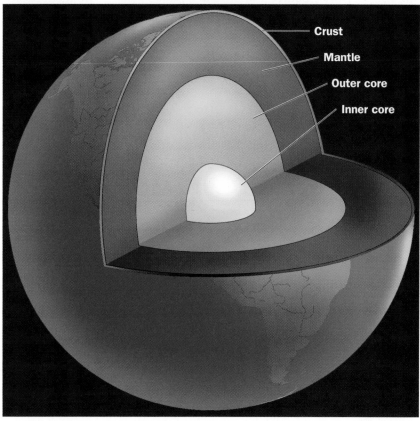

Crust

Mantle

Outer core

Inner core

Did You Know?

- The oldest rocks on Earth date back 4 billion years.
- Only Earth has the temperature range that permits liquid water to exist, and only Earth has developed an oxygen-rich atmosphere. These two factors enable Earth to support life.

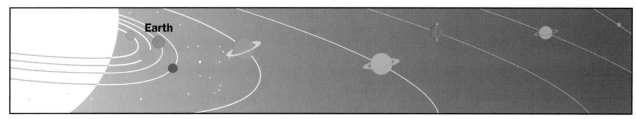

Earth

* 9.78 m/s²

The Space Name Game

Dr. Michael F. A'Hearn knows his way around space. Dr. A'Hearn, a professor of astronomy at the University of Maryland, is also an office-holder in the International Astronomical Union (IAU), the organization responsible for naming celestial bodies. Scientists, space agencies, and authorities around the world recognize and use IAU's names. Here, Dr. A'Hearn answers some common questions about the space "name game," or how astronomical bodies get their names.

Q: How are asteroids named?
A: First, an asteroid is given a set of numbers and letters that tells when it was first discovered. Once the asteroid's orbit is well known, a permanent number is assigned—in numerical order. After that, a name is assigned. The discoverer of the asteroid can suggest a name, but the IAU has final approval.

For example, an asteroid discovered by P. Wild on March 5, 1973, was given the designation "1973 EB." This means that the asteroid was identified in 1973 in the first half of March (E) and was the second (B) asteroid discovered in the first half of that month. Once we understood the orbit of 1973 EB, we gave it the permanent number of 2001 because that's how many asteroids had been discovered by then. This asteroid was named Einstein in memory of Albert Einstein, the greatest scientist of the 20th century.

Q: How often are asteroids discovered?
A: New asteroids are discovered nearly every day! However, people tend not to search during the full Moon because the background light interferes too much. Most discoveries are made around the new Moon, when our cameras can "see."

Q: How often are comets discovered? Are they named the same way as asteroids?
A: Many new comets are discovered every month. They are generally named for their discoverers. Comet Halley was named after astronomer Edmund Halley, who was the first to predict the return of this particular comet. But like asteroids, comets are given codes that reflect their discovery date.

Dr. Michael F. A'Hearn

Q: What about stars?
A: A few bright stars easily seen from Earth have ancient, traditional Arabic names, such as Sirius. We have identified hundreds of millions of stars. To study them, we need to be able to find them, so they are simply known by catalog numbers. By looking up its number in a huge catalog, we can find a star's precise coordinates, or position in the sky.

Q: Is it true that people can pay to have a star or a planet named after them?
A: Some companies claim to offer such services for a fee. However, those names are completely invalid. As an international scientific organization, the IAU has nothing to do with the commercial practice of "selling" fictitious names of stars, planets, moons, or any other space "real estate."

If you're interested in stars and space, go to your nearest planetarium or local observatory. Have someone show you real stars through a telescope. You also may want to join a local astronomy club. Someday you may discover a new asteroid or comet that could be named after you! □

18

Fossils as Evidence of Asteroid Impact

An asteroid impact in what is now Mexico may have caused the mass extinction of many organisms, including the dinosaurs.

ARTIST: DON DAVIS/NATIONAL AERONAUTICS AND SPACE ADMINISTRATION

INTRODUCTION

An enormous rock falls from the sky—appearing to come from nowhere. Flames of orange engulf the land. All life near the point of impact is destroyed instantly. Particles of melted rock, dust, and debris hover like a dusty blanket and eventually fall back to the planet's surface.

This may sound like a scene from a science fiction movie, but this describes an event that took place again and again throughout Earth's geological history—an asteroid impacting the planet. In fact, scientists now think that a large asteroid hit Earth 65 million years ago and caused the extinction of the dinosaurs and many other organisms that inhabited Earth at that time. How do scientists know which organisms died and which survived? They examined the fossils contained in rocks dating from that time. In this lesson, you will explore how fossils help us trace the history of asteroid and comet impacts on Earth.

OBJECTIVES FOR THIS LESSON

Analyze what the properties of a fossilized rock tell us about how the rock formed.

Brainstorm what you know and want to know about fossils.

Watch a DVD about the relationships among fossils, dinosaur extinction, and asteroid impact.

Model fossil excavation, identification, and formation.

Getting Started

1. Remove the limestone rock from your group's plastic box of materials. With your group, examine it with a hand lens. Discuss the properties of the rock.

2. How do you think this rock formed? How did the imprints of the shells get on the rock? Discuss your ideas with the class.

3. Brainstorm with the class what you know and want to know about fossils.

4. Watch the DVD *Dinosaur Extinction*.

5. Discuss as a class how the properties of rocks can help scientists learn more about the history of a planet. Consider the following:

What did scientists conclude by looking at the layers of the earth in Mexico?

Why are rocks and fossils important for scientists who study the history of a planet?

MATERIALS FOR LESSON 18

For you
1 pair of disposable gloves

For your group
1 sample of fossiliferous limestone
2 hand lenses
1 black china marker

MATERIALS FOR INQUIRY 18.1

For you and your partner

1 softened fossil-bearing mound
1 plastic wide-mouthed container
  of warm water, with lid
1 excavating stick
1 paintbrush
1 dropper bottle of water
1 pair of forceps
1 small resealable plastic bag
1 pair of goggles (optional)
  Wet and dry paper towels
  Newspaper or other
  table covering

For your group

1 "Fossils Through Time" poster

Figure 18.1 *Use your excavating tools to dig for fossils. Be careful not to damage the fossils.*

Inquiry 18.1
Excavating Fossils

PROCEDURE

1. Discuss what you already know about paleontologists—scientists who study life forms of the past—and how they excavate fossils.

2. Cover your work area with newspaper. Wear gloves. Collect one fossil-bearing mound for you and your partner. Remove the mound from its container of water. Use your excavating tools (dropper bottle, excavating stick, pair of forceps, and paintbrush) to dig the fossils from your "rock," as shown in Figure 18.1. Work over a paper towel.

3. After you have found the fossils, use your container of water and tools to try to remove as much plaster from them as possible. Dry them. Then clean your work area.

4. Use your hand lens to examine each fossil. Draw a picture of each fossil in your notebook. Use the fossil identification chart in Table 18.1, your group's fossil poster, fossil books, Figure 18.2, and the class Fossil Collection boxes to identify the name of each of your fossils. Write down the name and approximate age of each of your fossils in your notebook. Create a table to organize your information.

5. Use your black china marker to write your name and your partner's name on a small plastic bag. Place your clean fossils in the bag and seal it.

Table 18.1 Fossil Identification Chart

Tooth (shark)

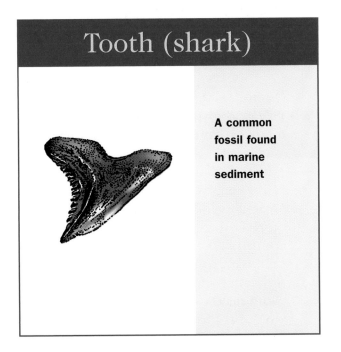

A common fossil found in marine sediment

Mollusk – Gastropod

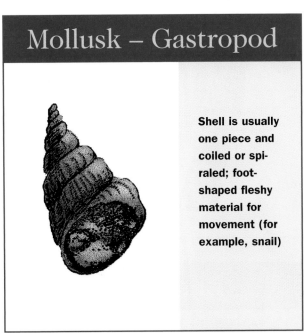

Shell is usually one piece and coiled or spiraled; foot-shaped fleshy material for movement (for example, snail)

Mollusk – Cephalopod

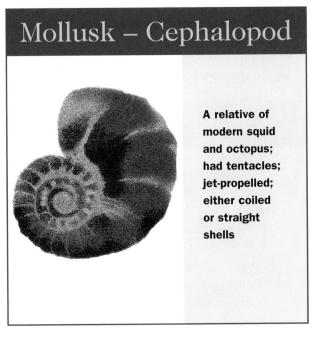

A relative of modern squid and octopus; had tentacles; jet-propelled; either coiled or straight shells

Bone (dinosaur)

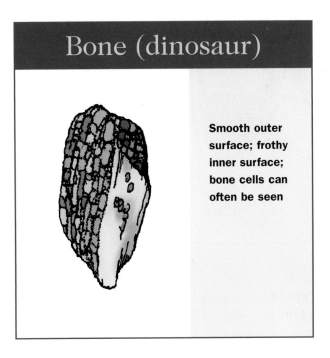

Smooth outer surface; frothy inner surface; bone cells can often be seen

Table 18.1 Fossil Identification Chart, continued

Crinoid stem

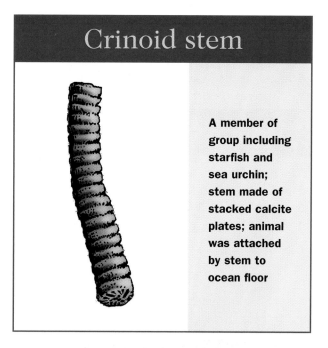

A member of group including starfish and sea urchin; stem made of stacked calcite plates; animal was attached by stem to ocean floor

Coral

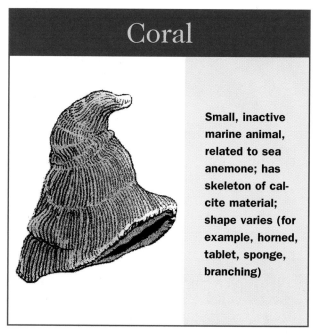

Small, inactive marine animal, related to sea anemone; has skeleton of calcite material; shape varies (for example, horned, tablet, sponge, branching)

Brachiopod

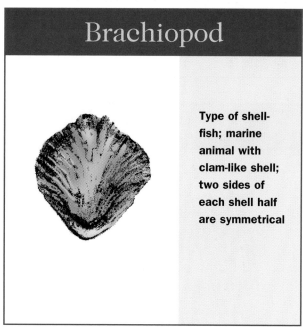

Type of shellfish; marine animal with clam-like shell; two sides of each shell half are symmetrical

Bivalve

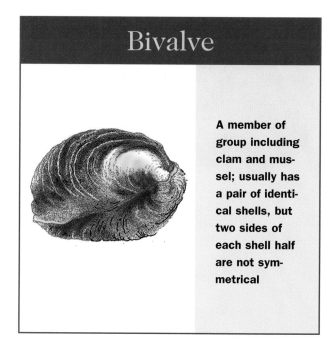

A member of group including clam and mussel; usually has a pair of identical shells, but two sides of each shell half are not symmetrical

Table 18.1 Fossil Identification Chart, continued

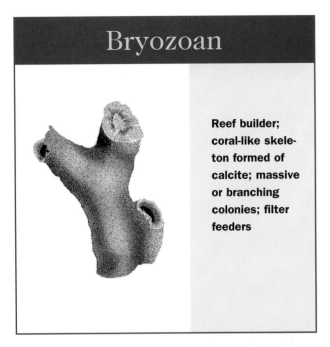

Bryozoan

Reef builder; coral-like skeleton formed of calcite; massive or branching colonies; filter feeders

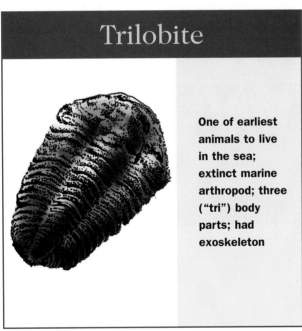

Trilobite

One of earliest animals to live in the sea; extinct marine arthropod; three ("tri") body parts; had exoskeleton

MATERIALS FOR INQUIRY 18.2

For you and your partner
1 set of fossils (from Inquiry 18.1)
2 shark teeth
1 plastic wide-mouthed container
1 plastic spoon
1 black china marker

For your group
1 cup of gravel, with lid
1 cup of red sand, with lid
1 cup of all-purpose sand, with lid
1 cup of black sand, with lid
1 cup of diluted glue, with lid

Inquiry 18.2
Examining the Relative Ages of Fossils

PROCEDURE

1. Discuss with your class how sediments are layered and how organisms become buried in the layers.

2. Examine Figure 18.2 and its extended caption. Answer the following questions in your notebook, then discuss them with your class:

A. Which layer of rock is probably the youngest? Why?

B. How can the order of rock layers help scientists estimate the age of a fossil?

C. How can the age of a fossil help scientists estimate the age of a rock layer?

D. Why is it important for scientists to know the age of a rock or fossil?

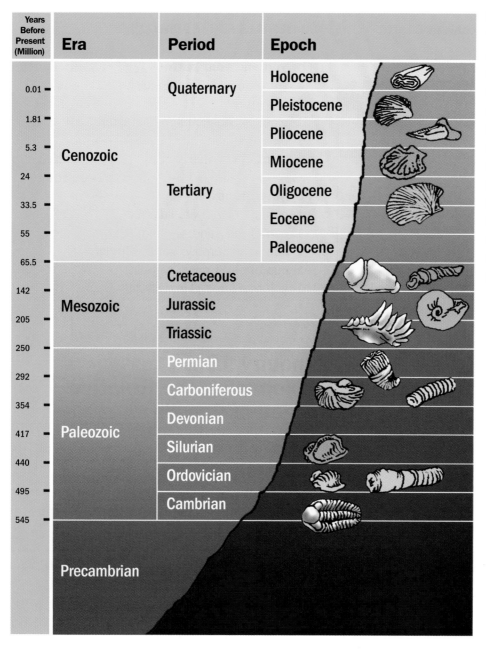

Figure 18.2 *Much of what we know about the relative ages of rocks comes from the study of fossils. Since certain types of fossils are always younger than others, we can say that one rock is older than another based on the fossils it contains. If sediments on Earth had remained undisturbed over time, the oldest rock would always be on the bottom and the youngest rock would always be at the top.*

3. Put a thin layer (around 1 cm thick) of gravel in the bottom of your wide-mouthed container. (In nature, the layers are called "strata.")

4. Bury the oldest fossil from Inquiry 18.1 in this layer. (Look at your notes to find out which of the fossils is the oldest.) If you don't know the ages, just select any one of your fossils.

5. Now pour a thin layer of sand (any color) into your container until the gravel is covered. Place the next-oldest fossil on top of this sand layer. Harden the sand into rock by covering it with a small amount of diluted glue. (In nature, chemicals seep into sediment and cement the sediment into rock.) Draw a picture of each buried fossil as you work.

6. Repeat Procedure Step 5 with another layer of colored sand and another fossil. Harden the layer with diluted glue. Continue this process until all your fossils are buried (see Figure 18.3). Plan to bury the shark teeth in the final top layer. (What would the top position of the shark teeth tell you about their age relative to the other fossils? Discuss this with your group.)

7. Use the china marker to write the ages of each layer on the outside of your container (see Figure 18.4). The sediment should be the same age as its fossil. Make up an age if the age of your fossil is not available. For example, if the fossil in the bottom layer was from 440 million years ago, mark that layer 440 MYA (**Million Years Ago**). If a shark tooth is on the top

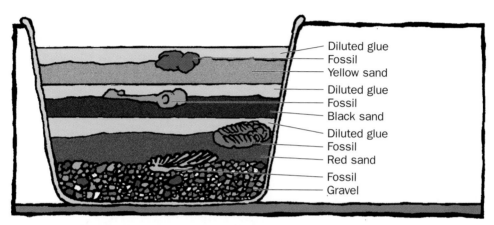

Diluted glue
Fossil
Yellow sand
Diluted glue
Fossil
Black sand
Diluted glue
Fossil
Red sand
Fossil
Gravel

Figure 18.3 *Cross-section of container with strata and buried fossils*

Figure 18.4 *Bury the fossils in each layer. Write the age of each fossil on the outside of the container. The oldest sedimentary layers should be on the bottom.*

layer, it may have been from 2 million years ago, so mark the top layer 2 MYA.

8. Draw a picture of the final strata in your science notebook. Record the location and approximate age of each fossil.

9. Exchange your container of hardened strata with the other pair of students in your group. Excavate the fossils from the other team's hardened strata, as shown in Figure 18.5. Can you tell how old each fossil is, based on the age of the layer in which you found it?

Figure 18.5 *Excavate another group's strata and determine the approximate or relative ages of their fossils.*

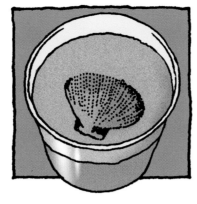

MATERIALS FOR INQUIRY 18.3

For you and your partner
- 1 plastic wide-mouthed container
- 2 shells
- 1 cup of plaster (premixed by your teacher)

For your group
- 1 resealable plastic bag of craft dough

Inquiry 18.3
Modeling Molds and Casts

PROCEDURE

1. Read "Fossils." In your science notebook, answer the questions at the end of the reading selection. Notice that some fossils are molds (impressions) of an organism, while others are casts. You will model these two fossil processes during this inquiry.

Figure 18.6 *Making a mold and cast of a fossil*

2. Fill the bottom of the plastic wide-mouthed container with half of the craft dough from your group's bag. Flatten the dough.

3. Press one shell, textured-side down, into the dough.

4. Remove the shell from the dough. What does the dough look like? Look back at the reading selection "Fossils." What kind of fossil is an impression of an organism? Discuss this with your group.

5. Repeat Procedure Steps 3–4 with the other shell if there is room in the dough to do so without disturbing the first imprint.

6. Now use what you know about fossils to create a cast. Fill just the imprint of the shell with plaster as shown in Figure 18.6 and allow the plaster to sit overnight. Label the container with your initials and class period.

REFLECTING ON WHAT YOU'VE DONE

1. Once it has hardened, remove the plaster cast from its mold.

2. Share with the class what you've learned about fossil excavation, identification, and formation. Revisit your class list from "Getting Started."

3. Discuss with your class how the molds and casts you made are types of fossils. Why are many fossil molds and casts— like those found in your fossiliferous limestone—made from shells and not from the organism within the shell?

4. Read "The Great Asteroid and the End of the Dinosaurs." Answer the questions at the end of the reading selection in your notebook, and then discuss them with your class.

Fossils

Fossils are the preserved remains of an organism from Earth's past. When a plant or animal dies, it usually decomposes. Bacteria break down its tissue, and over a period of months or years, the tissue disintegrates. But sometimes animal or plant remains are protected from the elements and bacteria that would normally break it down. When this happens, traces of the fleshy parts of the organism may be preserved as a fossil. However, usually only the mineral parts of an organism, such as shells or skeletons, are preserved.

Fossils can be formed in many different ways. One type of fossil is an animal bone, tooth, or shell that has been preserved—often for millions of years. Fossils also can be formed when minerals seep into the pores of a slowly decaying shell or bone and replace the organism's cells with mineral material. Ancient wood preserved in this way is called "petrified wood," which is actually stone. An organism preserved in this way does not continue to decay.

Two other kinds of fossils are molds and casts. A mold is formed when acids dissolve a bone, tooth, or shell and leave an imprint or mold of the object in sediment. One way to think about a mold is to imagine pushing a seashell into wet sand. When you pull the shell away, the shape of the shell has been pressed into the sand. If the sand hardened over time, the impression of the shell would be preserved as a mold. A tiny sea creature's skeleton found in a piece of sandstone is an example of a mold. A cast is formed when sand or other minerals fill a cavity-shaped mold over time, and then harden to form a replica of the original organism.

(continued)

COURTESY OF THE HARDIN FAMILY PRIVATE COLLECTION

Is it a rock or is it wood? This petrified wood was found in Navajo, Arizona, and probably formed more than 225 million years ago. This fossil is four times as hard as granite rock. The colors are the result of different kinds of minerals that replaced the organic material in the wood.

COURTESY OF THE HARDIN FAMILY PRIVATE COLLECTION

This rock was found in Cap Rock, Texas. How many molds or casts of organisms can you find?

Sometimes an entire animal is preserved as a fossil. For example, 30 million years ago a fly may have gotten caught in tree resin. Eventually, that resin hardened into a clear, rocklike substance called "amber" with the fly entombed inside it. Sediment covered the amber and buried it deep inside the earth. Eventually, erosion may have brought the amber with the perfectly preserved fly to the surface to the lucky person who found it. The oldest amber fossil ever found is about 300 million years old.

COURTESY OF CAROLINA BIOLOGICAL SUPPLY COMPANY

This fly was trapped when it landed on sticky resin. In time, the resin turned to amber and the fly was preserved. This piece of fossilized tree resin was found in the Dominican Republic and dates back 24–34 million years.

This mammoth was trapped in the La Brea Tar Pits of southern California. Saber-toothed tigers are in the foreground.

Being trapped in tar also can fossilize animals. In the La Brea Tar Pits in southern California, tar bubbled up to the surface and formed pools in which many animals became trapped. In rare cases, freezing can also preserve an entire organism. Wooly mammoths, woolly rhinoceroses, and musk oxen are animals that were once frozen and have been recovered. Another method for preserving fossils is mummification. Mummification involves the air-drying of soft tissues such as muscles and tendons before the organism becomes buried.

Fossils also can include tracks, burrows, borings, nests, or any other preserved indication of the activities of an organism. Even an organism's feces (solid waste) can become fossilized. Fossilized waste can provide important information about diet and the size of the animal that produced it.

(continued)

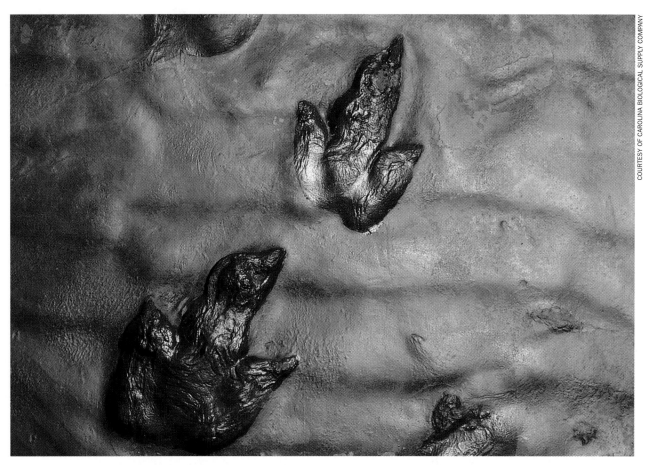

This fossil records the tracks of a three-toed Archosaurus. It was found near Summit, New Jersey. Sediment washed over the tracks and in time, hardened into stone, preserving the tracks.

The fossilized remains of microorganisms and organisms with skeletons or shells are abundant. Even the fossilized bones and teeth of dinosaurs and sharks are more common than you may realize. The next time you find yourself on a beach, don't just look for shells—look for the fossil of a shell in a piece of sandy rock. You might be surprised at what you will find! □

QUESTIONS

1. Name three types of fossil preservation and describe how they form.
2. Look back at your own fossils from Inquiry 18.1. Can you tell how each formed?
3. What could happen to an organism after it dies?
3. What do you think fossils can tell us about Earth's history as a planet?

The Great Asteroid and the End of the Dinosaurs

Imagine an asteroid larger than Mt. Everest hurtling toward Earth at a speed of 54,000 kilometers per hour. Could anything survive its impact? This scene may sound like something taken from a science fiction tale. But this event really did take place, and many scientists believe it changed life on our planet forever.

Impact!

More than 65 million years ago, dinosaurs ruled the Earth. *Tyrannosaurus rex* roamed the plains while winged reptiles soared in the skies above. Strange and exotic vegetation covered the land, while bizarre creatures swam the seas. There was little warning before disaster struck—perhaps just a momentary shadow across the sky.

The asteroid slammed into Earth with the force of a hundred million hydrogen bombs. It struck in the area now known as Chicxulub (*cheek-shoe-lube*), on the Yucatan Peninsula of what is now Mexico. Trillions of tons of rock vaporized or exploded into the atmosphere. Giant waves known as "tsunamis," possibly

(continued)

ARTIST: DON DAVIS/NATIONAL AERONAUTICS AND SPACE ADMINISTRATION

Artist's concept of the asteroid impact that may have been responsible for the mass extinction of many plants and animals, including the large dinosaurs.

several kilometers high, destroyed everything in their paths. Trees and plants burst into flames for thousands of miles in every direction. Violent earthquakes shook the planet, while searing winds whipped the landscape. Poisonous gases filled the air. Countless types of creatures and vegetation may have become extinct within hours. Many more would perish within the following days or months, probably because of a lack of habitat or food.

The debris that exploded into the air when the asteroid struck began spreading throughout the atmosphere. Soon the entire planet was blanketed in a thick cloud of dust that blocked most of the Sun's rays. Earth was plunged into a cold and terrible darkness. Organisms that could not adapt to the plunging temperature and lack of light began to die.

Plants draw their energy from the Sun and so were probably the first to be affected by the climate changes. Once the plants died, the herbivores (plant-eating creatures) began to starve. And with most of their prey dying off, the carnivores (meat eaters) were forced to attack one another before finally dying themselves. On the basis of fossil records of the time, scientists believe that the only land animals that survived the effects of the asteroid impact weighed

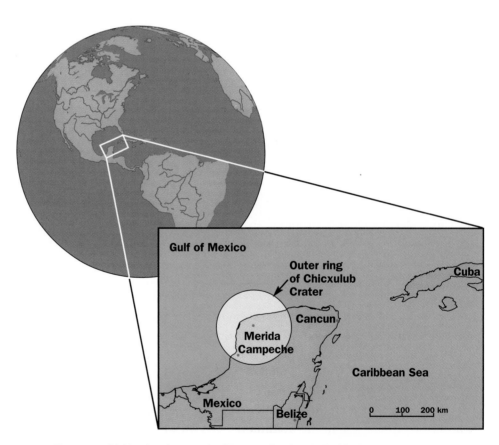

The asteroid hit what is now the Yucatan Peninsula in Mexico.

COURTESY OF WALTER ALVAREZ

This group of scientists at the University of California at Berkeley formulated the theory that an asteroid impact 65 million years ago killed off the dinosaurs. From left are Luis Alvarez, Walter Alvarez, Frank Asaro, and Helen Michel. Notice the sample of rock containing the dark band of clay that contains the mineral "iridium."

22 kilograms or less, and they probably lived on the remains of the larger dead creatures. Many families of birds became extinct. Only the hardiest species of fish, sharks, plankton, and invertebrates survived.

Scientists estimate that when the dust cloud surrounding Earth settled several months later, only one-third of the organisms living on Earth at the time of the asteroid impact lived to see the Sun again. Most cold-blooded reptiles and dinosaurs perished. The smaller, warm-blooded mammals survived to become the dominant creatures on the planet.

Our Future

The question everyone asks is, "Could a disaster like this occur again?" "Yes," says Walter Alvarez. Alvarez is a professor at the University of California at Berkeley and the geologist who—along with his father, award-winning physicist Luis Alvarez, and scientists Frank Asaro and Helen Michel—unlocked the mystery of the great asteroid and dinosaur extinction. Alvarez states, "It can happen and it will happen again in the remote future. But if we keep looking in the sky and we are prepared for it, hopefully our scientists will do a better job of preventing a real natural disaster than the Hollywood people did in the movies."

Even though dinosaurs inhabited Earth far longer than humans have, we are the first species on the planet with the ability to save ourselves from such a rare and random threat coming from outer space. ◻

How Do We Know What Happened 65 Million Years Ago?

In 1980, scientists made an educated guess about the location of the impact crater at Chixculub after studying differences in mineral deposits in the soil. In 1990, a NASA-generated image from space confirmed the existence of a crater in that area. Over the course of 65 million years, the crater has been nearly filled with earth and sediment. But a few telltale clues helped scientists unlock the mystery.

First, quartz rock in the area showed signs of great stress that result from a meteorite impact. This quartz is known as "shocked quartz." Second, large amounts of a mineral called "iridium," which is found only in meteorite dust or debris from an asteroid impact, was detected at Chixculub.

Meanwhile, paleontologists were studying fossil records from Chicxulub and other places around the world. When they reached a certain layer in the strata, paleontologists could see a dramatic change in the types of fossils in the soil. More importantly, between the layers of strata where the dramatic change occurred, scientists found a thin layer of iridium. The fossils that lay beneath the iridium are the organisms that lived before the impact. The fossils above the iridium are the organisms that either survived the impact or evolved from them. Working as "time detectives," scientists could reasonably determine that nearly two-thirds of all organisms on Earth vanished at the same time as the asteroid impact.

QUESTIONS

1. On the basis of fossil records, how did an asteroid 65 million years ago affect life on Earth?
2. If the asteroid impact had not occurred, how might life on Earth be different?
3. How might the effects of the asteroid impact have been different on another planet?

COURTESY OF DAVID A. KRING, NATIONAL AERONAUTICS AND SPACE ADMINISTRATION/UNIVERSITY OF ARIZONA SPACE IMAGERY CENTER

Layer of iridium shown as a dark band. Layers below the dark band were laid down before the impact. Layers above the dark band were laid down after the impact. The pocket knife is shown for scale.

The Age of Planets:
DATING ROCKS

Scientists believe that our solar system is about 4.6 billion years old. How did they make that estimate? Scientists use a process called radiometric dating to help them determine the age of rocks that are found on Earth and the Moon and to date meteorite samples. By comparing the ages of these materials, scientists can make predictions about the age of the entire solar system.

Radiometric Dating

Radiometric dating uses radioactive elements to help determine the age of rocks (and sometimes fossils) by measuring the age of radioactive elements in them. It works like this: Over time, radioactive elements decay and form new elements. For example, organisms take up carbon from the environment. This carbon eventually decays into nitrogen. When an organism dies, it stops taking up carbon, but its supply of radioactive carbon continues to decay at a particular rate. Scientists can measure the amount of radioactive carbon in the organism to calculate when the organism died. This method works for organisms that lived up to 70,000 years ago.

This process of carbon decay does not happen quickly. In fact, it takes 5730 years for just *half* the carbon in a sample to decay into nitrogen. This time is called the "half life" of radioactive carbon. This concept is pretty simple for the first half life, but it gets more complicated after that.

Imagine that you have a 100-gram sample of radioactive carbon. If you could check on that

(continued)

All organisms absorb carbon from the environment. This carbon decays, but is replaced by new carbon until the organism dies. After death, the carbon in the organism continues to decay at a steady rate, which tells us how long ago the organism died.

carbon after 5730 years, you would find that half the carbon had decayed into nitrogen. You would have 50 grams of radioactive carbon and 50 grams of nitrogen. If you could come back after another 5730 years (or after a total of 11,460 years) you would find that half the carbon that was left the previous time had decayed, so you would have 25 grams of radioactive carbon left. Then, 5730 years later, you'd have 12.5 grams of radioactive carbon left. As time passed, the amount of radioactive carbon would get smaller, but it would take a very long time for all the carbon to decay.

For scientists who want to study something as old as rocks, they need to select a radioactive element that has a much longer half-life than that of radioactive carbon, such as radioactive potassium, or potassium-40. Potassium-40 turns into argon as it decays, and its half-life is 1,280,000,000 years (or 1.28 billion years). Scientists use potassium-40 to date rocks. By comparing the amount of radioactive potassium to the amount of argon in a rock sample, they can determine the age of the rock.

Rocks 3.5 billion years old have been found on all continents. However, scientists believe that Earth is even older than this. They believe that these 3.5-billion-year-old rocks were not part of Earth's original crust, but were formed later from lava flows and sediments. Crystals from Australia, dated to be 4.4 billion years old, are believed to be some of the oldest materials on Earth.

UNITED STATES GEOLOGICAL SURVEY

A technician of the U.S. Geological Survey in Denver uses a mass spectrometer to determine the radioactive "age" of a sample of igneous rock. A mass spectrometer allows scientists to precisely analyze rocks and minerals ranging in age from 10,000 years to 0.56 billion years.

The Ancient Solar System

In their efforts to determine the age of the solar system, scientists have not limited themselves to studying Earth. They have also studied rocks from the Moon. Many of these samples were collected during NASA's Apollo missions.

Scientists have determined that the oldest of these lunar rocks are between 4.4 and 4.5 billion years old, which indicates that the Moon is about as old as Earth.

Scientists also have studied meteorites to determine the age of the solar system. Since meteorites are not subject to planetary processes such as volcanism, they are excellent indicators of the age of the solar system. Using radiometric dating, scientists have now determined the age of more than 70 meteorites, all of which are about 4.5 billion years old. Scientists believe that this is the age of our solar system.

As scientists continue to study new mineral samples from other planets, it will be possible to test rocks from other places in the solar system. Those samples may allow scientists to confirm the age of the solar system. ☐

COURTESY OF JOHN W. VALLEY, UNIVERSITY OF WISCONSIN—MADISON

Outcrop in Western Australia. Zircon crystals (see below) near the hammer were dated 4.4 billion years old. These crystals are pieces of the earliest known crust on Earth. (From left to right: John Valley and Aaron Cavosie, University of Wisconsin–Madison, and Simon Wilde, Curtin University.)

COURTESY OF
JOHN W. VALLEY,
UNIVERSITY OF
WISCONSIN—MADISON

Microscopic view of a zircon crystal determined to be 4.4 billion years old

Comparing Planets: Is Earth Unique?

Earth is teeming with liquid water, oxygen, and abundant life forms.

NATIONAL AERONAUTICS AND SPACE ADMINISTRATION/JOHNSON SPACE CENTER

INTRODUCTION

Earth teems with liquid water, oxygen, and abundant life forms. But it wasn't always this way. The primitive Earth—like Venus today—had an atmosphere thick in carbon dioxide. This gas caused a greenhouse effect with high surface temperatures on Earth. Earth's surface was covered with volcanoes, just as Venus' surface is today. Is Earth unique? Or could Venus be a young Earth?

The presence of life on Earth and its abundant liquid water sets our planet apart from the rest of the planets in our solar system. In this lesson, you and your classmates will present your planetary travel brochures and mission designs. You will compare Earth to the other planets in the solar system and consider how the conditions on each planet—such as distance from the Sun, surface gravity, atmosphere, and temperature—affect our ability to study the planet more closely in the future. You also will consider the delicate balance of conditions on Earth that allow life to exist.

What might life on Earth be like if its conditions were different? What conditions might be necessary for life to exist on other planets? Let's find out.

OBJECTIVES FOR THIS LESSON

Present your travel brochure and your team's mission design to the class; explain how a planet's features affect scientists' ability to study it.

Compare Earth to other planets in the solar system.

Explore the effects of climate change on Earth.

Getting Started

1. With your group, brainstorm how Earth compares to the other planets in our solar system. How is Earth like other planets? How is it different? List your group's ideas in your notebook.

2. Examine the list of ideas. What conditions or characteristics allow life to exist on Earth? Identify them in some way on your list.

3. Read "Climate's Link to Life." Answer the questions at the end of the selection in your notebook, and then discuss them as a class.

MATERIALS FOR LESSON 19

For you
1 completed copy of Student Sheet 10.1c: Planetary Chart
1 completed planetary travel brochure

For your team
1 completed future mission design

Inquiry 19.1
Comparing the Planets

PROCEDURE

1. Listen as other students present their planetary travel brochures to the class. Compare the data you have recorded on Student Sheet 10.1c with the data presented by each student. Be prepared to ask questions and debate ideas. Revise information on Student Sheet 10.1c if needed.

2. After all the students have presented their brochures, get together with your mission design team. Present to the class your ideas for a future mission to your planet. What features of the planet did you consider when designing your mission? Share your ideas with the class.

REFLECTING ON WHAT YOU'VE DONE

1. With your group, compare the nine planets in each category listed on Student Sheet 10.1c. Look for patterns and exceptions to the patterns. (For example, does the distance of a planet from the Sun relate to its mass? Does the mass of a planet determine how many moons it can have? If a pattern in mass and distance exists, is there a planet that doesn't follow this pattern?) Decide with your group how to record the patterns you discover.

2. Analyze any patterns or exceptions to the patterns by answering the following in your notebook, then discuss them as a class:

A. Which categories listed on Student Sheet 10.1c seem to be related? Explain why you think they are related.

B. Which categories seem to stand alone, with little or no relation to the others?

C. Which planet breaks a pattern and in which category?

D. Look back to the Mission reading selections in Lessons 11–17. What patterns do you observe in the planets' atmospheres? Which categories seem to be related to whether a planet has an atmosphere? Explain your thinking.

3. Read "Little Things Mean a Lot." Then answer the questions at the end of the reader in your notebook. Discuss your answers with your class.

Climate's Link to Life

Earth has a lot going for it—it has the best position of any planet in the solar system. If Earth were much closer to the Sun, all of its water would boil away, as it has on Venus. If our planet were farther from the Sun, Earth's water would freeze, as it has on Mars.

All the other planets in our solar system are either too hot or too cold to support life as we know it. But on Earth an incredible range of life forms exists, from algae to zebras. No doubt about it—Earth's position and conditions are just right. That doesn't mean, however, that Earth's climate is the same everywhere on the planet, or that it never changes.

Climate Differences in Place and Time

Tour the planet and you'll find different climates that support different plants and animals. Around the equator, the climate is hot and wet, which is perfect for monkeys, snakes, and orchids. But those life forms wouldn't last long in the frigid, dry Arctic. And can you imagine a polar bear

(continued)

This photo of Prince William Sound, Alaska, demonstrates Earth's conditions in balance.

from the Arctic surviving in the tropics?

Not only does Earth have a wide variety of climates, but over time—a long time—the planet's climate has changed.

Throughout Earth's 4.5 billion-year history, there have been many ice ages when snow and ice covered much of the planet for long periods. Eventually, higher temperatures melted most of the ice and put an end to each ice age. But there were losers each time the climate changed.

Different climates support different plants and animals on Earth.

During Earth's last ice age, woolly mammoths and mastodons thrived. We know this because scientists have found many of their bones and analyzed these fossils to determine their ages. This research makes one thing perfectly clear: These prehistoric giants died out at the end of the last ice age. They did not survive the change in climate. Their disappearance helped make way for newer species of plants and animals that were better suited to the warmer climate.

Thousands of years from now, Earth will likely enter another ice age. But first, the planet is in for some pretty hot times.

Greenhouse Gas

Earth typically experiences a warm period between ice ages, but something else is happening on our planet. Earth is getting even warmer than it usually would between ice ages! For a clue about why this is happening, think about the climate on Venus. It is one of the hottest planets in our solar system because its thick atmosphere is made up of mostly carbon dioxide (CO_2). Carbon dioxide is a "greenhouse gas." That means that it lets the Sun's heat in, but it does not let it back out again. This CO_2 traps a planet's heat like a thick woolen blanket. Earth may be heading for a similar situation.

(continued)

This prehistoric giant died out at the end of the last ice age.

Gasoline-burning cars, trucks, jet skis, leaf blowers, and lawn mowers release carbon dioxide, a colorless gas, into the air. And this gas, along with other pollutants and water vapor, absorbs the Sun's heat—heat that would normally escape into space—and traps it in Earth's atmosphere.

Global Warming

Temperatures on Earth appear to be rising. Scientists predict that increased hot spells may cause more drastic changes due to the heat. Numerous frog species already have been wiped out in Central America because of these changing conditions. Some scientists believe that the world's coral reefs may be gone by 2050 due to global warming. The population of Adelie penguins on the Antarctic dropped 40 percent in the last quarter of the 20th Century. Scientists think that warmer temperatures make it harder for penguins to find food and breed.

Higher temperatures also will melt glaciers and ice sheets, causing oceans to rise. Models indicate that the glaciers in Glacier Park, Montana, may be gone by 2030. Rising sea levels in Maryland's Blackwater National Wildlife Refuge are driving away many species of birds. Coastal areas around the planet—including places such as Florida in the United States, and countless low-lying countries like the Netherlands—could get buried under water.

It's true that Earth is the best planet in the solar system to call home. But let's not forget: The climate has a whole lot to do with it. ☐

Venus

QUESTIONS

1. Do you consider that Earth is in a state of balance (or equilibrium)? Explain your answer.
2. Why could Earth's state of balance be considered "delicate"?
3. Why might Earth's climate be its "link to life"?
4. Look at the photograph of Venus. How does Earth's climate compare to other planets?

LITTLE THINGS
Mean a Lot

Throughout this course, you read a series called Missions. The information about Earth's solar system is very detailed—and perhaps confusing at times.

"Why does this all matter?" you might ask. "Is it really important that Earth is 149.6 million kilometers from the Sun? Or that Earth's surface gravity is much less than that of Jupiter? Or that the Moon is 382,400 kilometers from Earth?"

These details do matter. They matter because it's the balance of many factors—mass, dis-tance from the Sun, rotation rate, and other factors—that makes life as we know it possible on Earth. These factors also make Earth, its sister planets, and the Sun work together as a whole—as a system.

Two scientists, Stephen Dole and Isaac Asimov, described the importance of little things in *Habitable Planets for Man,* a book published in the 1960s. In it they speculate about life on Earth if some things were changed. Let's examine a few.

What if Earth were twice as massive?
Greater mass would mean a greater surface gravity. This would have a significant effect on plant and animal life. Trees would be shorter and have thicker trunks. Animals would have heavier leg bones and muscles. Mountains would not be as high because they would not have the strength to support their weight. Waves in the ocean would be lower, and erosion would be faster.

What if Earth were closer to the Sun?
If Earth's mean distance from the Sun were 10 percent less than it is now, less than 20 percent of Earth's surface would be habitable. The habitable areas would lie in two bands between latitudes 45 degrees and 64 degrees North and South. A broad area of intolerable heat would separate these two bands. There would be no polar ice, and the level of the oceans would be higher.

What if Earth rotated once every 100 hours, rather than every 24 hours?
Temperature differences between day and night would be extreme. The Sun would seem to crawl across the sky. Few forms of life would be able to tolerate both the intense heat of the long days and the bitter cold of the long nights.

What if the Moon were much closer—for example about 152,000 kilometers away from the Earth, instead of 384,400 kilometers away?
If the Moon were much closer to Earth, tidal forces might be strong enough to halt the rotation of Earth with respect to the Moon. A "day" on Earth would last a month, and Earth would be uninhabitable. By contrast, if the Moon were more than 713,600 kilometers away, Earth could not hold it in orbit. Organisms dependent on the rhythm of the tides would die out, and nights would always be dark.

As we can see from these examples from *Habitable Planets for Man*, life on Earth is possible only because of a delicate balance that exists in the solar system. Change just one thing and we might be in for trouble. Details do matter! □

QUESTIONS

1. Which of Earth's characteristics allow life to exist on the planet?
2. How might Earth change if any of its conditions were even slightly changed?
3. Examine the planet you studied for your planetary travel brochure. What conditions would you have to change on the planet for life to exist on it?

SCIENCE FICTION— SCIENCE FACT

Author and scientist
Isaac Asimov

What kinds of books do you like to read? Many people turn to science fiction. Adults may enjoy writers such as Isaac Asimov and Arthur Clarke, whose works are modern classics. Younger people may prefer a writer like Madeleine L'Engle, who wrote *A Wrinkle in Time* and *A Swiftly Tilting Planet.*

Why is science fiction so popular? One reason is that science fiction tells a good story that removes us from our ordinary surroundings. Authors who make good use of their imaginations can create convincing and inventive worlds.

But science fiction is different from fantasy—it is not based on imagination alone. Real science fiction is based on scientific principles and a solid understanding of the real world and how it works. Some of the best-known authors of science fiction are scientists themselves. Asimov had a Ph.D. in chemistry and he taught in a medical school—whenever he wasn't writing one of his hundreds of books!

Asimov defined science fiction as writing that is concerned with the "impact of scientific advance on human beings." He thought science fiction was a good way to make science more accessible to everyone.

Once you know what science fiction is, you can see how something that was once featured in science fiction can become science fact. In 1865, the French author Jules Verne wrote a book, *From the Earth to the Moon,* that described a manned voyage to the Moon. Most French people at the time were probably skeptical—*"C'est impossible!"* they may have said.

(continued)

SMITHSONIAN INSTITUTION LIBRARIES

Jules Verne's book From the Earth to the Moon

Author Jules Verne surrounded by illustrations of some of his ideas

Some citizens fled their homes in panic after hearing the radio broadcast "War of the Worlds."

But just about 100 years after Jules Verne imagined a trip to the Moon, U.S. astronaut Neil Armstrong and his team landed the spaceship *Eagle* on the Moon's surface. Other works by Jules Verne describe underwater vessels—what we now call submarines—and even something similar to today's television sets decades before these things were invented.

Science fantasy can be great reading. One of the most famous books of the late 1800s was *War of the Worlds* by H.G. Wells. In that story, Martians invaded Earth. A radio broadcast based on the book aired on Halloween night in 1938 and caused millions of people to believe that an invasion from Mars was actually taking place. Some people even decided to evacuate their cities!

Scientists doubted Wells's fantastic theory about Martians. And when *Viking I* landed on Mars in 1976, people learned that this famous author had indeed been writing science *fantasy* and not science *fiction*. There were no signs of life on the planet. Wells's book is good reading—but his tales are not necessarily based on true science.

Science fiction helps shape our vision of how we will live tomorrow. If something can be imagined, has practical applications, and is scientifically possible, chances are it will become a reality. Jules Verne, one of the greatest science fiction writers of all time, was able to imagine the future.

Why don't you give it a try? Let your imagination soar. Can you think of something that is science fiction today—but may become science fact tomorrow? ☐

QUESTION

1. How would you describe your team's mission to another planet—science fiction or science fact? Explain your answer.

Exploring Space Technology

This skier's boots use space technology to help the skier bend and move swiftly downhill.

COURTESY OF THE ROSSIGNOL COMPANY

INTRODUCTION

How has the space program helped advance our life on Earth? The use of satellites alone has affected our daily living in almost every aspect, from telephone calls to television. Space technology from NASA has been used in many different products for decades. For example, Apollo engineers developed special Moon boots for astronauts who would walk on the lunar surface. The circuitry in the boot could warm or cool the astronaut's feet in the Moon's extreme temperatures. Later, a footwear design firm used this technology to create built-in rechargeable footwarming devices for ski boots. The footwear design firm also adapted the accordion-like joints originally developed for NASA spacesuits for use with the boot's tongue. This design increased the flexibility of the boot tongue so that it could bend without cracking.

In this lesson, you will learn more about products that use space technology. First, you will read about some products and processes—called "spinoffs"—that were originally created for the space program that have been adapted for use

OBJECTIVES FOR THIS LESSON

Read about products and processes—called "spinoffs"—that scientists and engineers developed for the space program that have been adapted for use on Earth.

Select a spinoff product, research the product, and record information about it.

Review the concepts and skills addressed in Parts 2 and 3 of *Earth in Space.*

on Earth. You will explore other spinoff products developed by the space program and select one product to research further. In Lesson 21, you will present information about this product through a **S**pace **T**echnology **A**nd **R**esearch (STAR) poster.

Getting Started

1. Read "Spinoffs From Space." Discuss the reading selection with the class.

2. What does the term "spinoff" mean to you? Discuss your ideas with the class.

3. Brainstorm other everyday products that you think may use space technology.

MATERIALS FOR LESSON 20

For you

1 copy of Student Sheet 20.1: STAR Poster

1 copy of Student Sheet 20: Solar System Review Access to a computer lab and the Internet or classroom resource center

Inquiry 20.1
Researching a Space Spinoff Product

PROCEDURE

1. Read the STAR Guidelines in this lesson. Then discuss the guidelines as a class.

2. Get one copy of Student Sheet 20.1: STAR Poster. Discuss the information with your class.

3. Discuss with your teacher how you will be assessed on this activity.

4. If possible, go to the computer lab or library to learn more about other space spinoff products.

5. Select a specific spinoff product or process for your STAR poster. Examples are listed in the Guidelines. Record information about your product on the sheet. Turn the completed STAR in to your teacher during Lesson 21.

REFLECTING ON WHAT YOU'VE DONE

1. Get one copy of Student Sheet 20: Solar System Review. Review your lab notes, review the reading selections in Lessons 11–21, and complete the sheet to prepare for the assessment in Lesson 22.

STAR Guidelines

The **S**pace **T**echnology **A**nd **R**esearch (STAR) activity focuses on a product or process—called a spinoff—that was originally created for the space program but that became useful to people on Earth. During this lesson, you will select one space spinoff product and conduct your research. During Lesson 21, you will present your research to the class on a STAR-shaped poster. You may use Student Sheet 20.1 for your star-shaped poster or you may create one of your own out of poster board.

1. Choose a product or process.
Select one spinoff product to research. For example, the following products or processes use space technology:

- Global Positioning System (GPS)
- Lightweight bicycle helmet
- Scratch-resistant lens
- Zero-gravity pen
- Shoe shock absorber
- Plant minder
- Solar water heater
- Miniature earthmover
- Supercooling refrigerator

2. Research the product.
Conduct your research to find out more about the space spinoff you have selected. Information on your selected topic may be difficult to find if it is a relatively new development in space science. You should use at least one resource. Your teacher will tell you which Internet sources, books, magazines, and newspaper articles you may use in your research.

3. Make your STAR poster.
Prepare your final STAR poster. You can use the star on Student Sheet 20.1 or you can make your own poster (see Figure 20.1). (It should be shaped like a star.) Each point of the star should address some type of information about the product. For example, you may want to try

to present information that addresses the following questions:

- How was this product originally used in space?
- Was this product originally proposed for a mission? Which one?
- How is this product now used on Earth?
- Did the design, form, or function of this product change when it was adapted for use on Earth? How?
- What other information do you have about this space spinoff?

Record your research about questions such as these on each point of your STAR.

4. Create a model.

As an option, you may choose to design and/or build a model of your selected product. If possible, show how the product works. Your model can include any one of the following:

- A three-dimensional working model of the product
- Your own drawing or labeled diagram of the product
- A set of photographs or illustrations of the product taken from other sources
- A Web page, slide show (PowerPoint®), or other technology-based presentation displaying your product

Remember to use your school's guidelines for giving credit to the sources for any images you use.

5. Present Your STAR project.

During Lesson 21, you will give a brief class presentation to discuss your research and show the class your STAR poster.

Figure 20.1

Two completed STAR posters on poster board.

Spinoffs From Space

A space spinoff isn't a piece of equipment abandoned and left in orbit after a space mission. A spinoff is an invention that scientists originally created for the space program that may be adapted for products used on Earth. Let's look at some spinoffs from space science.

Hang gliders were developed from a spacecraft retrieval system.

Hang Gliders Take Off With NASA's Wings

During the Gemini and Apollo projects, NASA wanted a better way to retrieve spacecraft after splashdown. Engineers designed a triangular set of wings to help a descending spacecraft hit its landing target. NASA never used those wings, preferring to continue using parachutes instead. However, makers of hang gliders have found a use for the wings: They help the fliers control their direction and speed when descending.

A Drill for Rock Is Good for Wood and Bone

Scientists originally created a tiny jackhammer for drilling rocks on Mars; when it is put to work, it will do an excellent job of revealing their composition. But the jackhammer also

(continued)

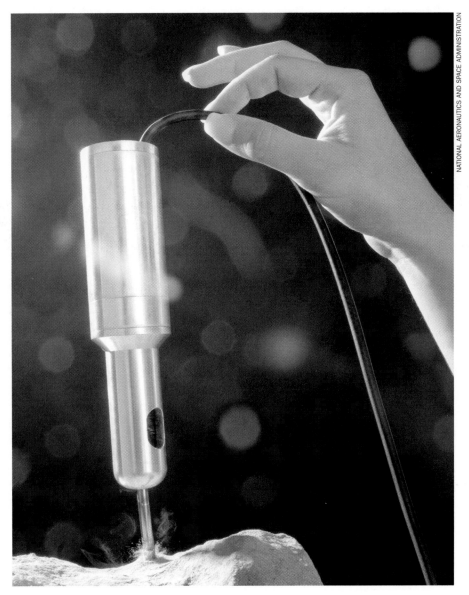

A tiny jackhammer designed for drilling on Mars may be used by craftsmen and orthopedic surgeons.

will be a popular tool for carpenters—and orthopedic surgeons. These doctors need to drill holes in bones when they set fractures or implant artificial joints. Ordinary medical power drills can harm bones because they generate excessive heat with their traditional rotary action. Not "Tiny Jack." It uses ultrasonic (frequencies above the range of human hearing) and sonic vibrations that do not rely on weight, and it does not generate heat.

From Spacecraft Insulation to Emergency Rescue Blankets

NASA developed lightweight metal insulation for use in a spacecraft—which eventually led to the creation of a new type of emergency rescue blanket. The emergency rescue blanket, made with plastic milk bottles, has the same "honeycomb" texture as the insulation in spacecraft. These blankets are four times warmer—and they dry five times faster—than blankets made from wool.

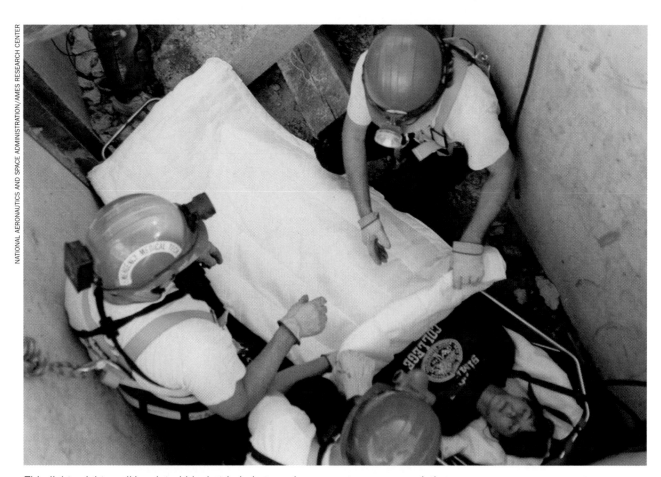

NATIONAL AERONAUTICS AND SPACE ADMINISTRATION/AMES RESEARCH CENTER

This lightweight, well-insulated blanket is being used on emergency rescue victims.

An Alarm for Every Home

Are you familiar with that smoke detector in your home? You can thank space science for it. Scientists invented smoke detectors to warn astronauts of fires in their spacecrafts. It certainly makes sense for ground-based homes to have them, too!

A Star Sensor for Your Ears

NASA scientists use infrared sensors to help measure the age of faraway stars. These sensors can also be used to measure a patient's temperature. An infrared thermometer placed in the ear can measure the amount of invisible infrared radiation, or heat, coming from the eardrum.

(continued)

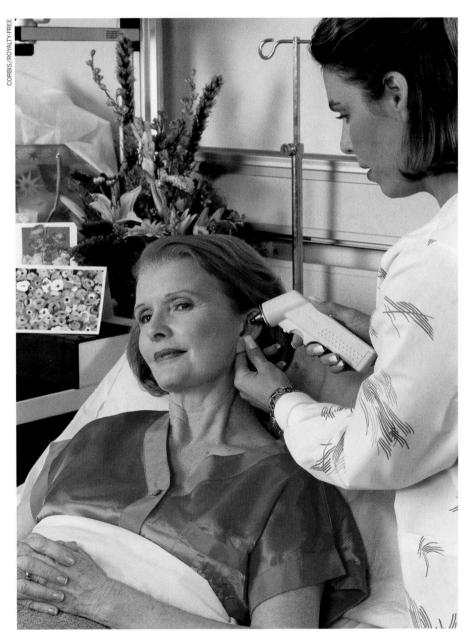

Infrared ear thermometers can calculate body temperature.

The Cool Suit

Stevie has a rare skin disease. He may die if he is exposed to warm temperatures. Stevie was restricted to staying indoors until a special outfit—originally created for astronauts—was adapted and custom-made for him. The adapted suit circulates coolant that runs through tubes in the vest and headpiece. The suit prevents Stevie from overheating—and lets him do things we all enjoy.

A Portable Ice Rink

Imagine a perfectly smooth and portable ice rink. As a result of NASA's research on solar energy, such a thing actually exists. Touring ice shows use the portable ice rinks. You can also find them at amusement parks, sports arenas—and even shopping malls. A portable ice rink is built on a layer of rubber tubing covered with water. Chilled antifreeze is pumped through the tubes, freezing the water smooth as glass in no time.

Cool suits can keep children who have a rare skin disease healthy and safe.

Portable ice rink

A Future Mars Mission May Help Clean Earth's Air Today

Future missions to Mars will include infrared lasers to analyze the Red Planet's soil and atmosphere. These same lasers, placed beside roadways on Earth, can easily detect pollution in car and truck exhaust. Drivers who violate emission standards will be told to fix their vehicles—or keep them off the roads. ☐

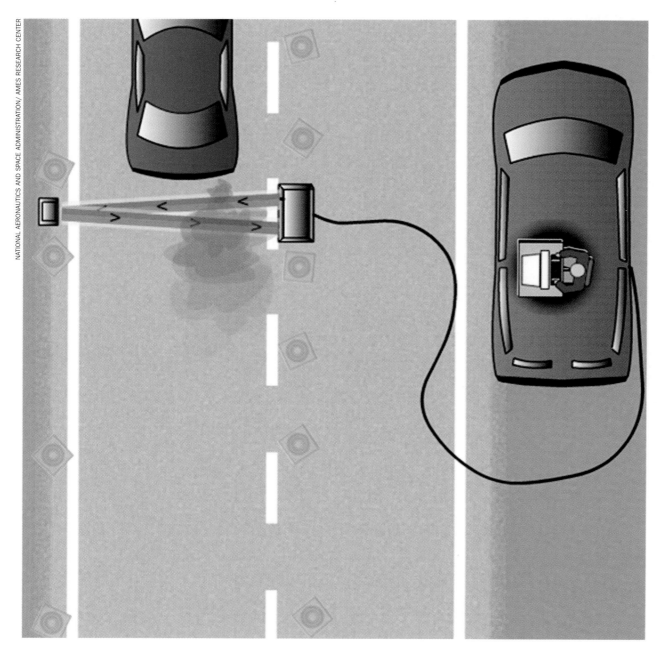

This infrared laser can detect pollution in car and truck exhaust.

NATIONAL AERONAUTICS AND SPACE ADMINISTRATION/ AMES RESEARCH CENTER

Presenting the Space Technology And Research (STAR) Posters

In this lesson, you will present your STAR poster to the class.

JEFF McADAMS, PHOTOGRAPHER, COURTESY OF CAROLINA BIOLOGICAL SUPPLY COMPANY

INTRODUCTION

In the last lesson you researched a technology product that was developed for the space program and was later adapted for use on Earth. Now it is time for you to tell other students about your space technology spinoff. First, you will present your five-point **S**pace **T**echnology **A**nd **R**esearch (STAR) poster to the class. You will share your ideas with the class and evaluate other students' presentations. At the end of the lesson, you will prepare for your final assessment in Lesson 22.

OBJECTIVES FOR THIS LESSON

Present information about a space spinoff product or process.

Discuss and ask questions about other students' explanations of their products.

Evaluate designs or products that use space technology.

Review the concepts addressed in Lessons 11–21.

Inquiry 21.1
Communicating Our Findings

PROCEDURE

1. You will be invited to present your STAR poster to the class. Share with the class any props, photographs, or product models that you might have.

2. Discuss your ideas about each product or process with the class.

3. Discuss other students' explanations about their space product or process and ask questions.

MATERIALS FOR LESSON 21

For you
1 copy of your completed STAR
1 copy of your completed Student Sheet 20: Solar System Review

REFLECTING ON WHAT YOU'VE DONE

1. Evaluate other students' space spinoff designs or products. Which form of space technology seemed the most common in the products presented?

2. Brainstorm some of the other space spin-off products that you think scientists and engineers have adapted for use on Earth.

3. Read "Sugars in Space." How is technology being used to search for life in other galaxies?

4. To prepare for your final assessment in Lesson 22, review Student Sheet 20 with your teacher.

Sugars in Space

For as long as humans have looked at stars in the night skies, we've been asking the same question: Is there any life out there? And as we study the universe with telescopes, we might wonder whether alien astronomers are peering back at us.

As far as our own solar system is concerned, it is almost certain that we don't have any nosy neighbors. In fact, it seems increasingly unlikely that we have neighbors at all. After decades of exploring the nearby planets, scientists have

(continued)

Is there life among the stars in our galaxy?

NATIONAL AERONAUTICS AND SPACE ADMINISTRATION/SPACE TELESCOPE SCIENCE
INSTITUTE/ASSOCIATION OF UNIVERSITIES FOR RESEARCH IN ASTRONOMY

not found a single sign of life. But that doesn't prove that there is no life out there—so we keep looking.

Among the things that scientists look for are the essential building blocks of life—water, oxygen, and organic chemicals. Wherever these building blocks exist, scientists say, it is at least possible that life could exist.

What building blocks of life have scientists found in space? We know that there is plenty of water on Mars, and almost all of it is frozen. On Europa, one of Jupiter's moons, there seems to be a great liquid sea under a surface made entirely of ice. And on the Moon, a recent space probe detected the possibility of ice, located in a crater at the Moon's south pole. Where there is water, there might be life.

Another amazing discovery was made recently by a group of American scientists, including Dr. Jan M. Hollis of NASA Goddard Space Flight Center. Using a large radiotelescope at Kitt Peak Observatory in Arizona, these scientists looked at a giant cloud of gas and dust near the center of the Milky Way galaxy. In that cloud, they found a chemical called glycolaldehyde (gly-co-LAHL-dee-hyde), that belongs to a family of chemicals that we know by a much more common name: sugars.

A radiotelescope works just like any other radio—except that it's much more powerful. To give you a rough idea of how powerful it is, imagine sitting on a park bench in New York City and being able to hear a cricket chirping in Los Angeles!

© 1995, 1966 NATIONAL RADIO ASTRONOMY OBSERVATORY

Radiotelescope at Kitt Peak

Clouds of dust and gas condensed to form the Sun and nine planets.

When these astronomers aimed their radio-telescope at the dust cloud, they detected a faint radio signal emitted by the sugar molecules. As those molecules spin around in space, they emit radio waves at a precise frequency just like the signals you receive from different radio stations. When the scientists detected the signals from the dust cloud, they knew those signals could only have been produced by glycolaldehyde.

Glycolaldehyde is a small molecule that is composed of carbon, oxygen, and hydrogen. It combines with other molecules to form either ribose or glucose. Ribose is a building block of RNA and DNA, the molecules that carry the genetic codes of all living things. Glucose is a sugar that is found in fruit.

Why are sugar molecules floating around our galaxy in giant dust clouds? We know that the dust clouds are remnants of ancient exploding stars and that they are made up of different elements and compounds, many of which are necessary for life. Eventually, the clouds will condense to form new stars and planets. That's what happened with the Sun, Earth, and other planets of our solar system, about 4.5 billion years ago.

The presence of glycolaldehyde and other organic chemicals in space means that the essential building blocks of life are scattered over the Milky Way galaxy. Perhaps someday we may detect astronomers in other parts of the universe, searching through the barrels of their telescopes as they try to find answers to the same questions that we have been asking all these years! ☐

Solar System Assessment

How does the distance of a planet from the Sun affect its orbital period? Use a string and washer to test your ideas in this lesson.

INTRODUCTION

You have now completed the second half of the module *Earth in Space*. In this lesson, you will be assessed on your ability to show both what you know and what you can demonstrate about the solar system. The assessment is divided into three parts. During Part A, you will conduct an investigation and record your data, observations, and conclusions. In Part B, you will complete multiple-choice and short-answer questions about the planets, asteroids, comets, and Earth's history as a planet. You will review diagrams and analyze data organized in a table. Finally, during Part C, you will review the ten questions that you answered in Lesson 1 of this module. Your teacher will use the results of this assessment to determine how well you can apply the concepts, knowledge, and skills you have learned in this module.

OBJECTIVES FOR THIS LESSON

Review concepts and skills from Part 2: Solar System and Part 3: Earth's History as a Planet.

Complete a two-part assessment of the concepts and skills addressed in Parts 2 and 3.

Revisit questions from Lesson 1.

PROCEDURE

Part A

1. Collect one copy of the Planning Sheet, one copy of Inquiry Master 22.1a, and one copy of Student Sheet 22.1a for yourself.

2. Listen as your teacher describes Part A of the assessment.

3. Discuss with your teacher how you might set up a data table.

4. Review with your teacher how you will be assessed on your work in this lesson.

5. Complete your Planning Sheet.

6. Review the Safety Tips. Collect your lab equipment. Although you might share a set of materials with another student, you will complete the written portion of the assessment individually.

7. Complete your investigation by following your Planning Sheet. Record your data, graph, observations, and conclusions. Remember to relate your conclusions to the motion of the planets in our solar system.

MATERIALS FOR LESSON 22

For you

- 1 copy of the Planning Sheet
- 1 copy of Student Sheet 22.1a: Solar System Performance-Based Assessment (Part A)
- 1 copy of Student Sheet 22.1b: Solar System Assessment Answer Sheet (Part B)
- 1 class copy of Inquiry Master 22.1a: Solar System Performance Task (Part A)
- 1 class copy of Inquiry Master 22.1b: Solar System Written Assessment (Part B)
- 1 pencil with eraser
- 1 pair of indirectly vented safety goggles

For you and your partner

- 1 student timer
- 1 metric measuring tape
- 1 piece of string, 1 m
- 1 small metal washer

SAFETY TIPS

Wear goggles at all times.

Do not spin the washer above your head.

Leave plenty of space between groups. Make sure the swinging washer will not hit students or objects.

Do not let go of the string while the washer is in motion.

Part B

1. Your teacher will distribute the questions and answer sheet for Part B of the assessment. Do not write on the question sheets. They may be used by other classes throughout the day. Put all answers on your answer sheet. Your teacher will go over the assessment with you.

2. Begin Part B of the assessment when your teacher directs you to do so.

3. Turn in Part B of your assessment after you have answered all of the questions.

Part C

1. With your class, examine the ten folders with Questions A–J from Lesson 1.

2. Answer the ten questions from Lesson 1 again independently and in writing. You can refer to Procedure Step 1 in Lesson 1 for the specific questions.

REFLECTING ON WHAT YOU'VE DONE

1. Review your scored assessments with the teacher.

2. Discuss with the class how your ideas about the solar system have changed since Lesson 1.

Glossary

amber: A type of fossil that forms when partial or complete insects and small arthropods become embedded in tree resin; fossilizes when the resin is buried and hardens into a clear shell. *See also* **fossil.**

angle of separation: Angle between lines originating from the eye of the observer toward two objects, such as a star—the Sun—and the horizon. *See also* **horizon.**

annular eclipse: A type of solar eclipse in which the Moon is too far from Earth to cover the Sun completely, so the outer edge of the Sun is seen as a ring. *See also* **solar eclipse.**

apparent: Seeming real or true; for example, the Sun's *apparent* motion across the sky is due to Earth's rotation, not the Sun's motion.

asteroid: A small, mostly rocky solar system object that orbits independently around the Sun; minor planet. *See also* **asteroid belt.**

asteroid belt: A large group of asteroids that orbits the Sun between Mars and Jupiter. *See also* **asteroid.**

astronomer: A scientist who studies the stars, planets, and other objects in space. *See also* **astronomy.**

astronomical unit: A unit of measure equal to the average distance between Earth and the Sun, about 150 million kilometers (93 million miles); abbreviated AU.

astronomy: The branch of science that studies the stars, planets, and other objects in space. *See also* **astronomer.**

atmosphere: The mixture of gases that surrounds a planet or moon.

aurora: Light display that occurs mostly near the poles when gases in Earth's atmosphere glow when hit by charged particles carried by solar winds. *See also* **solar wind.**

axis (plural: axes): An imaginary line that runs through the middle of an object (for example, from pole to pole) around which that object rotates; a line at the side or bottom of a graph.

basin: An area where rock dips toward a central point or depression, as in a crater. *See also* **crater.**

cast: Type of fossil that forms when sand, minerals, or other matter fill a cavity-shaped mold over time and then harden, forming a replica of the original organism. *See also* **fossil.**

celestial: Of or relating to things in the heavens.

chromosphere: The layer of the Sun's atmosphere below the corona. *See also* **corona.**

coma: The part of a comet that surrounds the nucleus and that is made of gas and dust. *See also* **comet.**

comet: A mass of frozen gas, cosmic dust, ice crystals, and organic material whose orbit around the Sun takes it outside the solar system.

constellation: An observed pattern of stars.

core: The center of a planet, star, or moon.

corona: The outer layer of the Sun's atmosphere that becomes visible from Earth during a total solar eclipse.

crater: A bowl-shaped pit on a planet, moon, or asteroid formed by the impact of an object; also formed by volcanoes. *See also* **basin.**

crescent: The phase of the Moon in which only a curved edge of the Moon's side that faces Earth is illuminated; occurs between a new moon and a quarter moon. *See also* **phase; waxing crescent; waning crescent.**

day: The time it takes a planet to complete one rotation on its axis; one Earth day is approximately 24 hours long. *See also* **year.**

degree: A unit for measuring angles and arcs; one degree equals $\frac{1}{360}$ of a circle.

Earth-centered: A description of the universe in which it was believed that all the planets, stars, Moon, and Sun revolve around Earth.

eclipse: The complete or partial block of the Sun or Moon's light that occurs when the Moon passes between the Sun and Earth and casts a shadow on Earth, or when the Moon enters the shadow of Earth.

ecliptic: The apparent path of the Sun, planets, and Moon in the sky as seen from Earth; the plane along which the Sun, planets, Moon, and other solar system objects orbit.

ellipse: An oval-shaped closed curve; the shape of a planet's orbit.

equinox: Either of two times of the year (fall or spring) during a planet's orbit when the north and south poles are equidistant from the Sun, causing day and night to be equal in length.

erosion: The process by which terrestrial planetary materials are broken down and moved from placed to place, for example, by wind and water.

first quarter: The phase of the Moon in which only the right half of the Moon's side is that faces Earth is illuminated; occurs when the Moon, Earth, and Sun form a 90° angle. *See also* **phase; third quarter.**

flyby: Method astronomers use to observe a planet or moon whereby a spacecraft "flies by" the planet or moon, taking pictures of it and gathering other scientific data as it does.

fossil: The preserved remains or impressions of organisms of Earth's geological past. *See also* **amber; cast; mold.**

full moon: The phase of the Moon in which the entire side of the Moon that faces Earth is fully illuminated; occurs when Earth is between the Moon and Sun. *See also* **phase.**

galaxy: A large system of dust, gas, stars, and other celestial bodies that has a particular shape.

gaseous planets: Planets composed of compounds that under normal Earth conditions would be gases; includes Jupiter, Saturn, Uranus, and Neptune.

gibbous moon: The phase of the Moon in which three-fourths of the Moon's side that faces Earth is illuminated; occurs between a quarter moon and full or new moon. *See also* **phase.**

gravity: A force of attraction between two objects; the strength of the force is due to the mass and distance between the two objects.

gravity assist: A technique that uses the pull of a planet's gravity to change a spacecraft's speed and direction.

greenhouse effect: The trapping of heat by a planet's atmosphere.

greenhouse gases: The gases in a planet's atmosphere, such as water vapor and carbon dioxide, that absorb energy radiated from the planet and prevent its escape into space.

horizon: The plane that extends from one's eye to the edge of Earth; the apparent connection between Earth and the sky.

Hubble Space Telescope: A telescope that orbits Earth 600 km above the surface.

inertia: The tendency of an object to remain either at rest or in motion unless acted on by an outside force. *See also* **Law of Inertia.**

lander: A spacecraft that lands on a planet to gather data directly from the planet's surface.

landform: A physical feature of a planet's surface, such as a mountain, plain, or valley.

latitude: An angular distance on a globe that runs parallel (east and west) to the equator; measured in degrees north and south. *See also* **longitude.**

Law of Inertia: Law stating that a body in motion tends to travel in a straight line unless an outside force disturbs it. *See also* **inertia.**

Law of Universal Gravitation: Law stating that any two objects in the universe have gravity and will attract each other, and that attraction depends on how much mass each object has and their distance from each other. *See also* **gravity.**

longitude: An angular distance on a globe that runs perpendicular (north and south) to the equator; measured in degrees east and west. *See also* **latitude.**

lunar: Of or relating to the Moon.

lunar eclipse: The blocking of sunlight to the Moon; occurs during a full moon, when Earth's shadow lands on the Moon. *See also* **eclipse.**

maria: Dark, flat, low-lying regions on the Moon's surface.

mass: The total amount of matter in an object; not dependent upon gravitational pull. *See also* **weight.**

meteor: The streak of light that is produced when a meteoroid burns as it enters an atmosphere. *See also* **meteoroid; meteorite.**

meteorite: A meteoroid that strikes a planet, moon, or asteroid. *See also* **meteor; meteoroid.**

meteoroid: A solid object moving in interplanetary space, distinguished from asteroids and planets by its smaller size. *See also* **asteroid; meteor; meteorite.**

model: A representation that is used to study objects, ideas, or systems that are too complex, distant, large, or small to study easily firsthand.

mold: A fossil type that is an impression of a shell, bone, tooth, or other body part left in the rock after the organism is covered by soft material. *See also* **fossil.**

moon: A rocky object that orbits a planet; a natural satellite.

NASA: The National Aeronautics and Space Administration, an organization that oversees the United States' space program, established in 1958.

neap tide: Lower-than-normal high tide that occurs when the first or third quarter moon, Earth, and the Sun are at right angles to each other and the gravitational force of the Sun partially offsets the gravitational force of the Moon. *See also* **spring tide; tide.**

nebula: A concentration of dust and gas in space.

new moon: A phase of the Moon in which the side of the Moon that faces Earth is not illuminated at all; occurs when the Moon is between Earth and the Sun.

nuclear fusion: The reaction by which hydrogen gas changes into helium gas and releases energy in the form of heat and light.

nucleus: The main part of a comet, which is made of ice, gas, and dust.

orbit: (noun) The curved path of one object, such as a planet or moon, around a central object, such as a star or planet; (verb) to move in a circular or elliptical path around a central object. *See also* **revolve.**

orbital period: The time that it takes an object to orbit another object one complete time. *See also* **period of revolution.**

orbiter: A spacecraft that studies a planet by orbiting it rather than by flying past it.

paleontologist: Scientist who studies life forms of the past. *See also* **fossil.**

partial lunar eclipse: A lunar eclipse in which part of the full moon's illuminated disk becomes temporarily darkened by Earth's shadow; occurs when the Moon moves partially into the umbra of Earth's shadow. *See also* **eclipse; lunar eclipse.**

partial solar eclipse: A solar eclipse in which the new moon temporarily blocks part of the Sun's disk; occurs when the new moon, Earth, and the Sun are not completely aligned and the umbra of the Moon's shadow falls into space and viewers on Earth are located in the penumbra of the Moon's shadow. *See also* **eclipse; solar eclipse.**

penumbra: The lighter, outer part of a shadow cone. *See also* **umbra.**

penumbral lunar eclipse: Lunar eclipse—barely visible from Earth—that occurs when the new moon moves into the penumbra of Earth's shadow. *See also* **eclipse; lunar eclipse.**

period of revolution: The time it takes an object to orbit another object one complete time. *See also* **orbital period.**

period of rotation: The time it takes an object to spin on its axis in one complete rotation. *See also* **rotation.**

petrified wood: Fossil originally of wood in which the wood has been replaced by some mineral. *See also* **fossil.**

phase: Any of eight various stages in which the Moon appears to change its shape.

photosphere: The layer of the Sun's atmosphere below the chromosphere that provides the sunlight that reaches Earth. *See also* **chromosphere; corona.**

plane: A flat surface; an imaginary surface along which the planets orbit. *See also* **ecliptic.**

planet: A massive, usually spherical space object that orbits a star and shines by reflecting the star's light.

Polaris: The current star to which the North Celestial Pole of Earth points; also called the "North Star."

probe: Instrument that makes observations and takes measurements such as atmospheric content, turbulence, temperature, particle size, and radiation either on a planet's surface or in its atmosphere.

prominence: A loop of gas that comes from the Sun's surface, linking parts of sunspot regions. *See also* **sunspot.**

radiation: The process by which energy is transferred from one object, such as the Sun, to another object, such as a planet, without the space between them being heated.

rays: Spoke-like patterns of ejected material that radiate from a crater.

revolution: The movement of one object around a central object. *See also* **revolve.**

revolve: To move in a curved path or orbit. *See also* **orbit; revolution.**

rotate: To turn or spin around a central point or axis. *See also* **axis; rotation.**

rotation: The movement of one object as it turns or spins around a central point or axis. *See also* **axis; rotate.**

satellite: A natural (for example, the Moon) or artificial (for example, the Hubble Space Telescope) object that orbits another object in space.

scale: The ratio between the measurements on a map or model and the actual measurements of an object.

scale factor: A method for reducing all measurements by the same amount to achieve the measurement of the scale model.

season: One of four natural parts of the year on Earth, including spring, summer, autumn (or fall), and winter; seasons vary from planet to planet and depend on the planet's rotation on its axis and revolution around the Sun.

shadow: An area where light is blocked by an object.

solar eclipse: The blocking of the Sun's light that occurs during a new moon when the Moon's shadow falls on Earth. *See also* **eclipse.**

solar energy: Energy from the Sun.

solar flare: A sudden brightness near a sunspot; explosion of gas from the Sun's surface. *See also* **sunspot.**

solar noon: Time of day when the Sun reaches its highest point in the sky for a given place on Earth.

solar system: A star with planets and other objects in orbit around it; our solar system is made up of the Sun, nine planets, asteroids, meteoroids, comets, and other space objects.

solar wind: A stream of electrically charged particles (primarily protons and electrons) that flow outward from the Sun's corona.

solstice: Either of two times of the year during which the north pole (around June 21) or the south pole (around December 21) is most directed toward the Sun.

space probe: An unmanned spacecraft that collects information in space.

space shuttle: A reusable spacecraft designed to transport astronauts, materials, and satellites to and from Earth's orbit.

space weather: The conditions on the surface of the Sun that ultimately affect Earth and its atmosphere.

spinoff: A product or process that was originally created for the space program that has been adapted for use on Earth.

spring tide: Higher-than-normal high tide during the month that normally occurs during a new and full moon when the Sun, Moon, and Earth are in line and their gravitational forces are combined. *See also* **neap tide.**

star: A sphere of hot glowing gases that releases energy in the form of heat and light. *See also* **Sun.**

Sun: The star in the center of our solar system around which Earth and eight other planets revolve. *See also* **planet.**

sunspot: A relatively darker, cooler area on the Sun's surface that emits charged particles.

technology: The application of science principles in processes, tools, and devices.

tectonics: The change in a surface of a planet due to internal forces.

terrestrial: Of or having to do with solid rock; name given to the four inner planets (Mercury, Venus, Earth, and Mars). *See also* **planets.**

third quarter: The phase of the Moon in which only the left half of the Moon's side that faces Earth is illuminated; occurs when the Moon, Earth, and the Sun form a 90° angle. *See also* **phase; first quarter.**

tide: Periodic rising and falling of the surface level of an ocean and other waters resulting from the gravitational attraction of the Moon and the Sun on the solid and liquid surfaces of Earth. *See also* **neap tide; spring tide.**

total lunar eclipse: Eclipse in which the entire disk of the full moon is covered by the Earth's umbra. *See also* **eclipse.**

total solar eclipse: Eclipse visible on Earth from inside the Moon's umbra; occurs when the Sun's entire disk—except for the corona—is blocked by the new moon. *See also* **eclipse.**

umbra: The inner, darker part of a shadow. *See also* **penumbra.**

universe: The entirety of everything that is known to exist in space.

velocity: Speed and direction that an object travels over a specified distance during a measured amount of time; rate of motion.

volcano: A landform, usually cone shaped, produced by a collection of erupted material around a vent, or opening, in the surface of a planet or moon and through which gas and erupted material pass.

waning crescent: Phase of the Moon in which a narrow strip of the Moon's lighted hemisphere is visible from Earth; shaped like a crescent; light is on the left; occurs before a new moon. *See also* **phase.**

waning gibbous: Phase of the Moon in which the lighted portion of the Moon's side that faces Earth is getting smaller; occurs after a full moon. *See also* **phase.**

waxing crescent: Phase of the Moon in which a narrow strip of the Moon's lighted hemisphere is visible from Earth; shaped like a crescent; light is on the right; occurs after a new moon. *See also* **phase.**

waxing gibbous: Phase of the Moon in which the lighted portion of the Moon's side that faces Earth is getting larger; occurs before a full moon. *See also* **phase.**

weight: A measure of the force of gravity on an object.

year: The time it takes a planet to complete one revolution around the Sun; Earth's year is 365¼ days long. *See also* **day.**

Index

Photo Credits

Front Cover Image courtesy of National Aeronautics and Space Administration (NASA) Goddard Space Flight Center, compiled by Reto Stockli, NASA Earth Observatory. Data and technical support provided by the MODIS Science Team.

Part 1: Sun-Earth-Moon System xviii–1 Courtesy of Carol O'Donnell/© NSRC 2 National Aeronautics and Space Administration/Jet Propulsion Laboratory 4 (left) © Roger Ressmeyer/Corbis (right) National Aeronautics and Space Administration/Johnson Space Center 6 United States Geological Survey/Hawaiian Volcano Observatory 7 Brian McLeod 10 © 1993 The British Library 12 National Aeronautics and Space Administration 16 Smithsonian Institution, National Anthropological Archives 17 V & A Picture Library 22 English Heritage 36 National Oceanic and Atmospheric Administration (NOAA) Photo Library/NOAA Central Library 38 © Jonathan Blair/Corbis 39 © Reuters Newmedia Inc./Corbis 40 Chaco Archive/National Park Service 41 (top) Chaco Archive/National Park Service, Photographer: Fred Mang (bottom) Chaco Culture National Historical Park/National Park Service 42 National Oceanic and Atmospheric Administration (NOAA) Photo Library/NOAA Central Library 57 © 1997-2000 by Calvin J. Hamilton 59 National Optical Astronomy Observatory/Association of Universities for Research in Astronomy/National Science Foundation 62 Corbis/Royalty-Free 68 (all) Courtesy UCO/Lick Observatory 69 (all) Courtesy UCO/Lick Observatory 70 National Aeronautics and Space Administration/Johnson Space Center 71 (top) National Aeronautics and Space Administration/Johnson Space Center (bottom) National Aeronautics and Space Administration 72 National Aeronautics and Space Administration 73 National Aeronautics and Space Administration 74 Bill Livingston/National Optical Astronomy Observatory/Association of Universities for Research in Astronomy/National Science Foundation 83 Dennis di Cicco/Sky & Telescope 84 (all) National Aeronautics and Space Administration/Kennedy Space Center 86 Jim Zimbelman 88 National Oceanic and Atmospheric Administration (NOAA) Photo Library/NOAA Central Library 95 Harvard Smithsonian Center for Astrophysics 96 National Center for Atmospheric Research/University Corporation for Atmospheric Research/National Science Foundation 97 Courtesy of Steele Hill and SOHO. SOHO is a project of international cooperation between ESA (European Space Agency) and National Aeronautics and Space Administration. 98 National Aeronautics and Space Administration 101 National Space Science Data Center/Goddard Space Flight Center 102 Courtesy of SOHO/MDI (Michelson Doppler Image) Consortium. SOHO is a project of international cooperation between ESA (European Space Agency) and National Aeronautics and Space Administration. 106 Courtesy of Carol O'Donnell/© NSRC 107 Ana Morris 108 All Photos Courtesy of SOHO/MDI (Michelson Doppler Image) Consortium. SOHO is a project of international cooperation between ESA (European Space Agency) and National Aeronautics and Space Administration. 113 Scala/Art Resource, New York 114 National Aeronautics and Space Administration/Jet Propulsion Laboratory 115 National Aeronautics and Space Administration/Johnson Space Center 116 Smithsonian Institution Libraries, Dibner Library of History of Science and Technology 118 Erich Lessing, Art Resource, New York 119 Image 235116, 1929, Forest Service Photograph Collection, Special Collections, National Agricultural Library 120 Jan Curtis, Geophysical Institute, University of Alaska Fairbanks 121 (top) Courtesy of SOHO. SOHO is a project of international cooperation between ESA (European Space Agency) and National Aeronautics and Space Administration. (center) © Dick Hutchinson (bottom) Courtesy of David Miller, National Geophysical Data Center 122 Jeff McAdams, Photographer, Courtesy of Carolina Biological Supply Company 126 Courtesy of Wisconsin Fast Plants 127 (both) National Aeronautics and Space Administration

Part 2: Solar System   128–129 Jeff McAdams, Photographer, Courtesy of Carolina Biological Supply Company   **130** National Aeronautics and Space Administration/Johnson Space Center   **135 (all)** Jeff McAdams, Photographer, Courtesy of Carolina Biological Supply Company   **136** Jeff McAdams, Photographer, Courtesy of Carolina Biological Supply Company **137** © Bettmann/Corbis   **138** National Aeronautics and Space Administration   **140–141** National Aeronautics and Space Administration/Johnson Space Center   **146** National Aeronautics and Space Administration   **152** Smithsonian photo by Eric Long, © 1993, Smithsonian Institution   **153** Smithsonian photo by Alfred Harrell, © 1992 Smithsonian Institution **154–155** National Aeronautics and Space Administration   **156** National Aeronautics and Space Administration   **157** National Aeronautics and Space Administration. Image processing by United States Geological Survey.   **158 (left)** National Aeronautics and Space Administration/Jet Propulsion Laboratory **(right)** National Aeronautics and Space Administration/ Jet Propulsion Laboratory/Northwestern University **160** Artist: Don Davis/ National Aeronautics and Space Administration   **161 (top)** National Aeronautics and Space Administration. Image processing by United States Geological Survey. **(bottom)** Courtesy of Meteor Crater, Northern Arizona, USA   **162 (top left)** National Aeronautics and Space Administration/Johnson Space Center **(top right)** National Aeronautics and Space Administration/Jet Propulsion Laboratory **(center)** National Aeronautics and Space Administration/Jet Propulsion Laboratory **(bottom)** National Aeronautics and Space Administration   **163** J.P. Lockwood, United States Geological Survey   **169** National Aeronautics and Space Administration   **170** National Aeronautics and Space Administration/Ames Research Center **171** National Aeronautics and Space Administration **172 (all)** National Aeronautics and Space Administration/Jet Propulsion Laboratory   **174** National Aeronautics and Space Administration. Image processing by United States Geological Survey   **176** R.L. Shuster, United States Geological Survey   **177 (top)** © Brian A.

Vikander/Corbis **(bottom)** National Aeronautics and Space Administration/Jet Propulsion Laboratory   **178** © Adriel Heisey   **179** R.E. Wallace, United States Geological Survey   **182** National Aeronautics and Space Administration, Viking orbiter image   **183** National Aeronautics and Space Administration/Jet Propulsion Laboratory/Malin Space Science Systems **185** National Aeronautics and Space Administration. Image processing by United States Geological Survey   **186** © Lunar and Planetary Institute, 2000   **187 (top)** © Lunar and Planetary Institute, 2000 **(bottom)** National Aeronautics and Space Administration. Image processing by Brown University   **189** © Lunar and Planetary Institute, 2000   **191** National Aeronautics and Space Administration/Jet Propulsion Laboratory/ Goddard Space Flight Center   **192** National Aeronautics and Space Administration/Jet Propulsion Laboratory/Malin Space Science Systems   **193** National Aeronautics and Space Administration/Jet Propulsion Laboratory/Malin Space Science Systems **194** National Aeronautics and Space Administration/Jet Propulsion Laboratory   **195** National Aeronautics and Space Administration/Jet Propulsion Laboratory   **196** National Aeronautics and Space Administration/Jet Propulsion Laboratory   **197** National Aeronautics and Space Administration/Jet Propulsion Laboratory   **198** National Aeronautics and Space Administration/Jet Propulsion Laboratory/Malin Space Science Systems **200** National Aeronautics and Space Administration/ Johnson Space Center   **202** Courtesy of Carol O'Donnell/© NSRC   **210** National Aeronautics and Space Administration/Jet Propulsion Laboratory/University of Arizona   **211** National Aeronautics and Space Administration/Jet Propulsion Laboratory   **212–213** National Aeronautics and Space Administration/Jet Propulsion Laboratory   **214** National Aeronautics and Space Administration/Jet Propulsion Laboratory   **216** National Aeronautics and Space Administration/Jet Propulsion Laboratory   **229** National Aeronautics and Space Administration/Jet Propulsion Laboratory **231** National Aeronautics and Space Administration/Jet Propulsion Laboratory   **232–233** National Aeronautics and Space Administration/Jet Propulsion Laboratory **234–235** National Aeronautics and Space Administration/Jet Propulsion Laboratory **236** Space Telescope Science Institute, Kenneth Seidelmann, U.S. Naval Observatory, and National Aeronautics and Space Administration **237** National Aeronautics and Space Administration/Jet Propulsion Laboratory **238** National Aeronautics and Space Administration/Jet Propulsion Laboratory **238–239** National Aeronautics and Space Administration/Jet Propulsion Laboratory **240** National Aeronautics and Space Administration/Jet Propulsion Laboratory/United States Geological Survey **244** Dan and Marci Rivera, © 2000 **253** Courtesy of Carolina Biological Supply Company **254** (both) Courtesy of Carolina Biological Supply Company **255** (both) Images of New Brunswick, Images Du Nouveau-Brunswick; Photographer: Robert D.H. Warren **258–259** National Aeronautics and Space Administration/United States Geological Survey **259** (top) National Aeronautics and Space Administration/Jet Propulsion Laboratory (bottom) National Aeronautics and Space Administration. Image produced by University of Arizona **260–261** National Aeronautics and Space Administration **262** (left) National Aeronautics and Space Administration **262–263** Dr. R. Albrecht, European Space Agency/ESO Space Telescope European Coordinating Facility/National Aeronautics and Space Administration **264** (both) National Aeronautics and Space Administration

Part 3: Earth's History as a Planet **266–267** Jeff McAdams, Photographer, Courtesy of Carolina Biological Supply Company **268** © William James Warren/Corbis **273** (top) National Aeronautics and Space Administration/United States Geological Survey (bottom) National Aeronautics and Space Administration/Jet Propulsion Laboratory **274** Dennis di Cicco/Corbis **275** (top) National Aeronautics and Space Administration/Johnson Space Center (bottom) Courtesy of Ofer Gazbo **276–277** National Aeronautics and Space Administration **278–279** R. Evans, J. Trauger, H. Hammel, and the HST Comet Science Team and the National Aeronautics and Space Administration **280** United States Geological Survey **281** National Aeronautics and Spac Administration/Goddard Space Flight Center/image created by Reto Stockli, Nazmi El Saleous, and Marit Jentoft-Nilsen **283** Barbara Summey, National Aeronautics and Space Administration/Goddard Space Flight Center **284** (top) National Aeronautics and Space Administration/Johnson Space Center (bottom) National Aeronautics and Space Administration/Goddard Space Flight Center/MITI/ERSDAC/DARDS and U.S./Japan ASTER Science Team **285** National Aeronautics and Space Administration/Goddard Space Flight Center. Image by Jesse Allen, Science Systems and Applications, Inc. **286** National Aeronautics and Space Administration/Goddard Space Flight Center Scientific Visualization Studio, images by Greg Shirah **287** National Aeronautics and Space Administration, image by Brian Montgomery, Robert Simmon, and Reto Stockli, based on data provided by the MODIS Science Team **289** Courtesy of Elizabeth Warner **290** Artist: Don Davis/National Aeronautics and Space Administration **292** Courtesy of Carol O'Donnell/© NSRC **297** Courtesy of Carol O'Donnell/© NSRC **298** Courtesy of Carol O'Donnell/© NSRC **301** (both) Courtesy of the Hardin Family Private Collection **302** Courtesy of Carolina Biological Supply Company **304** Courtesy of Carolina Biological Supply Company **305** Artist: Don Davis/National Aeronautics and Space Administration **307** Courtesy of Walter Alvarez **308** Courtesy of David A. Kring, National Aeronautics and Space Administration/University of Arizona Space Imagery Center **310** United States Geological Survey **311** (both) Courtesy of John W. Valley, University of Wisconsin—Madison **312** National Aeronautics and Space Administration/Johnson Space Center **315** National Oceanic and Atmospheric Administration (NOAA) Photo Library/NOAA Central Library **318** National Aeronautics and Space Administration/Jet Propulsion Laboratory **321** (top) From the Isaac Asimov Collection in the Special Collections at Boston University (bottom) Smithsonian Institution Libraries **322** Smithsonian